II P B 10

SYSTEMS ANALYSIS

A Computer Approach to Decision Models

IRWIN SERIES IN QUANTITATIVE ANALYSIS FOR BUSINESS

Consulting Editor

ROBERT B. FETTER *Yale University*

BOWMAN & FETTER *Analysis for Production Management* Revised Edition

BIERMAN, BONINI, FOURAKER, & JAEDICKE *Quantitative Analysis for Business Decisions* Revised Edition

MARTIN *Electronic Data Processing* Revised Edition

BASS, BUZZELL, GREENE, LAZER, PESSEMIER, SHAWVER, SHUCHMAN, THEODORE, & WILSON *Mathematical Models and Methods in Marketing*

MORRIS *Analysis for Materials Handling Management*

FRANK, KUEHN, & MASSY *Quantitative Techniques in Marketing Analysis: Text and Readings*

HOWELL & TEICHROEW *Mathematical Analysis for Business Decisions*

MORRIS *Management Science in Action*

BOWEN *Mathematics: With Applications in Management and Economics*

BERANEK *Analysis for Financial Decisions*

McMILLAN & GONZALEZ *Systems Analysis: A Computer Approach to Decision Models*

THEODORE *Applied Mathematics: An Introduction: Mathematical Analysis for Management*

ELLIOTT & WASLEY *Business Information Processing Systems*

SYSTEMS ANALYSIS

A Computer Approach to Decision Models

By CLAUDE McMILLAN, Ph.D.

PROFESSOR OF MANAGEMENT

SCHOOL OF BUSINESS

UNIVERSITY OF COLORADO

and RICHARD F. GONZALEZ, Ph.D.

PROFESSOR OF MANAGEMENT

GRADUATE SCHOOL OF BUSINESS ADMINISTRATION

MICHIGAN STATE UNIVERSITY

1965

RICHARD D. IRWIN, INC.

HOMEWOOD, ILLINOIS

First Printing, January, 1965
Second Printing, October, 1965
Third Printing, March, 1966

Library of Congress Catalog Card No. 65–12415

To Our Families

Preface

THE AUTHORS of this text were motivated to produce suitable materials for a course in systems analysis in the business curriculum at the undergraduate as well as graduate level. At present the number of schools or departments of business administration or industrial engineering in which such course content is offered is small. However, if the growing interest in the systems concept and the extension of the "systems view" of the firm is to take on real substance, then the curriculum planner must turn his attention to procedures and techniques useful in the measurement and evaluation of the behavior of complex systems which make up the modern firm. This text introduces the student to the methodology of systems analysis via computer simulation. Uncertainty as well as complexity characterize the subsystems of the firm, and only by making use of the computer can we economically process realistic models of the systems.

Computer simulation allows students with modest backgrounds in mathematics and statistics to build and process systems models which produce operationally useful information at a modest investment of time and effort. We do not say that computer simulation is a substitute for formal analytical procedures. Neither are we unmindful of the many unanswered tactical questions about the methodology of simulation. Yet for helping to understand complex systems, as well as to develop information in order to improve decisions concerning the design or use of such systems, computer simulation is a legitimate and in our experience an interesting pursuit for the business student because it focuses on problems and situations which are known to him.

Because systems simulation requires the use of computer models, the student is introduced to a general programming language early in the text and from that point on the presentation is heavily dependent upon that language. A by-product of a course such as the one being proposed is that the student acquires basic programming skill as well as experience with a major computer application— simulation. One might consider that a course in systems analysis solves a current problem which perplexes the curriculum planner not only in business administration but in other disciplines: the problem of how to introduce the student to the computer—a problem for which various answers have been proposed. These range from computer appreciation courses in which students learn about the principal applications of the computer in their fields, to the proposal that all students regardless of major or field of concentration learn a general programming language so they may utilize the computer for any classroom problem-solving requirement. A third solution is for instructors in accounting, statistics, operations research, or management science to modify their courses to include computer processing of problems or data.

We would argue that a computer appreciation course is insufficient; that the student ought to be encouraged and given the opportunity to try his hand at the various applications in his field. The second recommendation when implemented usually results in a service course of short duration in which the student applies his programming skill to problems which are of little more than passing interest to him. The third proposed solution has met with little success because many instructors are not prepared to make the necessary modification. The requirement to teach programming, to demonstrate its application, and to cover the subject matter of the course (accounting, statistics, etc.) is simply not practical in many cases.

It is not our purpose to teach computer programming, but because we cannot presume that students typically have this background we have included it in the text. Specifically we have selected as a programming language, FORTRAN. There are arguments that a text should be "language independent" but we disagree. At some point, if the student is to actually use the computer, a language must be specified. We have chosen the most widely used general programming language. With the exception of input/output statements, the programs as listed in the text can be processed with little modification. If FORTRAN is not available, the programs are documented so that they may be written in whatever language is used at a particular installation.

Organization of the Text

This text is characterized by (1) progress from particular models to the general model or case, and (2) progress from consideration of subsystems to consideration of the complex of subsystems or the entire firm. Usually we undertake analysis in order to discover general solutions or propositions which may later be applied to specific cases. Yet we are coming to appreciate the utility if not the elegance of focusing attention on specific situations and then, as Professor Forrester has said, "We generalize as far as we dare." We note that decision makers in the real world are interested in solutions for particular problems or situations and we think that this approach is more meaningful to the student as well.

Progressing from analysis of subsystems to analysis of the complex of subsystems reflects the fact that it is still convenient organizationally and administratively to deal with the major subsystems of the firm before attempting to model and analyze the interconnections and interdependencies which exist among subsystems.

Chapters 1 and 2 of the text serve to define generally the concept of system and to apply the definition to the firm. The subject of model building, particularly the nature and use of computer models, precedes the discussion in Chapter 2 of the methodolgy of simulation.

Chapters 3 and 4 constitute an introduction to FORTRAN programming with emphasis on the necessary statements which are later required to build preliminary simulation models. The use of control statements is illustrated in Chapter 4 by reference to the inventory system under conditions of certainty in which the problem is to determine an optimum inventory reorder rule. We acknowledge that this problem has an analytical solution which may be obtained directly by a procedure discussed in the chapter. However the manner of computation using the computer, keeping in mind that it is our purpose to demonstrate particular features of FORTRAN, involves a solution by enumeration and evaluation of a series of possible reorder rules. At this point the student may well challenge the assumptions on which the inventory system under certainty is defined. Information about consumer demand as well as the supplier's lead time is not perfect and in fact these two variables are usually treated as random variables. Before moving to the analysis of the inventory system under uncertainty, we have included in Chapter 5 a brief review of some concepts of probability which the student will find useful if he is not acquainted with the subject.

In Chapter 6 the inventory system is analyzed by composing a computer model and conducting experiments with that model. The purpose of the first five chapters has been to prepare the student for the simulation which he conducts in Chapter 6. The student should be mindful that the problem posed in this chapter is not trivial and solutions or their approximations by formal methods of analysis would demand much greater time, effort, and mathematical sophistication than the student would typically be expected to have.

In Chapter 7 the model of the single-channel queue is developed. This model is basic to many of the physical distribution or physical service systems which we find in the firm. The queuing system model is first developed analytically and then computer simulation of the queuing system is presented in Chapter 9. Because the modeling of the queuing system requires that random samples be drawn from various kinds of nonuniform distributions, Chapter 8 is given to the development of generators for obtaining such samples. As more advanced statistical and programming concepts are required, they are introduced in this and subsequent chapters.

Chapter 10, "Management Planning Models," reflects again a special need of the analyst in simulating business systems. Demand is treated as a random variable, exogenous to the system, and the model builder as well as the business decision maker must devise ways to anticipate demand. A variety of short-range planning and forecasting routines are commonly employed; several of the important ones, including network planning methods are included in Chapter 10.

The first ten chapters provide the background and techniques to enable the student to propose and carry out fairly large and realistic computer models of the firm. By way of introducing the simulation of large-scale systems, we have included in Chapers 11 and 12 a brief review of some significant simulation efforts. Chapter 11 reviews some work of the Systems Development Corporation and the model of C. P. Bonini. Chapter 12 introduces industrial dynamics, a particular form of simulation. Conceptually, in industrial dynamics continuous change models are used as contrasted to those discussed in this text, which are discrete change models. Industrial dynamics models are composed in FORTRAN so that the student may distinguish the two model types and may engage in industrial dynamics model building without having to learn the special programming language, DYNAMO.

In Chapter 13 the student is presented with a hypothetical firm the model of which makes use of various subsystem models which were developed in the preceding chapters. The purpose is to not only construct a model of a firm but to use it in order to test and evaluate various decisions and policies.

Finally, in Chapter 14 we call to the student's attention the fact that many tactical questions involving the use of simulation have yet to be answered. There are some guides and procedures which the student should follow to preclude grossly inefficient experiments involving simulation methods.

From the preceding it is perhaps evident that not all the material included in this text can be covered in a single course of a quarter or even semester duration. Experimentally, at the undergraduate level, and assuming that Chapters 3, 4, and 5 required detailed treatment, it has been possible in a three-quarter-hour course to cover the materials through Chapter 7 plus some modified experiments involving the SIMCO model of Chapter 13. At the graduate level in a three-quarter-hour course, teaching FORTRAN outside the scheduled class when necessary, and omitting detailed consideration of Chapter 5, it is possible to cover most of the text materials and selected exercises.

As a reminder to both instructor and student we strongly urge that regular assignment of the exercises be made. The procedure of conceptualizing a problem and obtaining an operational computer model is an ill-defined procedure which can really only be learned through practice. The same applies to the acquisition of even minimum programming skills. No amount of discussion, exposition, or dry runs substitute for the experience and confidence gained from a successful composition of the computer program and its use to obtain information for improving the quality of decision making.

A course in systems analysis, particularly one that represents the first effort to teach a course which utilizes a computer regularly, will constitute a somewhat unique experience. The instructor will quickly realize that in terms of resources it is a costly course. Both instructor and student will experience a certain amount of frustration because of the physical arrangements and organization required to accommodate large numbers of students so that their programs may be prepared, debugged, and processed, with reasonably short turn-around time. For the most part central computer facilities on the typical campus are not organized primarily to service users who require the processing of large numbers of relatively short class problems. We do not mean to overstate such difficulties but merely call them to the instructors' attention.

To summarize, systems analysis, particularly in business administration, is a significant and growing body of knowledge. The analysis of complex systems can be done economically, even by undergraduate students of business, via the use of the computer utilizing the procedures of simulation. A course in systems analysis has as an important by-product the introduction and exposure of the student to the computer. Admittedly there are many ways in which such an exposure could be accomplished. We think that by focusing attention on an important application, systems analysis, that emphasis is properly placed on the computer as a tool. This text has purposely been designed to be self-contained, presuming nothing except a basic course in college mathematics as a prerequisite, and has been made FORTRAN-dependent in order to facilitate the process of formulating models and enabling the student to process them on the machine. If our experience is borne out generally we would expect that the subject matter of this text will not only be interesting and challenging to the student but will also stimulate his interest in the computer and cause him to make applications in other subject matter fields.

Acknowledgments

The authors are responsible for the selection, organization, and presentation of materials in this text. However, as the materials were developed and assembled, many individuals contributed, and we should like to acknowledge their help. A number of graduate instructors in the Department of Management at Michigan State University have taught the undergraduate version of the systems analysis course and their experience and critical suggestions have been useful. The group includes Messrs. E. Martin Basic, Rodney J. Boyes, John Demaree, David Fleckenstein, Stanley T. Hardy, John C. Moffett, and Ralph Trine. Mr. Fleckenstein assisted in the writing of the programs and preparation of the instructors manual.

Mrs. Peggy Cushion supervised the preparation of the manuscript through its several versions and we particularly acknowledge her assistance.

CLAUDE McMILLAN
RICHARD F. GONZALEZ

EAST LANSING, MICHIGAN
January 1, 1965

Table of Contents

XV

CHAPTER 1

Systems and Models

BEFORE DESCRIBING particular systems of the firm or the simulation of them, it is necessary to consider generally what is meant by *system*. The term has been used in many ways and has meaning in every form of organized research and learning. Referring to the business firm, we commonly use the terms *inventory system, distribution system, production system,* etc. We also speak of the *decision system* and the *information system.* For our purpose a somewhat ambiguous definition of system will serve:

A system is a set of objects together with relationships between the objects and between their attributes.[1]

The kinds of entities in the firm are limitless. Physical objects such as machines, raw materials, finished product, clerks, and machine operators may be entities of a system. Abstract objects may also comprise a system; for example, profit goals, sales quotas, production standards, and costs.

Attributes are the properties of entities, and an entity is described by listing its attributes. The entity, Machine Number 784, might have such properties as price, weight, color, machine speed, cost of operation, and production rate. Consider the attributes of inventory stock item XYZ; attributes of interest might be the quantity at a particular time, the monthly cost of storing a unit, or the number of units used last year. Thinking of the variety of entities which comprises business systems one needs to recognize that entities have many attributes. For much of our analysis we need be concerned with only a few attributes; the rest will be ignored.

[1] "The Definition of System," *Yearbook for the Advancement of General Systems Theory,* 1956, p. 18. See also A. D. Hall, *A Methodology for Systems Engineering* (New York: D. Van Nostrand Co., 1962).

Relationships which exist between and among entities and their attributes tie the system together. Were it not for relationships the concept of system would be meaningless. Relationships among entities of the firm are again limitless. We are familiar with relationships involving the price and sales volume attributes of a product. The discipline of economics treats this relationship under different competitive situations. Relationships between product cost and price are constantly being studied and quantified. Sales volume and advertising expenditure illustrates another common relationship. In inventory systems we will examine relationships among the attributes of the stock item, the quantity on hand, reorder quantity, demand, etc.

Given the set of entities and their attributes, we would be able to identify or postulate a great many relationships. Here, also, interest is limited to those relationships which we think have an important effect on the way the system undergoes change. Systems analysis may lead to a consideration of relationships which had previously been ignored or, as a matter of fact, had not been identified.

Having defined a system by its entities, attributes, and relationships, it is also necessary to identify the *environment* of the system. More precisely, then, the environment of a system may be defined as follows:

The environment is the set of all objects, a change in whose attributes affects the system, and also of those objects whose attributes are changed by the behavior of the system.[2]

It would seem to follow that everything not included in the system would constitute the environment, and one might suspect that the subdivision of a set of objects into the subsets, system, and environment is done arbitrarily. This conclusion is correct so long as we recognize that the partition is done for the convenience of the person who is analyzing the system.

Examples of the difficulty of separating system and environment will turn up later in modeling the firm. In some cases the consumer is considered part of the environment. Describing the consumer in terms of the attributes of taste and income—where a change in either would probably affect the firm—does not violate the definition of environment; one might even argue for including the consumer within an enlarged system without violating the definition of system. The same problem exists when deciding whether or not

---

[2] *Ibid.*, Hall.

suppliers or competitors are part of the system environment or of
the system itself.

One way of distinguishing system and environment is to consider
whether or not the activity in the system is influenced or subject to
management control.

It is necessary to differentiate between those activities which are
intrinsically related to management activity and those which are related
to the business environment. The basis for differentiation is whether
management activity can be expected to control the situation. The
activities of customers, banks, unions, vendors, competitors and the
ambient economy are some of the factors which have been categorized as
being environmental influences beyond the control of management
activity.[3]

From the definitions of system and environment it follows that a
system can be subdivided into subsystems. Subsystems of the firm
might follow an identification of the major functional areas: production, personnel, accounting, and distribution. We are not, however, restricted to this set of subsystems; the concept of system
permits other meaningful subsystem identifications, such as the information system of the firm.

Entities belonging to one subsystem are also part of the environment of another, or of several other subsystems. In the definitions of
system and subsystem we can agree with the frequent observation
that elements of a system may themselves be systems of a lower
order, or, put another way, that all systems are subsystems of the
next higher system. This implies a hierarchy of subsystems and
various subsystem levels within a system.

In studying a system one may choose to focus on the detailed behavior of the various subsystems (microscopic behavior) or one
might elect to study the behavior of the system as a whole (macro-
scopic behavior). Both approaches will be employed to analyze the
behavior of the firm. A significant step is taken when we move from
subsystem analysis to analysis of the whole system. In the latter
form of investigation, relationships among subsystems must be
evaluated. As most business firms develop, various factors influence the particular design of each subsystem, and rarely is there a
practical means to insure that the design of the several subsystems
is completely compatible. It is possible and frequently true that

---

[3] Jay B. Heyne, "Mark I Operational Specifications (*TM-536*)," Systems Development Corporation, Santa Monica, Calif., p. 3.

subsystems are observed whose objectives are imperfectly rational-
ized; i.e., the objectives are not consistent, complementary, or
mutually reenforcing. We would describe such a system as one that
lacks integration.

SYSTEM CLASSIFICATIONS

In developing the concept of system it is useful to classify systems
into several broad categories. The first would distinguish between
natural and *man-made* systems. In every respect the firm is thought
of as man-made even though the environment in which it operates
contains natural systems. In terms of complexity and dynamism the
firm, the man-made system, has few equals.

A second distinction contrasts *open* systems and *closed* systems:

Most . . . systems are open, meaning they exchange materials, energies,
or information with their environments. A system is closed if there is no
import or export of energies in any of its forms, such as information, heat,
physical materials, etc.[4]

An open system may become closed in two ways. If interaction
with the environment is cut off, or if we later choose to include in
the system that part of the environment which involved the inter-
change of energy, materials, or information, the system becomes
closed. It would seem unreasonable to consider the firm a closed
system. As a matter of fact, we are hard-pressed to name any part of
our physical or social world which is not environmental to the firm.

A third classification separates systems which are adaptive and
those which are not. Adaptive systems react to environmental
changes in a way that is desirable considering the purpose for which
the system was designed. March and Cyert[5] describe the firm as an
adaptive system, meaning that environmental change or shock
elicits a response (decision) which results in a new system state.
Successive shocks and responses, and the observation concerning
how successful the response was, become part of the "experience" of
the firm. Organizational learning is said to take place through time
as those responses which led to preferred system states are recalled
and applied.

The term *system state* was used above. Recall that a system is de-

---

[4] Hall, *op. cit.*
[5] Richard M. Cyert and James G. March, *A Behavioral Theory of the Firm*
(Englewood Cliffs, N.J.: Prentice-Hall, 1963).

fined as the set of entities and their interrelated attributes. Attributes through time will take on different values. At any point in time we may describe the state of the system by observing the current value of those attributes.[6] In describing the state of the firm one may list the values of such variables as profit, back orders, sales, production, etc. Having selected a set of variables, one can then identify sequential states of the system through time.

If the values of the attributes of a system remain constant, or within defined limits, the system is stable. In contrast, if the values of the attributes fluctuate widely, the system is unstable. At times the system will be unstable, and at other times stable. An example of this behavior will be found in the analysis of subsystems involving waiting lines. A waiting line of variable length develops at a service center (tool crib, customer checkout counter, complaint desk, ticket selling booth, etc.) because of the relatively fixed capacity of the facility as well as the varying demand for service placed against it.

In analyzing these systems it is common to find that, when the service center is opened at the beginning of the day, there is an initial interval during which the length of the waiting line increases and decreases erratically. After this initial period the length of the line varies within narrow and predictable limits. The term *transition state* defines the interval during which the erratic behavior occurred. References are also made to an *exploding state*—when the values of the variables (the attributes) indicating the state of the system take on ever-increasing, fluctuating values. The longer the system operates, the greater the fluctuations.

Equilibrium can be defined in terms of system state. A system is in equilibrium if, in the absence of external shock, its state remains unchanged. If an external shock to the system is followed by a return to an equilibrium state, then the system is said to be stable.[7] This definition of stability supplements the one given above.

Finally we may consider systems in which a portion of their output is regularly "fed back"; that is, introduced as an input to influence future states. The portion of the output which is fed back for purposes of control consists of information, and we refer to these

---

[6] Alternatively, the state of the system means the existing entities and the current values of their attributes. See Harry N. Markowitz *et al.*, SIMSCRIPT: A Simulation Programing Language (Englewood Cliffs, N.J.: Prentice-Hall, 1963).

[7] E. F. Beckenbach (ed.), *Modern Mathematics for the Engineer* (New York: McGraw-Hill, 1956), p. 31.

systems as information-feedback systems. The term *servomechanism* defines man-made systems utilizing feedback. A further definition of the information-feedback system is given by Professor Forrester:

> An information-feedback system exists whenever the environment leads to a decision that results in action which affects the environment and thereby influences future decisions. Examples of systems of information-feedback control abound in all parts of our physical world. In the business situation we can point to the following illustrations.
>
> In business, orders and inventory levels lead to manufacturing decisions that fill orders, correct inventories, and yield new manufacturing decisions.
>
> A profitable industry attracts competitors until the profit margin is reduced to equilibrium with other economic forces, and competitors cease to enter the field.
>
> A competitive need for a new product leads to research and development expenditure that produces technological change.[8]

There are many perplexing problems in the design of information-feedback systems. The recent work of Professor Forrester is a significant contribution to our understanding of the design and behavior of these systems in business. Forrester has given the name Industrial Dynamics to the study of such systems through simulation.

MODELS

The methodology of systems simulation involves experimentation with systems models. Model building and the use of models is so integral to simulation that one author has suggested "that simulation occurs whenever a model of any sort is employed."[9]

Analysis begins with observation of a system or event. From observation, familiarization, and thinking about the system comes the formulation of hypotheses which are possible explanations of the system behavior. Model building has been explained as an extension and formalization of the statement of hypotheses.[10] As an ab-

---

[8] Jay W. Forrester, *Industrial Dynamics* (Cambridge, Mass., and New York: The M.I.T. Press and John Wiley & Sons, 1961), p. 14.

[9] W. K. Holstein and William R. Soukup, *Monte Carlo Simulation,* Institute Paper No. 23, Institute for Quantitative Research and Economics and Management, Graduate School of Industrial Administration, Purdue University, Lafayette, Ind., 1962, p. 1.

[10] Edward H. Bowman and Robert B. Fetter, *Analysis for Production Management* (Homewood, Ill.: Richard D. Irwin, Inc., 1961), p. 29.

straction, simplification, or idealization of the system or event, the model helps to describe or in some sense duplicate it. Models cannot replace the real world; at best they reduce a complex system to manageable proportions or serve to crystallize our thinking and perception.

Once the analyst has achieved a parallelism between the real world situation and his model, it is usually easier to manipulate the model to study the characteristics in which he is interested than it is to try to work with the real world system. . . .

By abstracting from the real world system the analyst can focus his attention on a much simpler system without great loss because some details have been ignored.

A model is useful in a practical sense when it accurately duplicates the behavior of the real world system. If a model does not accomplish this, it is useful only insofar as it provides information and insight into the development of the new model.[11]

Models are neither true or false; their value is judged by the contribution they make to our understanding of the systems they represent.

Having observed the situation, specified the problem, formulated a hypothesis, and rendered the hypothesis specific by building a model, we then seek to evaluate the model. The testing or validating of a model can be done by making further observations and measurements of the system, or by experimentation. As new data is obtained, the model is checked against it to determine the correspondence between the model and the real system. If subsequent observations cannot be accounted for by the model, then it needs revision. The same principle is true in testing the model by experimentation; if the model does not confirm the hypothesis implicit in the model, we must modify the model.

"When a model has been tested, and is acceptable, then understanding has been added to the problem. The model which usefully described a given situation is capable of prediction in the sense that changes in the situation can be logically (mathematically) followed through the model."[12] Another writer summarizes model building and formal analysis:

The scientific method is basically the establishment of models (sometimes more abstractly called hypotheses) which must have two properties:

[11] Ellwood S. Buffa, *Models for Production and Operations Management* (New York: John Wiley & Sons, 1963), pp. 9–10.

[12] Bowman and Fetter, *op. cit.*, p. 32.

First, they must account for all known facts, and secondly, they must enable us to make predictions which may be tested by any unbiased and independent observer. Newton's law of gravity explained all the observations of the positions of celestial bodies. So did many previous models of the universe. Newton's Law has survived because, in addition it could be used, for example, to construct—a thousand years in advance—tide tables whose correctness may be observed by any businessman on a weekend. . . .

Once established by fitting known facts and tested by making predictions for which there are independent observational data, the model is used for experimentation, by which the results of various ways of running the business may be determined. Actual tests on real customers are often expensive, and worse they disturb the situation so that the results are either biased or leave a permanent perturbation.[13]

Classification of Models

Models may initially be distinguished by their correspondence to the system being modeled; i.e., how nearly are they like the real thing? Physical models retain some of the entities of the system they represent. A physical model looks like its referent.[14] It may be scaled down, but it behaves like the real thing.

Models which have been constructed from a set of physical objects not found in the real system are called *physical analogues*. For example electrical components may be used to build a system that behaves analogously to a mechanical system. An electrical system (analogue computer) may be constructed to behave like a hydraulic system, an oil refinery, or perhaps like a distribution system for transporting natural gas.

Schematic models are representations in pictorial form and vary in degree of abstraction. Flow diagrams and organizational charts are examples. Marked abstraction characterizes these models. Their components are lines, symbols, etc., which are not found in the physical world.

A *mathematical model* of a system consists of a set of equations whose solution explains or predicts changes in the state of the system. The use of mathematical models is a consequence of analytical efforts to abstract and describe the real world. Qualitative descriptions of systems (verbal symbolic models) are of limited help in predicting or precisely specifying the state of a system.

---

[13] E. F. Beckenbach, *op. cit.,* pp. 211–12.

[14] The word *referent* is used to mean the system or the class of systems being modeled. The referent of a model is the real system(s).

The inadequacy of words becomes apparent when a model is presented quantitatively. It is in the attempt to present relationships with precision, as well as quantitatively, that the use of mathematics is growing in model development. The vagueness, the ambiguity, the lack of clear and specific definitions of the character of a situation described verbally are faults which can be avoided by formalized mathematical presentation of problems. This objective is not always achieved. In the minds of many, formalized models take on an aura of authenticity and accuracy which can lead to misapplication. However, the attempt to develop a formalized, mathematical model in a given situation demands a more thorough analysis of the situation than would otherwise be demanded, and, consequently, problems are often more properly analyzed.

Translating problems stated in verbal terms to precise mathematical problems is not an easy task because most languages do not lend themselves to precise, unambiguous statements.[15]

Mathematical models are highly abstract. Yet it is abstraction that makes mathematical models general, subject to manipulation, and precise in terms of the information gained from their use. A *computer model* (for the present) is simply defined as a mathematical model expressed or written according to a particular set of rules so that the model may be processed by the computer. The set of rules and notations which constitute the algebraic computer programming language, FORTRAN, is the subject of Chapter 3.

Partial and General Models

Models are also classified according to the degree to which they have been confirmed and accepted, which in turn is the measure of their generality.[16]

Morris points out that the degree to which a model becomes accepted is often determined by its generality, meaning the number of systems it purports to explain. He notes that in management science the model builder is constrained when making observations by the level at which management activity takes place:

If, for example, one is concerned with granting credit to customers, the firm with a relatively small number of customers can treat them as individuals in the matter of credit risk, but the firm with a large number of customers must set down policies based on the characteristics of large groups of people. Again, the salesman has to make decisions about the

---

[15] James E. Howell and Daniel Teichroew, *Mathematical Analysis for Business Decisions* (Homewood, Ill.: Richard D. Irwin, Inc., 1963), pp. 283–84.

[16] William T. Morris, *Management Science and Action* (Homewood, Ill.: Richard D. Irwin, Inc., 1963), p. 84.

individual accounts but the sales manager may have to act with respect to whole classes of accounts. Thus, to some extent, the management scientist is not free to choose his level of observation or units of ultimate analysis. These tend to be fixed for him by the nature of the action management contemplates. Although the ultimate level of observation or analysis is fixed, one has the opportunity of reaching this level by starting at lower levels of observation. For example, if we need a prediction of total annual sales for a company, we could start by predicting sales by product, customers, or by industry or by month.[17]

The level of observation, as it determines the partial or general nature of a model, is still another way of classifying models, but we need not become entangled in cross-classifications. We may infer from Morris' comment that many models in business tend to be partial rather than general because the focus of the analyst is directed by the activities of the management of a firm, and the model which results treats a particular system rather than a class of systems. Such models lack widespread confirmation and, hence, acceptance.

Deterministic and Probabilistic Models

Mathematical models may be subdivided into deterministic models and probabilistic models. The use of either type is indicated by the nature of the system being studied. We might have a system for which, theoretically, there is an optimum design or optimum mode of operation within defined and unvarying conditions. The model of such a system would be deterministic. However, such optimums are almost totally unknown because of the complexity of interaction among system variables or because we lack the mathematical sophistication required to express them and solve the model. In practice there is difficulty in identifying and estimating the numerical values for what we called the defined and unvarying conditions.[18]

Systems which deterministic models represent are devoid of uncertainty, and changes of state can be perfectly predicted. The way in which the system behaves can be evaluated according to measures of effectiveness, such as cost, profit, time, etc. However, we may lack sufficient understanding of the system and so fail to include or

17 *Ibid.*, p. 85.
18 Beckenbach, *op. cit.*, p. 213.

properly evaluate some characteristics of the system which have an important bearing on the measure of effectiveness which we are trying to maximize (profit) or minimize (cost). If the model is enriched so that it accounts for all important variables and relationships, we may find that we lack the mathematical methods to solve the model for the optimum solution. Until the mathematical techniques are discovered, partial models which we can manipulate mathematically are used, and the solutions gained are recognized to be less than optimum, or to be subject to assumed conditions of complete knowledge; i.e., certainty.

More typically, systems are characterized by attributes that take values which are the result of factors whose interaction is at best poorly understood. These attributes or variables are "produced" by successive trials of stochastic processes. Such processes are described as repetitions of "experiments" whose results are probabilistic; i.e., determined by chance. If in a system periodic values of certain attributes are determined probabilistically, knowledge of the system is less than perfect. Uncertainty exists, and future system states are anticipated subject to qualifications about the probable occurrence of a sequence of events, usually in the environment.

Probabilistic models, by definition, are those which include the representation of stochastic processes or their results. Because uncertainty is more the rule than the exception, most of our models will be probabilistic.

There is a difference between the kind of information which a probabilistic model renders and that which is available from a deterministic model. It is not correct to say that the solution, or rather the processing, of a probabilistic model results in an optimum solution. Given that we have adequately modeled a stochastic process with which we can trace probable future system states, there is never complete assurance that the variables will take on the sequence of values which the model outputs simply because the process is stochastic. Models of this type output emperical data. In effect, we manipulate a system model (having probabilistic elements) and synthetically produce future events. We are thus in a position to sit back and ask: "What would the state of the system be with a given system design; or what would be the state if a particular decision were made?" The answers are in the form of inferences based on observations of experiments with the model.

SUGGESTIONS FOR FURTHER STUDY

BROSS, IRWIN D. J. *Design for Decision.* New York: The Macmillan Co., 1953.

MORRIS, WILLIAM T. *Management Science in Action.* Homewood, Ill.: Richard D. Irwin, Inc., 1963.

OPTNER, STANFORD L. *Systems Analysis for Business Management.* Englewood Cliffs, N.J.: Prentice-Hall, 1960.

TEICHROEW, DANIEL. *An Introduction to Management Science.* New York: John Wiley & Sons, 1964.

CHAPTER 2

Simulation

Definition

IN ITS MOST general sense, simulation means the representation of reality. Hence, verbal description and schematic or diagrammatic representation of some part of the real world constitutes simulation. Holstein and Soukup observe, however, that these forms of simulation are not new. On the other hand,

If . . . simulation necessarily involves the use of mathematical expressions and equations which closely approximate random fluctuations in the simulated system, and which are so complex as to be impossible of solution without the aid of massive electronic computers, then simulation is a very recent development.[1]

Another writer defines simulation as *dynamic representation achieved by building a model and moving it through time.*[2] The model—a mathematical model—is an abstraction of a system which has its counterpart in the real world.

In these definitions we note the references to mathematical models and the computer. Since the system models are processed by the computer, they are *computer models* as the term was defined in the previous chapter.

We use the term "computer model" to denote a special kind of formal mathematical model, namely a model which is not intended to be solved analytically but rather to be simulated on an electronic computer. Simulating a computer model consists in using a digital or analogue computer to trace numerically or graphically the time paths of all endogenous

---

[1] W. K. Holstein and William R. Soukup, *Monte Carlo Simulation,* Institute Paper No. 23, Institute for Quantitative Research and Economics and Management, Graduate School of Industrial Administration. Purdue University, Lafayette, Ind., 1962, p. 1.

[2] William Arthur, "To Simulate or Not to Simulate: That Is the Question," *Educational Data Processing Newsletter,* Vol. 2, No. 4, p. 9.

variables [for example, profit, inventory, price, output] generated by the model.[3]

Before we pursue the definition of computer simulation it is useful to note briefly what has been done using this technique to analyze business systems. The Eastman Kodak Company simulated a system for roll-film spooling, in which product mix and length of production runs varied, to solve problems of equipment design, utilization of operators, and maintenance.

General Electric Company used simulation to test alternative production scheduling procedures. A model of a production system was processed to learn the effect of different machine loading, scheduling, and dispatching procedures. The company thus avoided the cost of trying out new scheduling procedures in the real system.

Imperial Oil modeled its physical distribution system, including hundreds of field warehouses and product flows throughout the system. Results of the simulation were used to determine the feasibility of central warehousing operations.

United Airlines modeled the operations of a large airport; and several months of activity were simulated in a matter of minutes. The model treated weather conditions, maintenance, aircraft, and manpower. This simulation proved useful for planning changes in the requirements for spare aircraft and standby personnel, and for testing the profitability of alternative operating plans.

Other simulations reported in 1959[4] included one by the Humble Oil Company to simulate oil-tanker scheduling. The Port of New York Authority simulated traffic patterns and demands for service prior to designing a central bus terminal. Thompson Products was one of several firms to simulate inventory systems under conditions of uncertainty.

At the same time that system-design and operating problems were being resolved with simulation techniques, nonbusiness systems also were being modeled. Economists employed simulation to predict the rate of economic growth in underdeveloped countries. Sociologists modeled populations so as to better understand and predict voting behavior. In 1960 simulation was used to predict the influence of religion on voting behavior. And psychologists are modeling

---

[3] Kalman J. Cohen, "Simulation of the Firm," *The American Economic Review,* May, 1960, p. 534.

[4] *Report of the Second System Simulation Symposium,* American Institute of Industrial Engineers, Evanston, Ill., 1959.

the learning process and making use of simulation to test the reasonableness of their explanations of this phenomenon. What we have indicated about the widespread use of systems simulation in business, economics, and the social sciences is only a modest start if it is compared with the use of simulation in the physical sciences. There, as in the social sciences, the computer has increased the power of the technique.

From the preceding we may conclude—as one author has—that there has been a veritable explosion of simulation in recent years. However, it is not simply the popularity of a technique nor the ease with which it may be employed that recommends it to students of management. We need to understand *why* the technique is applied and *what distinguishes* it from more formal analytical problem solving methods.

Why Systems Simulation?

[Systems] simulation is useful in the study of a class of problems wherein the operating rules, policies, procedures, and other elements that control production, inventory, etc., are under question . . . [and in which the] number of variables involved, the uncertain nature of inputs, among other things, makes these problems, which are referred to generally as a system, difficult to analyze.[5]

Or, stated somewhat differently:

Mathematical analysis is not powerful enough to yield general analytical solutions to situations as complex as are encountered in business. The alternative is the experimental approach.

The mathematical model of the industrial system is constructed. Such a mathematical model is a detailed description that tells how conditions at one point in time lead to subsequent conditions at later points in time. The behavior of the model is observed and experiments are conducted to answer specific questions about the system that is represented by the model.

"Simulation" is a name often applied to this process of conducting experiments on a model instead of attempting the experiments with their real system. . . .

In business, simulation means setting up in a digital computer the conditions that describe company operations. On the basis of the descriptions and assumptions about the company, the computer then generates the resulting time charts [time paths or series] of information concerning

---

[5] D. G. Malcolm, "The Use of Simulation in Management Analysis: A Survey," *Report of the Second System Simulation Symposium,* American Institute of Industrial Engineers, Evanston, Ill., 1959, p. 18.

finance, manpower, product movement, etc. Different management policies and market assumptions can be tested to determine their effects on company success.

Instead of going from the general analytical solution to the particular special case we have come to appreciate the great utility, if not the mathematical elegance, of the empirical approach. In this we study a number of particular situations, and from these we generalize as far as we dare.[6]

In summary then:

1. Simulation is a problem solving technique.
2. It is an experimental method.
3. Application of simulation is indicated in the solution of problems of (*a*) systems design and (*b*) systems analysis.
4. Simulation is resorted to when the systems under consideration cannot be analyzed using direct or formal analytical methods.

Now let us consider several of these points in greater detail.

Properties of Simulated Systems. The definitions of simulation described systems (for which simulation methods are appropriate) as complex, subject to random fluctuations, and having relationships which are difficult if not impossible to analyze mathematically. By *complexity* we mean that the system is large in terms of the number of variables, parameters, relationships, and events to which the system is responsive.

The existence of *random variables* was implied in the definition which referred to "the uncertain nature of inputs" of a system. Much of the discussion which follows in this text treats the manner in which random variables, or rather the processes (sequences of events) which assign successive values to the variable, are modeled.

The third property of systems for which simulation is an appropriate method of investigation concerns the relationships among system entities and attributes which are not well-behaved, or, as the mathematicians would say, are *not mathematically tractable.*[7] We do not expect that this property, so briefly described, will be immediately meaningful to the student. However, in subsequent expositions of various models the student should develop an awareness that simulation does indeed facilitate the analysis and evalu-

---

[6] Jay W. Forrester, *Industrial Dynamics* (Cambridge, Mass., and New York: The M.I.T. Press and John Wiley & Sons, 1961), pp. 17–18.

[7] For example, a relationship which determines values conditional on existing information. (See the discussion of "decision rules," which follows.)

ation of complex, dynamic relationships which, in many instances, cannot be expressed mathematically except with advanced concepts and difficult evaluation procedures.

System Design

The two applications of simulation listed were the *design* of systems and the *analysis* of system behavior. Design or the design problem simply means that typically the analyst has alternative ways of putting system components together. Given the specification of the desired output of the proposed system, he seeks a design that optimizes some measure of system behavior, such as profit, cost, time, resource utilization, stability, etc. A model of the system is processed incorporating successive changes which correspond to alternative designs. The influence of design on the measure of effectiveness is traced, and the analyst then has a basis for selecting the design which most effectively achieves the desired result or system output. This application, the comparison of alternative designs, is comparable with those experiments that use physical models of aircraft in wind tunnels or ship models in laboratory basins. When we referred to simulation as a kind of management laboratory, we had this application in mind.

To illustrate, consider the problem of designing a retail inventory system.

FIGURE 2-1

$$\text{Materials} \atop \text{Information}\Big\} \xrightarrow{\text{Inputs}} \boxed{\text{Inventory} \atop \text{System}} \xrightarrow{\text{Outputs}} \Big\{ \text{Materials} \atop \text{Information}$$

The inputs to the system are receipts of new stocks from suppliers and customer orders, which are designated "information inputs." The outputs are orders shipped and some form of customer billing. (These sets of inputs and outputs are actually incomplete, but they are sufficient for our discussion.) Average time to process or fill an order is arbitrarily selected as the measure of system effectiveness. (Obviously, other measures of effectiveness could have been selected.) The box labeled Inventory System represents the set of entities, stock items, clerks, documents, etc., which the designer may arrange in any order to minimize the average order processing time.

FIGURE 2-2

Simulation for System Design

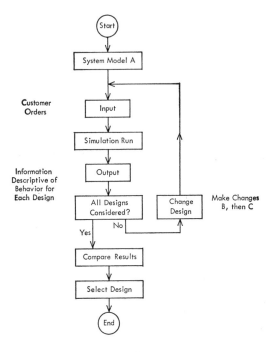

When he specifies the contents of the box (entities, attributes of entities, and relationships; for example, the way in which attributes take on values) the designer is proposing a design alternative. Assume in this case that the analyst wishes to consider and compare design alternatives A, B, and C (and assume that Design A is the standard or reference configuration, and that B and C represent changes or alterations from design A). When Design A is modified we have indeed specified a different system, but it is convenient to simply speak of changes in a model rather than different models.

Alternative designs may differ in the number of clerks, amount of documentation, order in which customers are serviced, rules for reordering stock, etc. Now suppose that a system model of Design A is provided with information about a sequence of customer orders and that the model is processed or "run" so that it traces the activity of processing orders and replenishing stocks of the inventory items. Assume also that the model can be made to report periodic values of various attributes: inventory level, stock on order, back orders, etc. From this information the analyst can obtain the measure of effectiveness dependent on Design A.

Next, Design A is modified so that the alterations or changes we summarized as Design B are introduced. The procedure is repeated. Then changes corresponding to design alternative C are made and the model is processed. Using the three values of the measure of effectiveness, the analyst has a comparative basis for settling on one of the designs for implementation; i.e., construction in the real world. This procedure is shown schematically in Figure 2-2. It should also be noted that our principal use of simulation in this text will be for the purpose of deciding what the design of particular systems should be.

Systems Analysis

The second general application of simulation is to analyze the behavior of systems. The analyst observes systems inputs and outputs and seeks to explain how the transformation is achieved. He postulates a configuration of the system in terms of entities and their relationships, composes a computer model of his theoretical system, provides the model with inputs like those in the real system, and attempts to produce outputs from the model that correspond to those of the real world. The degree to which he succeeds is taken as a measure of the validity of the model; i.e., verification that the analyst can explain what took place in the real system.

The two applications appear to be similar, but in fact they are not. In the first case, simulation is used to obtain information about a system(s) which the analyst has created and about which he knows a great deal. In the second case, the analyst uses simulation to test hypotheses about a system which he does not know well, and whose behavior he can explain only by presuming the existence of particular entities and relationships. The procedure for systems analysis via simulation is diagrammatically shown in Figure 2-3.

FIGURE 2-3

Simulation-Systems Analysis

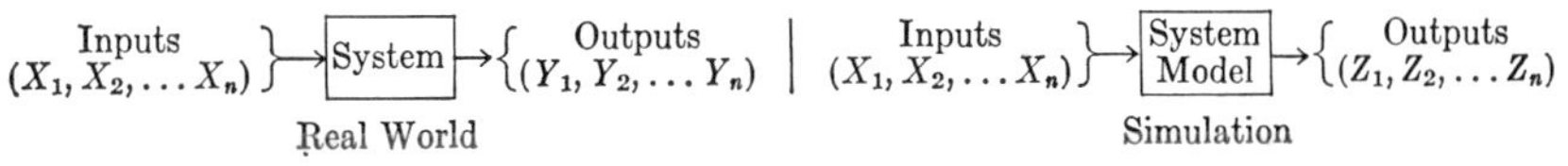

$$\begin{matrix} \text{Inputs} \\ (X_1, X_2, \ldots X_n) \end{matrix} \Big\} \to \boxed{\text{System}} \to \Big\{ \begin{matrix} \text{Outputs} \\ (Y_1, Y_2, \ldots Y_n) \end{matrix} \quad \Big| \quad \begin{matrix} \text{Inputs} \\ (X_1, X_2, \ldots X_n) \end{matrix} \Big\} \to \boxed{\begin{matrix}\text{System} \\ \text{Model}\end{matrix}} \to \Big\{ \begin{matrix} \text{Outputs} \\ (Z_1, Z_2, \ldots Z_n) \end{matrix}$$

Real World   Simulation

The analyst frequently views the real world system as a "black box," the contents of which he wishes to describe by inferring from the observations of system inputs and outputs. As stated before, the theory of system behavior represented by the model is validated by comparing differences between outputs of the real world system, $Y_1, Y_2,...Y_n$, and outputs of the system model, $Z_1, Z_2,...Z_n$. Modifications are made and the model is rerun until the outputs are arbitrarily similar—or until the analyst discards his particular theory in favor of another. In Chapter 11 we shall study a major effort (the model of C. P. Bonini) to use simulation to test a behavioral theory of the firm.

METHODOLOGY

In the following we present the general methodology of computer simulation (regardless of the application), but it is of course the purpose of the text to illustrate in detail how the methodology is implemented. The flow chart, Figure 2-4 outlines the procedure.

FIGURE 2-4

Simulation Procedure*

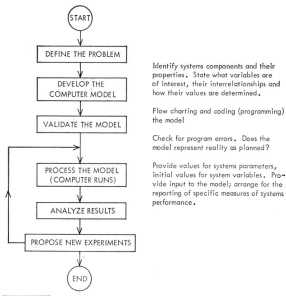

START

DEFINE THE PROBLEM

Identify systems components and their properties. State what variables are of interest, their interrelationships and how their values are determined.

DEVELOP THE COMPUTER MODEL

Flow charting and coding (programming) the model

VALIDATE THE MODEL

Check for program errors. Does the model represent reality as planned?

PROCESS THE MODEL (COMPUTER RUNS)

Provide values for systems parameters, initial values for system variables. Provide input to the model; arrange for the reporting of specific measures of systems performance.

ANALYZE RESULTS

PROPOSE NEW EXPERIMENTS

END

* Adapted from Daniel Teichroew and John F. Lubin, "Computer Simulation: Discussion of the Technique and Comparison of Languages," Working Paper No. 20, Graduate School of Business, Stanford University, Stanford, Calif., 1964, pp. 27–29.

Computational Concepts in Simulation.[8]   Reference has been made to a number of concepts which should now be defined. Attributes of system entities may change through time, in which case we call them *system variables* or, alternatively, *state variables*. The latter term is often used since the set of attribute values at any point in time defines the "state of the system." The state of our inventory system at any time would be obtained by noting the values of such attributes as Inventory on Hand, Inventory on Order, etc., which are attributes of the entity, Stock Item. Attributes of other system entities would also be noted.

Parameters are considered to be those attribute values which do not change during the simulation. For example, a stock item might have the attribute Cost per Unit. For certain cases this attribute would be fixed during a simulated time, and it is necessary to state only initially what the parameter value is. System or state variables, on the other hand, must be given an initial value, but relationships in the system are periodically evaluated so that the system model is said to generate values for these variables. And (not to add to the confusion) we might point out that because these values are generated within the model, and depend on what happened earlier in the simulation, these values—or rather the variables to which the values are assigned—are called *endogenous variables*. Thus we will use the three terms interchangeably: *system, state,* and *endogenous* variables.

To process a model it is necessary not only to state parameter values and initial values for system variables, but some provision must be made for "moving the model through time." We are interested in the dynamic behavior of the system. Typically, the simulation begins at time zero, at which time the parameters and system variables have the initial values provided by the analyst.

Next, various events are generated or input to the model which cause changes to take place and which result in new values for the system or state variables. For example, in the inventory system the receipt of the first customer order (an event) results in changes in inventory and in the value of customer billings (or accounts receivable). The reduction in inventory might occasion an order to the supplier for new stock. In the computer all this activity takes place in a fraction of a minute but it corresponds, let us say, to the firm's activity during a full day.

Now provision for advancing the clock or the calendar is required;

---

[8] *Ibid.* (Figure 2-4), pp. 32–33.

that is, we move to the next day or we input the next exogenous event and the model processes the information, describing the event, and, according to the relationships contained in the model, a second set of values of the state variables is computed. The process continues until all events have been input or until the simulation has run for the desired length of time.

Finally, two additional computational requirements exist in order to conduct simulations. We shall not detail them here since we have already alluded to them—and since their exploration must be deferred to those chapters which review some elements of probability and descriptive statistics. The requirements, however, are the provision for generating values of random variables, which are treated as the outcomes of exogenous events, and the summarization and analysis of the results of the simulation.

SIMULATION AND DECISION MAKING

Relationships among entities and attributes take several forms. One kind of relationship may be illustrated with reference to an inventory system by considering the attributes, BEGINNING INVENTORY, ENDING INVENTORY, CUSTOMER ORDERS. These attributes (variables) may be related in the fashion:

ENDING INVENTORY = BEGINNING INVENTORY −
CUSTOMER ORDERS.

We imply that the values have meaning at certain times; that is, at the beginning and end of the day or at some other points in time, and that the magnitudes are expressed in common units, dollars or physical units. When modeling a system it is necessary that we express many such relationships in order to obtain sequential values of state variables.

Another and more interesting relationship might be illustrated by the following expression:

When INVENTORY ON HAND $\leqq$ 50 units; order 200 units.

This relationship is known as a *decision rule*. Whether or not an order is placed is conditional on the value of INVENTORY ON HAND. However, the relationship serves to compute the value of an attribute which we might call INVENTORY ON ORDER. At the start of the simulation the value of this state variable might be zero and would remain so until INVENTORY ON HAND $\leqq$ 50 . At that time the model would employ the decision rule to order 200 units and the value of INVENTORY ON ORDER would be 200. Thinking ahead we can see that this variable would be decreased whenever an order from a supplier was received. A second relationship, describing INVENTORY ON HAND , INVENTORY ON ORDER , and INVENTORY RECEIVED , would have to be specified.

Simulation is especially powerful for testing and comparing the way decision rules affect system behavior. Many design changes are changes of the parameters of decision rules (50 and 200 in our example) as well as changes of the form of the rule. For example, we might wish to substitute as a reorder rule the following:

Order 100 units every day .

Not all decision making is so unambiguous. Neither are certain decisions made regularly. Yet, as we have implied, decision making can be interpreted literally as modifying the state of a system.

Decision Making

The decision-maker is assumed to act periodically to influence the design of the system in order to transform a set of inputs into a set of outputs which have economic value. We assume further that the system has been designed to achieve transformation or conversion of inputs in a reasonably effective fashion. However, we may observe that in the best designed systems conversion does not always measure up to the designer's plans. Things go wrong—availability of inputs of required quantity or quality are not completely controllable. Faulty production occurs, orders are delayed in processing, machines break down, the market places changing values on the product or service output of the systems, and so on.

The effects of such events change the system state in a way that prompts the decision-maker to modify something about the system. Perhaps he rearranges the set of inputs, or changes its composition. These changes, modifications, or redesign of the system constitute decision making of a particular kind. The decision-maker elects to modify the system in order to better achieve the purpose(s) or ideal set of outputs for which the system was created, given information that outputs are not being achieved according to the measure of effectiveness. Decisions of this type may also be made on the basis of anticipated environmental changes which could lead to unsatisfactory system behavior.

There is a second type of decision, unlike that described above, which is imposed irregularly on the decision-maker. Some decisions are routinely required simply because the system is not automatic. Here we might imagine that activity takes place within the system and that the conversion of inputs proceeds to a particular state, the description of which is available to the decision-maker. He then initiates one of several regular courses of action. He is constrained by existing policy or he uses the information in conjunction with a decision rule of the form described above.

Courses of action usually involve commitments either to purchase or to hire resources: for example, the decision rule that when the inventory of stock item $Z \leqq x$ units, order A number of units from the supplier; or, if the number of jobs scheduled today $> H$ number of machine hours, start up the standby machine; or, if plant utilization $< P$ percent this week, lay off workers, etc.

In both cases, decision making is a response by the manager who tries to control the behavior of the system. Conditions, or rather events exogenous to the system, can compel the manager to make decisions; or decisions may in part be planned and periodic responses required to sustain activity in the system. Simulation is used to improve the quality of both kinds of decision making.

AN ILLUSTRATIVE EXAMPLE

To summarize many of the concepts and the simulation methodology, let us consider a small exercise in simulation which is intended merely to demonstrate certain features of the procedure. The student should not hazard an evaluation of simulation on the basis of the example in which simplifying assumptions are made and methodological short cuts used.

We fall back on the classical problem of the newsboy who seeks to fashion an inventory ordering rule so that the amount of his profit is maximized. Uncertainty exists in this situation because the number of papers purchased daily by his customers cannot be predicted. In such an inventory system we have the entities Newspapers, Customers, Newsboy, and Profit. The entity Newspapers has attributes: NUMBER ORDERED, NUMBER SOLD, COST, and PRICE. Profit has a single attribute of interest, AMOUNT. Attributes of Newspapers are recorded in units; the attribute of Profit, AMOUNT, in dollars.

A relationship can be written to express the way in which AMOUNT takes daily values:

$$AMOUNT = (NUMBER\ SOLD)(PRICE) - (NUMBER\ ORDERED)(COST).$$

COST and PRICE refer to per unit values and we assume that unsold inventory has zero value. In the example we shall disregard the cost of unfilled demand; COST and PRICE are defined as parameters; and we shall assign the values: COST = $0.05; PRICE = $0.15.

The state variables NUMBER ORDERED and NUMBER SOLD must be generated. NUMBER ORDERED will take values determined by the evaluation of a decision rule which our newsboy elects to employ. The rule will be to order each day the number of papers demanded the preceding day. Thus each day:

$$NUMBER\ ORDERED(DAY) = NUMBER\ DEMANDED(DAY - 1),$$

where the value of the subscript (DAY) represents the current date. This illustrates the need for a system calender variable, which we designate DAY, which takes on the values 1, 2, 3, ..., n.[9]

The variable, NUMBER SOLD, is determined in part by the exogenous event, CUSTOMER DEMAND. NUMBER SOLD also depends on the NUMBER ORDERED. If CUSTOMER DEMAND is equal to or less than NUMBER ORDERED, the newsboy can satisfy all customers. If CUSTOMER DEMAND is greater than NUMBER ORDERED, the newsboy can only sell an amount equal to NUMBER ORDERED. This relationship, used to determine NUMBER SOLD, can be expressed:

If CUSTOMER DEMAND ≦ NUMBER ORDERED,
then NUMBER SOLD = CUSTOMER DEMAND,

and

If CUSTOMER DEMAND > NUMBER ORDERED,
then NUMBER SOLD = NUMBER ORDERED.

---

[9] The notation used here anticipates the computer language, FORTRAN, which is introduced in the next chapter. Conventionally, we would write the subscripted variables as $NUMBER\ ORDERED_i$, $NUMBER\ SOLD_{i-1}$.

To generate values for CUSTOMER DEMAND we now resort to a shortcut, the implications of which are fully developed in Chapter 6. Suppose the newsboy knows from past experience that CUSTOMER DEMAND (daily) may be 15, 16, 17, 18, 19, or 20 newspapers. He also knows from his experience the relative frequency with which each value occurred and can thus construct the following table.

Customer Demand	Relative Frequency
15	1/12
16	2/12
17	4/12
18	3/12
19	1/12
20	1/12
	12/12

He regards that the value of CUSTOMER DEMAND is determined by chance, but that in the long run the values occur with the frequencies noted. Therefore our newsboy constructs a type of roulette wheel in which the area is divided into six segments, each marked with a value of the variable, and each segment proportional in size to its relative frequency:

Each day the wheel is spun and the number of the segment taken to be the value of the variable, CUSTOMER DEMAND. He is now ready to simulate the system and test his proposed reorder rule. Table 2-1, which shows an average daily profit of $1.62, summarizes his activity for 10 days.

To begin the simulation, our newsboy spins his CUSTOMER DEMAND wheel and lets the first value represent demand the preceding day. This is necessary since his reorder rule requires a prior value (in our example this value was 18). Therefore the NUMBER ORDERED for DAY NUMBER 1 is 18. Next the wheel is used to generate CUSTOMER DEMAND for the first day. As we performed the simulation this value turned out to be 17. Comparing

Table 2-1

Newsboy Simulation

Day	Customer Demand	Number Ordered	Customer Demand	≤	Number Ordered	Customer Demand	>	Number Ordered	Number Sold	Amount	Amount (Cumulative)
1	17	18		✓					17	1.65	1.65
2	17	17		✓					17	1.70	3.35
3	16	17		✓					16	1.55	4.90
4	17	16					✓		16	1.60	6.50
5	15	17		✓					15	1.40	7.90
6	17	15					✓		15	1.50	9.40
7	18	17					✓		17	1.70	11.10
8	20	18					✓		18	1.80	12.90
9	17	20		✓					17	1.55	14.45
10	18	17					✓		17	1.70	16.15

CUSTOMER DEMAND and NUMBER ORDERED for DAY NUMBER 1, CUSTOMER DEMAND was less than NUMBER ORDERED. The NUMBER SOLD, employing our rule, is therefore 17 and AMOUNT is

$$(17)\,(0.15) - (18)\,(0.05) = \$1.65.$$

The variable "DAY" is given the value $DAY = DAY + 1$, which has the effect of moving us to the next day. The process is repeated, and the results are shown in Table 2-1.

The newsboy could now propose changes in the system, specifically in the reorder rule. He might wish to test a rule in which, for example, he orders an amount equal to average sales over perhaps the last three or five days. Other changes might be proposed. If he had reason to believe that the variable CUSTOMER DEMAND might change, he could model the anticipated change. We are not suggesting that a short, ten-day simulation run produces reliable information, nor that we have considered all properties of the system, but the illustration serves to point out (in an elementary fashion) how the methodology is implemented. The meanings of such concepts as entities, attributes, state variables, parameters, decision rule, calendar, etc., are, hopefully, a little more meaningful.

The illustration points up another aspect of simulation. If we were to expand our model and propose a simulation run of several hundred or several thousand days for each of a series of system designs, we can readily appreciate the amount of effort involved. It is precisely for this reason that we call in the digital computer, and it is to the subject of computer programming that we turn in the next chapter.

SUGGESTIONS FOR FURTHER STUDY

FORRESTER, JAY W. *Industrial Dynamics*. Cambridge, Mass., and New York: The M.I.T. Press and John Wiley & Sons, 1961.

ORCUTT, G. H.; GREENBERGER, M.; KORBEL, J.; AND RIVLIN, A. H. *Microanalysis of Socio-Economic Systems*. New York: Harper & Row, 1961.

TOCHER, K. D. *The Art of Simulation*. Princeton, N.J.: D. Van Nostrand Co., 1963.

CHAPTER 3

Introduction to Programming

PROGRAMMING is the composition of programs. A computer program, as we shall see, is a model. It is a unique model in two ways: (1) It is constructed in conformance with a number of rather rigorous conventions, peculiar to computer logic, and thereby (2) The model itself is intelligible to a computer in the sense that if the model is introduced or "fed into" the computer, the computer will respond by performing certain operations which the model calls for.

Programs may be written in any of a number of "languages," but the computer itself understands only one language: so-called "machine language." Developing fluency in machine language requires a great deal of study, and constructing programs in machine language is tedious and slow. Fortunately, there are a number of other languages which require minimal effort to understand and to use in building powerful computer models. When programming is done in any language other than machine language, it must first be "translated," by means of a special intermediary program called a *compiler,* into machine language. A computer equipped with the proper compiler can do the translating.

FORTRAN (an abbrevation for FORmula TRANslation) is a language for which compilers are rather universally available. There are many variations in FORTRAN compilers, but most versions are sufficiently similar that minor modifications in any FORTRAN program will make it susceptible to translation by most FORTRAN compilers, and hence usable on most computers.

Thus FORTRAN becomes a somewhat universal language, ideally suited to analytical model building, and a good "basic language" from which to learn other computer languages when the need arises.

A FORTRAN program consists of a number of statements, or instructions, to the computer. To develop some fluency in FORTRAN we will first examine some of the basic conventions governing FORTRAN programming, and then we will explore the mechanical process by which a FORTRAN program is prepared for submission to the computer for compiling and subsequent execution.

ALGEBRAIC EXPRESSIONS, MEMORY, AND THE SEQUENCE OF OPERATIONS

There are a number of different kinds of statements that make up the list of possible FORTRAN instructions. The basic algebraic statement is one of these. It consists of a variable, an equal sign, and some expression to the right of the equal sign. When such a statement is encountered the computer gives to the variable on the left side of the equal sign the value of the expression on the right side of the equal sign. Thus, upon encountering the statement AHC = 40.00, the computer stores in its "memory" the value 40.00 for AHC. Later, if we call for the value of the variable AHC to be printed out for us, the value 40.00 will be printed out (assuming that the value of AHC has not been changed through subsequent operation).

The expression to the right of the equal sign can be a more involved mathematical expression; for example: AHC = 70.00 + 20.00 − 50.00. The computer will perform whatever computation is called for by the expression to the right of the equal sign, and then will give to the variable on the left of the equal sign the value resulting from the computation. It should be emphasized that a variable—and only one variable—can appear to the left of the equal sign in an algebraic statement in FORTRAN. The following has no meaning in FORTRAN: AHC + 10.00 = 50.00.

The computer reads statements (instructions) in a program from the top down unless specifically instructed to do otherwise. Furthermore, a succeeding algebraic statement can supersede a prior one. For example, the variable AHC is given two different values in the following three statements: AHC = 40.00, AOC = 25.00, and AHC = 60.00. The computer, on encountering the first of the above statements, stores 40.00 for the variable AHC; but by the time the last statement has been executed AHC has the value 60.00, the 40.00 having been replaced by 60.00.

Thus far we have used only constants to the right of the equal sign in our algebraic statements. In most programs variables also appear on the right side of the equal sign. An appropriate FOR-TRAN algebraic statement might also be: TAC = AHC + AOC.

Upon encountering the above algebraic statement the computer would add together the values currently stored for the variables AHC and AOC, and would store the value of the sum for the variable TAC. (By the time a statement such as that above is encountered, the variables AHC and AOC should, of course, have been given the desired values.)

A great deal of flexibility is permissible in writing variable names; however, there *are* a few rules, and several of the most important are:

1. Variables can consist of no more than six letters or six letters and numbers;
2. Every variable must begin with a letter;
3. All letters must be capitals (there are no lower case letters in FORTRAN);
4. It is unwise to end a variable with the letter F (for reasons which will be enlarged upon later).

OPERATIONAL SYMBOLS

Some FORTRAN operational symbols are like ordinary mathematical symbols, but some are not. The customary mathematical symbols, their meaning, and the corresponding FORTRAN symbols which will concern us most appear below:

Mathematical Symbol	Meaning	Corresponding FORTRAN symbol
+	add	+
−	subtract	−
÷	divide	/
×	multiply	*
( )^2	raise to a power (square)	**2
$\sqrt{}$	take the square root of	SQRTF( )

A few examples will illustrate the use of these symbols and will increase our understanding of FORTRAN programming.

The compound interest formula, which gives the amount (S) to which an initial deposit (P) will grow in n years when compounded at r percent annually, is $S = P(1 + r)^n$.

We might instruct the computer to determine the amount to which \$1,000[1] invested at 4 percent compounded annually would grow in six years by the following program segment:[2]

$$P = 1000.00$$
$$R = .04$$
$$N = 6$$
$$S = P * (1.0 + R) **N$$

A question might be raised at this point: How, in the final statement above, does the computer know whether to multiply P times the quantity $(1 + R)$ *before* or *after* raising the quantity $(1 + R)$ to the 6th power? There is a *hierarchy of operations* in FORTRAN, and it should be *memorized*.

THE HIERARCHY OF MATHEMATICAL OPERATIONS IN AN ALGEBRAIC EXPRESSION

The computer first scans everything that appears to the right of the equal sign in an algebraic expression, then

Everything which appears inside a set of parentheses is done first.
Exponentiation is done next.
Then *multiplication and division* are done.
Finally, *addition and subtraction* are done.

Whenever one of the above rules does not answer the query, What should be done next? the computer moves from left to right, executing operations called for in that order.

As we will see, parentheses can be used extensively to group portions of a complex algebraic expression in order to minimize the likelihood of error. Also, parentheses can be "nested," with one set inside another.

At the end of the above program the computer would have stored for the variable S the value of our deposit at the end of the sixth year.

---

[1] In FORTRAN, commas cannot be used to group digits in an algebraic expression; also the dollar sign (\$) must never appear in an algebraic statement.
[2] This job could also, of course, have been done by the statement:
$$S = 1000.0*(1.0 + .04)**6.$$

THE PRINT STATEMENT

There are several FORTRAN statements whose purposes are to input and output data. The PRINT statement causes to be printed out for one or more specified variables the current values stored for those variables. Thus if the statement PRINT_____,N,S is inserted at the end of the compound interest program above, it would cause the value of N and the value of S to be printed out at the end of the program.

The blank in the PRINT statement above indicates that we have left something out. Specifically, we have left out reference to what is termed a FORMAT statement. A FORMAT statement is used to specify the format in which we want the print-out to appear; i.e., whether the values of N and S should appear side by side, one above the other, with some identifying terminology, or otherwise. More will be said about FORMAT statements shortly.

NUMBERED STATEMENTS AND THE GO TO STATEMENT

FORTRAN statements can be numbered. For a variety of reasons (which will soon become apparent) it is useful to number many FORTRAN statements. These numbers always appear to the left of the statement.

It was pointed out earlier that, unless otherwise specified, statements in a FORTRAN program will be executed in top-to-bottom order. The GO TO statement is one of a variety of statements which can be used to change this order of execution. Every GO TO statement must have a number after the words GO TO. Upon encountering a GO TO statement, the computer will proceed to the statement whose number appears after the words GO TO, whether the statement whose number is given appears prior or subsequent to the GO TO statement. To understand the use of the GO TO statement, examine the program segment in Figure 3-1.

With this program the computer is instructed to calculate the amount to which a deposit of $1,000, earning 4 percent compounded, would grow in one year. The value of the deposit at the end of the year, S, is printed out. This value is then viewed as the initial deposit (P is set equal to S in the next-to-last statement), and the

FIGURE 3-1

FIGURE 3-1

Program Segment Containing Go To Statement

$$P = 1000.00$$
$$R = .04$$
$$N = 1$$
$$2 \quad S = P * (1.0 + R) **N$$
$$\text{PRINT } \underline{\hspace{1cm}}, S$$
$$P = S$$
$$\text{GO TO } 2$$

computer is sent back to calculate the amount to which the new deposit will grow at the end of the next year by the statement: GO TO 2. As the program is written above there is nothing except failure of the equipment to prevent the process being repeated indefinitely.

COUNTERS

In many programs one finds need of a "counter" to count the number of times a repetitive program has been repeated. We might use a counter in the above program to keep track of the number of years our $1,000 has been on deposit, and to print this information out, along with the value of the balance on deposit at the end of each year. In the following program segment the variable YEAR serves as our counter, and every time statements number 2 through the GO TO statement are repeated the value of the variable YEAR is increased by 1.

$$\text{YEAR} = 0.0$$
$$P = 1000.00$$
$$R = .04$$
$$N = 1$$
$$2 \quad S = P * (1.0 + R) ** N$$
$$\text{YEAR} = \text{YEAR} + 1.0$$
$$\text{PRINT} \underline{\hspace{1cm}}, \text{YEAR,S}$$
$$P = S$$
$$\text{GO TO } 2$$

(Note: The choice of numbers to employ in numbering statements is limited only by the fact that statement numbers must be non-zero, positive integers of five digits or less. Where many numbers are employed in a program they *need not* appear in consecutive order.)

THE *IF* STATEMENT

The IF statement is a "conditional" GO TO statement, and is best illustrated by an example: IF (YEAR − 10.0)2,4,7.

When the above statement is encountered, the computer will evaluate the expression which appears inside the parentheses after the word IF in precisely the same fashion that it evaluates the expression to the right of an equal sign in an algebraic statement. If the value of the result is negative, the computer will proceed immediately to statement number 2; if the value of the result is equal to 0, the computer will proceed immediately to statement number 4; if the value of the result is positive, the computer will proceed immediately to statement number 7. It does not matter whether statements number 2, 4, and 7 appear before or after the IF statement.

In our compound interest problem we might use an IF statement —in place of the GO TO statement—to stop the repetitive process of calculating the balance on hand at the end of, say, 10 years:

```
      YEAR = 0.0
      P = 1000.00
      R = .04
      N = 1
  2   S = P * (1.0 + R) **N
      YEAR = YEAR + 1.0
      PRINT_____, YEAR,S
      P = S
      IF (YEAR − 10.0)2,4,4
  4   CONTINUE
```

On the 10th iteration the value of the expression in parentheses becomes zero, and the flow of control is sent to statement number 4. In our program the expression in parentheses would never become greater than zero (positive), so we really need only statements number 2 and 4. However, all IF statements must mention three statement numbers after the parentheses, and each of the numbers must refer to a statement in the program. To conform to this FORTRAN convention we simply write: IF (YEAR − 10.0)2,4,4.

The CONTINUE statement serves only to provide a statement for the number 4. When the CONTINUE statement is encountered, the computer passes on to the statement which follows the CONTINUE statement.

THE *STOP* AND *END* STATEMENTS

The preceding program segment is a complete FORTRAN program except for the specification of the FORMAT for printing out the answer (left blank in the PRINT statement) and except for a terminal statement; that is, a STOP and an END statement. (STOP statements can be used at times without an END statement, but an END statement, which must terminate all programs, must be preceded by a STOP statement.)

Our complete FORTRAN program for determining the amount to which $1,000 would grow if compounded annually at 4 percent for 10 years (complete except for the FORMAT requirement referred to above) would be as follows:

```
        YEAR = 0.0
        P = 1000.00
        R = .04
        N = 1
    2   S = P * (1.0 + R) **N
        YEAR = YEAR + 1.0
        PRINT_____, YEAR,S
        P = S
        IF (YEAR − 10.0)2,4,4
    4   CONTINUE
        STOP
        END
```

THE *DO* STATEMENT

We could achieve the same results as those we've achieved in the above program by a simpler scheme using a powerful FORTRAN statement called the DO statement or the DO loop. Like the GO TO and the IF statements, the DO statement influences the order of execution of statements in a program. The DO statement is also best explained by an example: DO 4 J = 5,35,3.

The 4 following the word DO refers to a statement (statement number 4) which must *follow* the DO statement. Upon encountering the above DO statement the computer will give the variable J the value 5. It will then proceed down *through* statement number 4 as in any other program. Upon reaching statement 4 the computer will execute statement number 4 and then will return to the DO statement, whereupon it will increase the value stored for the variable J by 3 (making it 8), then it will proceed as before through statement number 4, returning again to the DO statement, increasing the value stored for the variable J by an additional 3 units (making it now 11), etc. This looping process will continue until J has grown to the point where to repeat the loop again would cause J to be greater than 35, whereupon the looping process is discontinued, and the computer proceeds to the statement which follows statement number 4 (the end of the DO loop) and continues through the remainder of the program.

Much more remains to be said about DO loops if their full potential is to be utilized, but we will allow ourselves only three comments at this point:

1. If only two numbers follow the equal sign in the DO statement, the third number (the amount by which the value of the variable is to be increased each time the loop is repeated) is presumed to be 1.
2. Variables, rather than numbers, *can* be used to the right of the equal sign in the DO statement, making it possible to cause the number of times the loop is to be repeated dependent upon prior calculations in the program.
3. The variable to the left of the equal sign in the DO statement can, *but need not necessarily,* be employed in the program anywhere else except in the DO statement itself.

Now that we have introduced the DO statement, we can write a more economical program (Figure 3-2) to cause the computer to calculate for us the balance of our $1,000 deposit after 10 years compounding at 4 percent per year:[3]

FIGURE 3-2

"Economic" Version of Sample Compounding Program

```
        P = 1000.00
        R = .04
        N = 1
        DO 3 J = 1,10
        S = P * (1.0 + R) **N
        P = S
     3  PRINT_____,J,S
        STOP
        END
```

---

[3] Admittedly, we could determine the answer to our compound interest problem more simply (as suggested in footnote 2). However, we have deliberately used the compound interest formula in this way so as to introduce the basic kinds of statements of which most FORTRAN programs are composed.

WRITING AND PUNCHING A PROGRAM

We now know enough about FORTRAN to write some rather powerful programs. However, before proceeding to use our knowledge of programming to deal with problems of this character, we would do well to explore the fashion in which a FORTRAN program is prepared to be "fed into" the computer for compiling and subsequent execution.

We have seen that a FORTRAN program essentially consists of a series of statements. To introduce a program into the computer we need to transpose our written statements to a set of punched cards. Transposition is achieved by simply typing, on the typewriter-like keyboard of a special card-punch machine, the FORTRAN statements in our program. Our FORTRAN statements become a "deck of cards," with holes punched in them. In general, each statement appears on a separate card, although, as will be shown, if a statement is too long to be punched on one card as many as ten cards can be employed to accommodate one statement.

When a letter, number, or other symbol is typed on the keyboard of the card-punch machine, one or more holes are punched in one or more of 12 possible positions in a vertical column on the card. The pattern of holes tells the computer which symbol is intended, and it is in this way that our FORTRAN instructions are communicated to the computer.

Figure 3-3 shows how the FORTRAN statement we've used in our compound interest program (to calculate the growth of our deposit in one year) might appear on a punched card.

A number of rather strict FORTRAN conventions govern the preparation of punched cards, and they must be learned. Most of these conventions have to do with the placement of symbols on the card. As shown in Figure 3-3, each card has 80 columns. Columns 1 through 5 are reserved for statement numbers, and FORTRAN statement numbers must be punched in any one or more of these columns. (Column 1 has an additional function which will be described shortly.)

Columns 7 through 72 are reserved for the FORTRAN statement proper. Except in FORMAT statements (discussed below), spaces may be employed rather freely in punching a FORTRAN statement. Thus the preceding statement could be punched as shown in Figure

FIGURE 3-3

FORTRAN Punched-Card Version for The Statement of the
Compound Interest Program

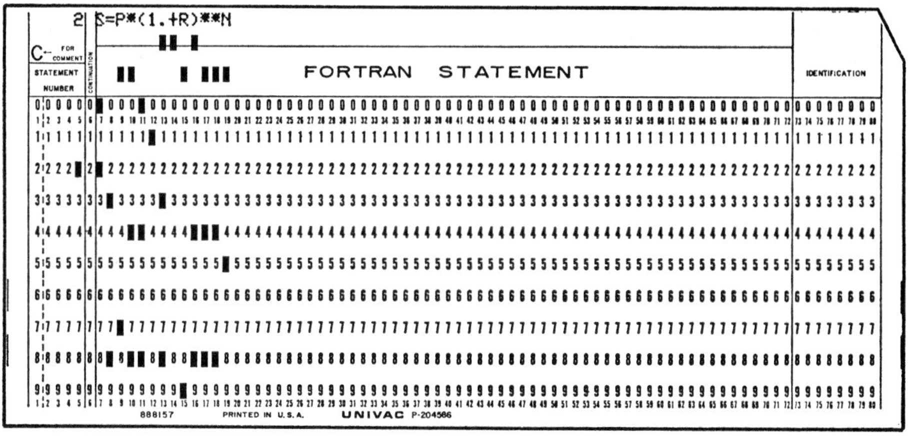

3-3 or it could be spread out to consume all the columns from 7 to 72.

Columns 73 to 80, inclusive, are ignored by the computer; they may be used by the programmer to number his cards or identify them in some other way for his own convenience.

Column 6 is employed to indicate a continuation where a statement is too long to be punched on one card. If one card is sufficient for a statement, column 6 can be left blank or punched with a zero. If additional cards are required for one statement, a non-zero integer must be punched in column 6 of each of the cards on which the continued statement is continued. A good practice is to leave column 6 blank if one card is sufficient for a statement. If more than one card is required, punch a zero in column 6 of the first card of the statement, punch a 1 in column 6 of the first continuation card, a 2 in column 6 of the second continuation card, and so on. (To repeat: no more than ten cards can be employed for one FORTRAN statement.)

A FORTRAN program is ready for submission to the computer when the statements have been punched in conformance with the rules described above and when the card deck is arranged in consecutive order—with the card corresponding to the first statement on top.

THE FORMAT STATEMENT

We have deliberately postponed introducing the FORMAT statement until the punching of cards was described. Of all FORTRAN conventions, those having to do with the FORMAT statement require the most rigorous attention to form, and rigorous attention to form means, chiefly, rigorous conformance to space specification requirements.

One use of the FORMAT statement has been mentioned: By use of a FORMAT statement we specify for the computer precisely the format in which we want data to be printed out for us following computations called for in the program. A second use of the FORMAT statement, in which data is read into the computer, will be described later.

In our previous use of the PRINT statement we employed a blank to indicate that something—a statement number—had been left out. Our complete PRINT statement for the program, shown in Figure 3-1, might be written: PRINT 8,S.

The number 8 refers to a FORMAT statement whose number is 8. (All FORMAT statements are numbered statements.) A set of parentheses must follow the word FORMAT in a FORMAT statement. Inside the parentheses, the arrangement of the data to be printed out is specified. The FORMAT statement referred to in our PRINT statement above might be written: 8 FORMAT (1HO,10X,F8.2).

The first expression in the parentheses, 1HO, specifies that prior to each print-out (i.e., prior to the printing out of each new value of our deposit S at the end of each succeeding year) we want the printing mechanism associated with the computer to double-space. Each succeeding value for S, therefore, will be printed on a separate line, with a blank line in between. With the expression 1H1 in the first position in the parentheses, we could cause each value for S to be printed out on a new page (hardly appropriate here, but frequently desirable). Finally, if we were content with single spacing, we would employ the expression   1H   (i.e., we would leave a blank space after the H).

In the third expression, F8.2, the F specifies that the value we expect to be printed out for S will have a fractional part; i.e., it will contain a decimal. Had we made provision throughout our program to deal only with integers, we would have used an I rather than an F specification. More will be said later about the need to distinguish between integers and decimal quantities.

The 8 in the 8.2 specifies that 8 columns or spaces should be reserved for printing out the various values of S. The .2 specifies that 2 spaces should be reserved for digits to the right of the decimal point. The space to be reserved for the printing out of data must be clearly specified in the FORMAT statement. One space must be reserved for each digit; one for the decimal point; and one for the *sign* of the number to be printed out (indicating whether it is a positive or negative quantity). If we expect the values of S to be 9999.00 or less, then 8 spaces would be adequate.

It is permissible to reserve more spaces than will be required, but care should be taken to reserve enough spaces so that no part of our answer gets truncated except that part which we want truncated. In the process of computing the values of S each time through our program, the computer will carry its calculations well beyond the two decimal places we are interested in as an answer. (How far beyond two decimal places the computation will be carried depends on the word length of the computer.) Each time the PRINT statement is encountered, the computer will round off the value of S to two significant digits (since we specified two digits to the right of the decimal point in the FORMAT statement to which our PRINT statement refers), and will print out only the *rounded* answer, dropping the decimal digits that were carried during the computation.

The second expression in the parentheses, 10X, specifies that the eight spaces reserved for printing out the value of S should begin 10 spaces to the right of the left margin of the sheet on which the values of S are to be printed out. Thus we specify *blank* spaces with the use of X's.

When a great deal of data is to be printed out—data of a number of different types—it is frequently useful to provide identifying remarks for the printed-out data. This can be done with an H specification. To understand how the H specification might be used, recall the PRINT statement of our final compound interest program (Figure 3-2): 3 PRINT 9,J,S.

We will let 9 refer to a FORMAT statement which we will write as follows:

9 FORMAT (1H ,22HAT END OF YEAR NUMBER ,I4,
5X,11HBALANCE = $,F8.2).

When our PRINT statement is executed, the computer will first cause to be printed out, beginning at the left margin, the following: AT END OF YEAR NUMBER. Twenty-two spaces were reserved for this group of words and spaces, as shown by the number 22 preceding the H, which precedes the first word of the group. The H indicates that the twenty-two characters and spaces which follow it should be printed out precisely as they appear inside the parentheses of the FORMAT statement.

In the next four spaces will be printed out the current value of the variable J, since four spaces are reserved for the value of J by the next expression in the FORMAT statement, I4. The next expression, 5X, will cause five spaces to be skipped. Next, the group for which eleven spaces were provided in the FORMAT statement will be printed out: BALANCE = $.

Finally, in the next eight spaces the current value of the variable S will be printed, since eight spaces were reserved for the value of S by the expression F8.2 in the FORMAT statement.

Our print-out for the first three times through the DO loop would therefore appear as follows:

```
AT END OF YEAR NUMBER    1    BALANCE = $ 1040.00
AT END OF YEAR NUMBER    2    BALANCE = $ 1081.60
AT END OF YEAR NUMBER    3    BALANCE = $ 1124.86
```

Notice that a plus sign would not get printed out for the values of S. Negative values are indicated by a minus sign on print-out, but positive values are simply given no sign at all, in conformance with algebraic custom. However, if a value is expected to be positive, space still must be reserved for the sign, whether or not it will be printed out.

In our PRINT and FORMAT statements above we have provided for printing out only two values, one for the current value of the variable J and one for the current value of the variable S. Note that the computer automatically associates the first variable mentioned in the PRINT statement with the space reserved by the first specification (the I specification) in the FORMAT statement, the second variable mentioned in the PRINT statement with the space reserved by the second specification (the F specification) in the FORMAT statement, and so on.

It is possible to have a PRINT statement and a corresponding FORMAT statement where no numerical values of program variables are to be printed at all. Instead of the scheme used above for identifying output data we might have used two sets of PRINT and FORMAT statements to create a two-column matrix for output data, with a heading above each column. Thus, before the DO statement in the program shown in Figure 3-2, we might have written:

```
     PRINT 10
 10  FORMAT  (1HO,2X,4HYEAR,2X,1OHBALANCE($))
```

Then, at the end of the DO loop, we might place the following two statements, with the first statement (the PRINT statement) *inside* the DO loop:

```
         PRINT 11, J,S
 11  FORMAT  (1H ,2X,I4,3X,F8.2)
```

With this arrangement the print-out, by the third time through the DO loop, would appear as follows:

```
     YEAR  BALANCE($)
      1      1 0 4 0 . 0 0
      2      1 0 8 1 . 6 0
      3      1 1 2 4 . 8 6
```

One has a rather high degree of freedom in arranging data print-outs since most computers are equipped to print up to 120 characters on one line. But note that there must be no unaccounted-for spaces inside the parentheses of a FORMAT statement, and that each specification group inside the FORMAT parentheses is separated from the others by commas.

More will be said about FORMAT statements as the need arises, but in many future discussions of FORTRAN programs the FORMAT statement will not be added. Reference to a FORMAT statement will be made, as before, by a PRINT statement with a blank following the work PRINT. Constructing FORMAT statements is a somewhat mechanical process and we are more interested in model-building concepts than in processing details.

SUGGESTIONS FOR FURTHER STUDY

FISHER, F. PETER, AND SWINDLE, GEORGE F. *Computer Programming Systems*. New York: Holt, Rinehart & Winston, 1964.

LEDLEY, R. S. *Programming and Utilizing Digital Computers*. New York: McGraw-Hill, 1962.

MARTIN, E. WAINRIGHT, JR. *Electronic Data Processing: An Introduction.* Homewood, Ill.: Richard D. Irwin, Inc., 1961.

McCRACKEN, DANIEL D. *A Guide to FORTRAN Programming.* New York: John Wiley & Sons, 1961.

ORGANICK, ELLIOT IRVING. *A FORTRAN Primer.* Reading, Mass.: Addison-Wesley, 1963.

EXERCISES

1. Write FORTRAN statements which will cause the computer to store in the variable RESULT the value of each of the following expressions (assuming the computer already has values stored for w, x, y and z).

a) $x + y^2$

b) $(x - y)^3$

c) x^4

d) $x + y/z$

e) $\dfrac{x - y}{z}$

f) $w + \dfrac{x}{y - z}$

g) $\dfrac{x + y}{y - z} + w^2$

h) $(x/y)^{z-1}$

2. In each of the following FORTRAN expressions remove parentheses, where parentheses *can* be removed, without changing the meaning.

a) $(A * B)/C$

b) $(A + X) * (B/Y)$

c) $(A/B) * C$

d) $(A ** (I - 2) + B ** (I + 3))$

3. Write each of the following as a FORTRAN statement.

a) $r = \dfrac{a + bx}{c - dx}$

b) $b = -\dfrac{1}{2x} + \dfrac{a^2}{4x^2}$

c) $fy = x \cdot \dfrac{x^2 - y^2}{x^2 + y^2}$

d) $j = 4k - 6k_1 k_2$

4. Smith deposits \$42,967.14 in the bank at the beginning of the year. Interest on Smith's deposit will be compounded annually at 5.75 percent per year. Write a FORTRAN program which will cause the computer to calculate and print out (a) SMITH BALANCE AT END OF YEAR _____IS \$_____ , and (b) Smith's balance at the end of each of ten successive years, with the number of the year in each case in the first blank space in the statement above, and the amount of the deposit at the end of that year in the second blank space in the statement above.

5. Write a FORTRAN program which will cause the computer to determine how many years Smith's money (Problem **4**) will have to remain on deposit at 5.75 percent, compounded annually, before it will grow to at least \$1,000,000.

6. Write a FORTRAN program which will cause the computer to determine the interest rate Smith will have to earn, compounded annually, for his initial deposit of $42,967.14 to grow to at least $1,000,000 in 10 years.

7. Peter Minuit, governor of the Dutch West India Company, is reputed to have purchased Manhattan Island from the Indians for $24 in 1626. Assume that the Indians invested their receipts at 6 percent, compounded annually, and write a FORTRAN program which would determine and print out the value of their investment at the end of each of the following years: 1676, 1726, 1776, 1826, 1876, 1926 and 1976. In your print-out identify the year associated with each investment value.

8. Monthly sales of Keynes Company, Inc., are increasing at a rate of 20 percent per month. The cost of sales is 90 percent of sales. Forty percent of sales are cash sales and the remainder are charge sales which are collected during the succeeding month. At the end of each month Keynes Company adjusts its stock level so that inventory is one-half of the month's sales. On January 1, Keynes Company accounts appear as follows:

Sales during previous month (SDM)	=	$300,000
Accounts receivable (AR)	=	$180,000
Inventory level (VEN)	=	$150,000
Cash on hand (COH)	=	$228,000

Assume that Keynes Company sales continue to increase 20 percent each month, and write a FORTRAN program which will determine and print out end-of-month statements for

SDM	COH
AR	COS (cost of sales)
VEN	GP (gross profit: SDM − COS).

Arrange to have these month-end statements printed out with each statement identified as to the month of the year to which it applies, and print out statements *through* the first month in which Keynes Company runs out of cash.

CHAPTER 4

The Inventory System Under Certainty

To SEE HOW our knowledge of programming can be applied to complex systems problems, and to learn a few more programming conventions, we will address ourselves to an inventory model. We will begin simply, gradually enriching our model by the introduction of complexities which will make it more representative of reality. And we will begin our development of the inventory system with an inventory problem under *certainty*.

A retailer stocks units of Item A for sale to his retail customers. Each Item A unit costs the retailer $500 delivered, and the retailer figures that the cost of holding a unit of Item A in inventory for one year is 20 percent of the delivered cost of the item.

The cost of processing an order for a new shipment of units of Item A is $20 per order.

Our retailer expects the demand for Item A to be 365 units during the year, and he expects the demand rate to be constant; that is, exactly one unit will be demanded by his customers per day, every day of the year.

Finally, our retailer knows that lead time (the time which elapses between the placement of an order for a new shipment of units of Item A and receipt of the new shipment) is exactly two days.

Since the retailer knows that daily demand will be one unit and that lead time is two days—that is, since there are no uncertainties—stockouts are easy to avoid. Our retailer can be assured that a stockout need never occur and yet he can contribute toward a low average inventory level simply by reordering whenever the stock level of Item A drops to two units: in two days the new order will arrive, and the two units on hand when the order was placed will have just been consumed. Thus the level of stock in Item A will drop to zero at the moment a new shipment arrives, and with the arrival of the new shipment a stockout is just avoided.

We have determined, therefore, that the optimum reorder point, $\hat{R}$, is two units.[1] To determine the retailer's best inventory management policy we need now to determine the optimum order quantity, $\hat{Q}$.

We might adopt a policy of ordering a new shipment of Item A every two days, ordering two units with each order. Our inventory "curve" with this policy would look something like that shown in Figure 4-1.

FIGURE 4-1

"Item A" Inventory Curve

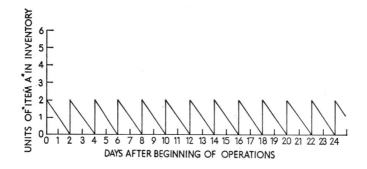

DAYS AFTER BEGINNING OF OPERATIONS

Under this policy the inventory level varies from a low of zero units to a high of two units. With this policy our retailer's average inventory level is one unit, and therefore annual inventory holding cost will be $100 (1 unit × 0.20 × $500).

An alternative policy might be to order a new shipment of Item A every 20 days, ordering 20 units with each order. Under this policy the inventory level would look something like that of Figure 4-2. With this policy our retailer's average inventory level is 10 units, and annual inventory holding cost will be $1,000 (10 units × 0.20 × $500).

---

[1] $\hat{Q}$ and $\hat{R}$ signify the optimum order quantity and the optimum reorder point, respectively.

FIGURE 4-2

Alternative "Item A" Inventory Policy

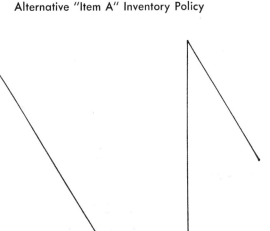

We are also concerned with ordering costs. Under the first policy our retailer is obliged to place 182.5 orders per year (at 2 units per order 182.5 orders will be required to meet the annual demand of 365 units). Annual ordering cost, therefore, would be $3,650 (182.5 orders × $20 per order).

Under the second policy our retailer is obliged to order only 18.25 times per year, and annual ordering cost is $365.

It is apparent that low inventory holding cost is achieved at the expense of high ordering cost, and that low ordering cost is achieved at the expense of high inventory holding cost. The nature of the inventory problem is demonstrated by the three cost curves shown in Figure 4-3.

Either extreme is bad, and the total cost curve—which is simply

FIGURE 4-3

Three Inventory Cost Curves

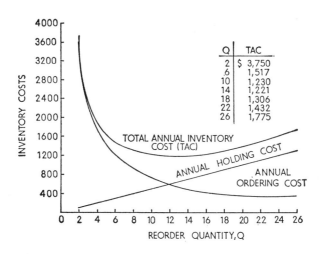

the sum of the holding cost curve and the ordering cost curve—has a minimum somewhere between the two extremes. Our objective is to find the optimum order quantity, $\hat{Q}$, which corresponds to this minimum point on the total annual cost curve.

We could do this in a number of ways, but we will do it by developing a mathematical model for our retailer's total annual inventory cost, TAC. Our model will consist of two parts:

1. *Annual holding cost:* $0.20\,(\$500) \times Q/2 = \$50Q$.
2. *Annual ordering cost:* $365/Q \times \$20 = \$7{,}300/Q$.

Total annual cost, TAC, would be the sum of these two parts, and our inventory model becomes

$$\text{TAC} = \$7{,}300/Q + \$50Q. \qquad (4\text{-}1)$$

SOLVING FOR THE OPTIMUM ORDER QUANTITY: $\hat{Q}$

Referring to our graph of the total cost curve (Figure 4-3) and observing its somewhat U-shaped character, it becomes apparent that we could deduce $\hat{Q}$ (4–1) by a simple iterative process. We could

a)   Select some small value for Q;
b)   Calculate TAC from 4–1;
c)   Increase Q by a small increment;

d) Recalculate TAC from **4–1**;

e) Compare the second TAC with the first TAC. If the second is smaller, then go back to *c)* above and repeat the process, comparing each time the new value of TAC with the value previously calculated until the new value is equal to or greater than the value previously calculated, at which point we reason that we've reached the bottom of our **U**-shaped curve, whereupon we stop and adopt as our optimum *Q* the one employed to get our lowest value for TAC.

If it has not already occurred to the reader, a moment's reflection should convince him that the simple iterative process we've described above is almost a computer program. All we need to do to make it a computer program, and thereby to cause the computer to solve our retailer's inventory problem, is to adopt FORTRAN statements. The following program (Figure 4-4) will do this. Note that in this program the variable TAC1 gets the value of the first calculation of TAC, and the variable TAC2 gets the value of the second calculation of TAC, in which *Q* has been increased by 1. In the IF statement, TAC2 is then compared with TAC1 to see if we are still "moving down the **U**-shaped curve" towards the bottom-most point.

FIGURE 4-4[2]

Conversion of Iterative Statements into FORTRAN Statements

```
    Q = 2.0
1   TAC1 = 7300.0/Q + 50.0 * Q
    Q = Q + 1.0
    TAC2 = 7300.0/Q + 50.0 * Q
    IF  (TAC2 − TAC1)1,2,2
2   Q = Q − 1.0
    PRINT 3,Q,TAC1
3   FORMAT  (1HO,12HOPTIMUM  Q  =  ,F8.2,2X,
        14HMINIMUM  TAC  =  ,F5.1)
    STOP
    END
```

Notice in the program above that when it has been determined in the IF statement that TAC2 is smaller than TAC1, TAC1 is then given the value of TAC2 by returning the computer to statement 1, whereupon TAC1 is recalculated using the Q which was previously

---

[2] Our page width will not accommodate on one line the full 72 characters which are available on a punched card. Henceforth in this text where indentation is encountered the indented part should be viewed as a continuation of the line above it, as in FORMAT statement Number 3, Figure 4-4.

employed to calculate TAC2. A new value for TAC2 is then calculated with an increased Q. This scheme is synonymous with giving P the value stored for S in our compound interest program (Figure 3-1, Chapter 3) in preparation for a new iteration.

Notice also that when the iteration is discontinued (i.e., when the computer goes to statement number 2) TAC1 is either equal to or less than TAC2. This suggests that TAC1 is likely to give us a better approximation of the minimum total annual cost than TAC2. We would, therefore, prefer to have printed out for us TAC1 and the value for Q which yielded it. Since the Q last employed was that employed to calculate TAC2, we subtract 1.0 from Q before arranging for a print-out.

Documentation: Flow Charting

We would do well to pause before further development of our inventory model and discuss documentation, an important computer programming practice. Sometime during the preparation of a computer program, and preferably before the program itself is written, all but the most elementary programs should be documented. When one documents a program he supplements it with anxiliary information to facilitate interpreting the program. Documentation may amount to no more than inserting COMMENT statements at appropriate places throughout the program so that the purpose of the statements immediately following the COMMENT statement can be more readily understood. Our inventory model above might be documented by this technique, shown in Figure 4-5.

The letter C, entered in column 1 on the punched card, identifies a COMMENT statement. The computer ignores COMMENT statements entirely, so that so far as the computer is concerned the documented program above is precisely the same as its successor in Figure 4-5.

Another way in which programs may be documented is by flow diagramming or flow charting. A flow chart is a pictorial representation of the flow of control and of the processing required for execution of a computer program. The choice of symbols to use in a flow chart, and the arrangement of the symbols, is arbitrary, but a somewhat prevalent convention for their use has come into being and we

FIGURE 4-5

Documentation of Inventory Model by COMMENT Insertions

```
C       INITIALIZE Q AT SOME SMALL VALUE
        Q = 2.0
C       CALCULATE TAC1
     1  TAC1 = 7300.0/Q + 50.0 * Q
C       INCREASE Q BY 1
        Q = Q + 1.0
C       CALCULATE TAC2
        TAC2 = 7300.0/Q + 50.0 * Q
C       COMPARE TAC1 WITH TAC2 AND DECIDE
           WHETHER TO CONTINUE ITERATION
        IF (TAC2 - TAC1)1,2,2
     2  Q = Q - 1.0
        PRINT 3,Q,TAC1
     3  FORMAT (1HO,12HOPTIMUM Q = ,F8.2,
           2X,14HMINIMUM TAC = ,F5.1)
        STOP
        END
```

will confine ourselves to a few more-or-less standard forms. Figure 4-6 is a sample flow chart which might be employed to document our inventory model. Processes (or procedures) are represented by

FIGURE 4-6

Optimum Order Quantity: Flow Chart for Determining Economic Order Quantity

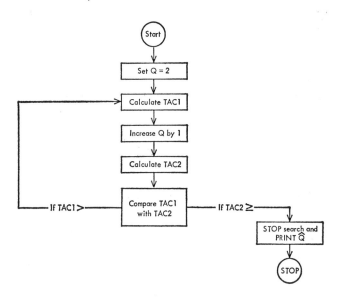

boxes, decisions are represented by a diamond, and arrows indicate the direction of flow.

It should be readily apparent that the undocumented program (Figure 4-4), the computer program documented with COMMENT statements (Figure 4-5), and finally the flow chart (Figure 4-6) say very much the same thing.

An experienced programmer probably would not bother to document a program as short and simple as that of our inventory model. As he becomes involved in composing more complex programs, however, even the experienced programmer finds some form of documentation useful. Long, complex programs can be written more easily if they are written from a flow chart which was composed in advance; and a flow chart also facilitates an individual's interpretation of another's program. If one adopts the practice of documenting his programs he will find that learning programming is easier, and that recalling the nature of programs which he has written some time in the past is much easier.

We will exploit our retailer's inventory problem to introduce several further comments about FORTRAN. Our retailer's inventory program might have been written in the form shown in Figure 4-7.

FIGURE 4-7

BIGNUM Variable in Retailer's Inventory Program

```
      BIGNUM = 999999.9
      DO 2 IQ = 2,1000
      Q = IQ
      TAC = 7300.0/Q + 50.0 * Q
      IF (TAC − BIGNUM)2,3,3
    2 BIGNUM = TAC
    3 IQ = IQ − 1
      PRINT 4, IQ, BIGNUM
    4 FORMAT (1H0,12HOPTIMUM Q = ,I3,2X,
        14HMINIMUM TAC = ,F8.2)
```

In this program the variable BIGNUM (Big Number) serves as the standard to which succeeding calculations of TAC are compared, as TAC1 did in the previous program. We load BIGNUM with a very large number to make certain that the first TAC we calculate will be smaller than BIGNUM.

Floating-Point and Fixed-Point Variables and Constants

Two features of the program in Figure 4-7 merit comment. First, we have chosen in this program, to designate the order quantity in the DO statement as IQ rather than simply Q. There are two classes of variables and constants in FORTRAN:

1. Integer variables and integer constants.
2. Floating point variables and floating point constants.

Integer constants are constants which do not have a fractional part; i.e., constants which require no decimal point. *Floating point* constants are constants which have a decimal point (fractions can be expressed in FORTRAN only in decimal form).

An important rule in FORTRAN is that a floating point value (constant) should not be given to an integer variable unless it is desired that the fractional part of the value be dropped. If a floating point constant is given as a value to an integer variable, only the integer part of the constant is stored; the fractional part will be lost. Unless truncation is desired—and sometimes it is—one should be careful not to intermix floating point and integer quantities in this fashion.

An integer variable is any variable whose first letter is an I, J, K, L, M, or N. If, in a given program, we do not expect to give a variable a value with a decimal part, we can use integer variables throughout. But we must be prepared for what are sometimes surprising results when division is involved. Thus, if the variable IST has a value of 3, the variable LDM has a value of 2, and the statement   KS = IST/LDM   is encountered, KS will have the value 1 stored for it. The fractional part of the quotient is truncated.

If we expect to have occasion to load a variable with a quantity which has a decimal part, we should use a floating point variable. Also, if we expect to add, subtract, multiply and divide variables on the right side of the equal sign in an algebraic expression, and if one of those variables is a floating point variable, then *all* should be floating point variables. This last rule does not apply, however, when exponentiation is involved. A floating point quantity may be raised to an integer power.

One of the rules of the DO statement is that any variables which appear in the DO statement must be integer variables. To convert Q to an integer variable in the preceding program, we simply added an I, making it IQ. Then, to prepare for using Q in subsequent computations, together with floating point quantities, we convert it back to a floating point variable in the statement immediately following the DO statement.

A second aspect of our inventory program (above) is that we have employed an IF statement to "get out of" the DO loop *before* the variable IQ has been given all the values called for in the DO statement. By specifying that IQ should take successive values up through 1,000, we have assured ourselves of this. The important thing to observe here is that one can transfer OUT OF the middle of a DO loop before the looping called for is finished, but one cannot get back into the middle of a DO loop. Entry into a DO loop must always be at the beginning of the loop, with the DO statement itself.

THE DECISION RULE

If we allow the computer to solve our retailer's inventory problem we find that his total annual cost, TAC, will be a minimum $1,208 per year if he orders 12 units with each new order. We have already determined that the best reorder point is two units. Therefore our retailer's *decision rule* for minimizing total annual inventory cost is: "When the stock level in Item A drops to two units, order a new shipment of 12 units."

THE COMPUTER PROGRAM AS A GENERAL MODEL

Anyone familiar with calculus will almost certainly be inspired to observe that calculus offers a simpler way to determine optimum $\hat{Q}$. Furthermore, such an observer might propose that, using calculus, we could even develop a *general model*. Thus, given the certainty conditions of our retailer's inventory system, we could reason:

1. *Annual holding costs are*   UHC × CPU × Q/2   *where:*

UHC = annual unit holding cost as a percent of the cost price/unit;
CPU = the cost price per unit;
   Q = the order quantity in units.

2. *Annual ordering costs are*   CPO × DPY/Q   *where:*

        CPO = the ordering cost/order processed ;
        DPY = the demand per year in units.

Our total annual inventory cost model, then, would be: $TAC = UHC \times CPU \times Q/2 + CPO \times DPY/Q$.

By use of calculus we could develop a general model for determining optimum Q in terms of all the other unknowns. Thus, differentiating TAC with respect to Q, we have:

$$\frac{dTAC}{dQ} = \frac{UHC \times CPU}{2} - \frac{CPO \times DPY}{Q^2}.$$

Equating the expression on the right side of the equal sign to zero, and solving for Q, we have:

$$\hat{Q} = \sqrt{\frac{2(CPO \times DPY)}{UHC \times CPU}}. \tag{4-2}$$

Four–2, above, would indeed be a general model for our retailer to use in determining optimum ordering quantity $\hat{Q}$, given

1. The cost price of one unit of Item A.
2. The cost of holding a unit of Item A in inventory for one year as percent of the delivered price of one unit.
3. The cost of processing one order.
4. The annual demand for units of Item A.

Herein, it may be argued, lies the power of the calculus.

However, in precisely this same sense, a computer program can itself be a *general model*. A computer program which is a general model for our retailer's inventory system, in precisely the same sense as 4–2, is shown in Figure 4-8.

FIGURE 4-8

Computer Program as General Model for Determining Optimum Order Quantity

```
      BIGNUM = 999999.9
      DO 2 IQ = 1,10000
      Q = IQ
      TAC = UHC * CPU * Q/2 + CPO * DPY/Q
      IF (TAC − BIGNUM)2,3,3
   2  BIGNUM = TAC
   3  IQ = IQ − 1
      PRINT 4, IQ, BIGNUM
   4  FORMAT (1H0,12HOPTIMUM Q = ,I4,2X,
         14HMINIMUM TAC = ,F8.2)
      STOP
      END
```

Like **4–2,** our program in Figure 4-8 requires that values for UHC, CPU, CPO and DPY be input into the model to determine optimum Q.

We could modify our program and approach the "perfect" $\hat{Q}$ with any degree of accuracy we desire, doing with our computer program anything which can be done with the general model developed by calculus.

As we go on we will further develop this concept of the computer program as a general model, and we will see that while (like analytical mathematical models) the computer program is restricted to operating within certain limits, the computer program can be used to simulate systems of much greater complexity than could be practicably simulated via pure analytical mathematical models of any kind.

EXERCISES

1. Which of the following are acceptable names of integer variables; which are acceptable names of floating point variables; and which are unacceptable names?

X	HPZ	HSQUARED	X1.4
I12G	NEXT	DELTA	(X61)
CAT	42G	MU	IA
X-Z	LAST	A*B	1X2

2. State the value of A or I as the result of the computer's execution of each of the following FORTRAN statements:

a) $A = 2 * 6 + 1$
b) $A = 2/3$
c) $I = 2 * (10/4)$
d) $I = 2 * (10./4.)$
e) $A = 1./3. + 1./3.$
f) $A = (4.0) ** (3./2.)$

3. Write a FORTRAN program which will cause the computer to calculate and print out the total annual inventory cost to Smith Company for ten successive order quantities ranging from 10 units per order through 100 units per order (by increments of 10), given that:

Cost price per unit $= \$200,$
Demand during year $= 1{,}825$ units,
Cost of holding inventory $= 20\%$ of cost/unit/year,
Cost of processing one order $= \$25.$

(Begin, before writing your program, by composing a flow diagram.)

4. Write a FORTRAN program which will cause the computer to calculate and print out the economic order quantity and the corresponding total annual inventory cost for Smith Company (Problem 3). *Note:*

Cause the economic order quantity to be determined within 5 units of the exact EOQ.

5. Write a FORTRAN program which will cause the computer to do what is called for in Problem 4 for each of the following five values of annual demand: *1,825, 3,650, 5,475, 7,300, and 9,125 units*.

Plot a curve showing the relationship between the economic order quantity and the annual demand for Smith Company. (Begin by composing a flow diagram.)

CHAPTER 5

Probability Concepts

AN IMPORTANT CHARACTERISTIC of a system that would lead us to consider the use of simulation is the presence of events whose occurrences cannot be predicted with certainty. The events alter the state of the system and we can learn what the new state will likely be if we can model the events and trace their effects as changes in the system variables.

We have been using a number of terms, including the term "event," without defining them. Modeling events and the processes of which they are a part requires that we review some basic definitions and certain notions that are part of the concept of probability.

Experiment. In mathematics an experiment is an act that can be repeated under a given set of conditions. The results of the act cannot be predicted with certainty.

This definition applies equally to acts that we can observe in the business systems although, as the mathematician phrases his definition, it seems to fit particularly well acts such as flipping coins or rolling dice. The idea of an experiment will be used to describe repeatable acts or situations in the firm or its environment, the outcomes of which are not predictable. We may sometimes beg the question of whether a sequence of such experiments was, or can be, performed under the same conditions. The meaning of experiment need not imply the act of a person singly nor, for that matter, a human act.

Stochastic Process. A sequence of experiments in which the results are uncertain is called a stochastic process. Precisely, the results of each experiment or trial depend on chance. For the most part, interest will be limited to processes with a countable (finite) number of repetitions or trials. When modeling the firm we will often assume that sequences of customers' orders, sequences of defective units of product, sequences of dollar amounts of particular costs, etc., are stochastic.

Outcomes. Each time an experiment is performed, one and only one of a set of elementary results occurs.[1] The set is called the outcome set of the experiment, and the assumption will be made that the number of elements of such sets is finite. By way of familiar example, the outcome set of the experiment of flipping a coin would include the elementary outcomes, heads and tails. Sometimes the phrases "logical possibilities" or "logical outcomes" are used to denote the outcome set.

Event. Given the outcomes of an experiment, an event is any subset of the outcome set. In the coin-flipping example, the outcome set A is $A = \{H,T\}$. Event B (the coin turns up heads) is the subset $B = \{H\}$. Event C (the coin turns up tails) is the subset $C = \{T\}$.

Because of the simplicity of the experiment, we note that the events are comprised of a single element of the outcome set. Such events are called simple events and the term is used interchangeably with the terms "outcomes" or "elementary outcomes."

Suppose instead that the experiment consisted of flipping two coins at a time and the event of interest is that at least one coin turns up heads. The outcomes set would be $A = \{ (H,H), (H,T), (T,H), (T,T) \}$. The event B would be the subset $B = \{ (H,H), (H,T), (T,H) \}$. Event B is said to occur if *any* of the elementary outcomes in set B is produced by the experiment.

Consider the experiment with outcome set $A = \{4,5,6,7,8\}$, where the integers stand for number of units of product ordered daily by customers. Suppose we are interested in the event D; the number of units ordered is six *or more*. D would be the set $D = \{6,7,8\}$.

Or perhaps we are interested in the events X, Y, Z, defined as:

$X =$ $\{4\}$ (number of units ordered is four *or less*),
$Y =$ $\{4,5\}$ (number of units ordered is five *or less*),
$Z =$ $\{4,5,6\}$ (number of units ordered is six *or less*), etc.

Probability of an Event. That the occurrence of an event cannot be predicted with certainty does not prevent us from making statements reflecting our belief that the event will or will not occur for a

---

[1] The outcomes are said to be mutually exclusive.

particular experiment or sequence of experiments. We speak of the likelihood or the probability that an event will occur. Sometimes "odds" are quoted in favor of the occurrence of an event.

Probability is the branch of mathematics that provides the framework for such assertions.[2] The theory of probability specifies the form in which our statements are made. It does not, however, compel us to make the statements nor does it tell us what probability measures (as the term will be defined) to use when evaluating a stochastic process or an event.

Probability theory defines a probability (probability measure) as a non-negative number assigned to an elementary outcome or simple event. Assignment is made to all the outcomes in the outcome set such that the sum of the probabilities is 1. It follows that the probability assigned to a single outcome is in the range of 0 to 1.

The *probability of an event* is the sum of the probabilities of the outcomes included in the subset which defines the event. In the example above for the event, number of units ordered is five or less if probabilities had been assigned to the elementary outcomes as follows:

Table 5-1

Assignment of Probabilities to Elementary Outcomes

Number of Units Ordered	Probability
4	0.1
5	0.2
6	0.2
7	0.3
8	0.2

The probability of the event is written:

P(Number of units ordered $\leqq 5$) = P(Number of units ordered = 4) + P(Number of units ordered = 5) = 0.1 + 0.2 or 0.3.

The probabilities one assigns usually reflect empirical or theoretical knowledge or information concerning the process. We are not concerned here that some probabilities are called objective while others are said to be subjective. As a practical matter, probabilities are the frequent result of combining judgment, intuition, and observation.

---

[2] See John G. Kemeny, *et al.*, *Finite Mathematics with Business Applications* (Englewood Cliffs, N.J.: Prentice-Hall, 1962), p. 134.

Equally Likely Outcomes. In the case of a set of outcomes which we believe to be equally likely, the same probability is assigned to each of the outcomes. The assumption of equally likely outcomes would seem to describe such processes as tossing coins, rolling a die, etc. Yet we frequently make the same assumption initially when modeling complex processes simply because we have insufficient knowledge of the process.

A convenient way exists for computing probabilities for events, given that the elementary outcomes are assumed to be equally likely. The probability of an event was defined to be the sum of the probabilities of the subset which identifies the event. It follows that the probability of the event is:

$$P(\text{Event}) = \frac{\text{Number of outcomes in event set}}{\text{Total number of outcomes}}.$$

The numerator is often described as the "number of ways the event can happen." Or sometimes the subset defining the event is referred to as the set of "favorable" outcomes, in which case the probability of the event becomes:

$$P(\text{Event}) = \frac{\text{Number of favorable outcomes}}{\text{Total number of outcomes}}.$$

Consider the process which daily results in a number of absentee employees. The outcomes and their probabilities might be as follows:

Number Absent	Probability
0	0.2
1	0.2
2	0.2
3	0.2
4	0.2

If our interest is the probability that *two or more* employees are absent in a day, the event is the subset $\{2,3,4\}$. The ratio of the number of ways the event can happen to the total number of outcomes is 3/5 or 0.6. The same probability measure could of course have been obtained, as before, by addition.

No matter whether one assumes outcomes to be equally likely or not, the student should recognize that once he has listed the set of elementary outcomes and has assigned probabilities to them, the way in which he selects the events is a matter left to his discretion. However, to compute the probability of an event the analyst employs theorems whose derivations and proofs are contained in probability theory.

Use of the equally likely or "equiprobable" measure will be frequent in subsequent chapters. An "experiment" will be discussed at the end of this chapter in which the outcomes are the decimal digits 1,2,3,4,5,6,7,8,9, and 0, and in which the probability measure 0.1 is assigned to each of the ten outcomes. Repeated trials of the experiment will result in a sequence of digits which we call "random numbers." Using the computational method known as *Monte Carlo*, we will employ a process with equally likely outcomes to model a second process whose outcomes are not equally likely.

Joint Probability. Of further interest when modeling events is the probability measure for a sequence of events. For example, what is the probability that the event, number of units ordered = 4, and the event, number of units ordered = 6, will occur on two successive days? Or what is the probability that event, number of absentees per day $\geqq 2$, will occur on five successive days?

The sequence is called a *compound event,* and its probability measure is called the *joint probability* of the event.

The events comprising the compound event are specified as independent. Colloquially, the occurrence of one has nothing to do with another. More precisely, the probability of an event is not influenced by the occurrence of preceding or succeeding events.

The joint probability of a compound event is the *product* of the probabilities of the independent events. To compute the probability of the compound event A, number of units ordered = 4 the first day, and number of units ordered = 6 the second day, we multiply the probabilities of the two events:

$$P(A) = P(4) \cdot P(6) = (0.1) \cdot (0.2) = 0.02.$$

The sequence or the compound event B, number of employees absent per day $\geqq 2$, occurring through five successive days would be:

$$P(B) = (0.6) \cdot (0.6) \cdot (0.6) \cdot (0.6) \cdot (0.6) = 0.078,$$

recalling that the earlier calculation of the probability of the event for a single trial produced the value 0.6.

Compound events can be visualized by the use of a schematic

model known as a tree diagram. For a single trial of a process having as outcomes the simple events A, B, and C, the diagram in Figure 5-1 would do.

FIGURE 5-1

Single Trial Tree Diagram

The line segments leading from the nodes are called branches. Now let us diagram several trials of the process.

FIGURE 5-2

Multi-Trial Tree Diagram

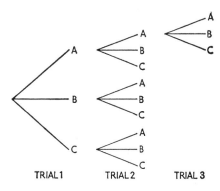

TRIAL 1   TRIAL 2   TRIAL 3

The compound events may be listed as the sequences:

A,A,A	B,A,A	C,A,A
A,A,B	B,A,B	C,A,B
A,A,C	B,A,C	C,A,C
A,B,A	B,B,A	C,B,A
A,B,B	B,B,B	C,B,B
A,B,C	B,B,C	C,B,C
A,C,A	B,C,A	C,C,A
A,C,B	B,C,B	C,C,B
A,C,C	B,C,C	C,C,C

As the number of trials increases arithmetically, the number of different sequences increases exponentially. Three trials produce 3^3, or 27, different sequences. Four trials result in 3^4, or 81, different sequences, etc. The compound event (sequence of simple, independent events) is depicted as a *path* through the tree. Bear in mind that the sequence of numerical values will represent values of system or environment random variables.

To complete the tree diagram, Figure 5-3 shows the probabilities of the simple events.

FIGURE 5-3

Tree Diagram Showing Simple Event Probabilities

Then, if we diagram the compound events which result from two trials, we have the situation shown in Figure 5-4.

FIGURE 5-4

Compound Events from Two Trials

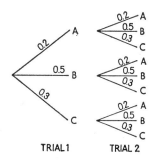

Probabilities of the compound events can be computed by multiplying branch probabilities; for example, the probability of compound event A_1A_2 is:

$$P(A_1A_2) = P(A_1) \cdot P(A_2) = (0.2) \cdot (0.2) = 0.04,$$

where the subscript denotes the trial number.

Random Variable. For the present, a random variable will be defined as one whose value is a number produced by the outcome of an experiment. When discussing the modeling of an event we implied that the event could be characterized as a value of a random variable. In an earlier example we spoke of a set of outcomes, each of which represented the number of units of product ordered or demanded daily. The random variable might be described simply as *daily demand*. Its values were the numbers 4,5,6,7,8, one of which was produced as a simple event on each trial of the demand process. The probability that the random variable takes a particular value is the probability of the simple event.

Outcomes not represented by numbers but, rather, attributes such as heads or tails, good or defective, success or failure, etc., may generate values of random variables. We are back to flipping two coins at a time, and the question is raised, "How many are heads?"

The question cannot be answered directly but it implies the random variable—number of heads—which suggests the events, number of heads = 0, number of heads = 1, etc. The experiment is summarized in Table 5-2.

Table 5-2

Outcomes Represented by Attributes Rather than Numbers

Outcomes	Number of Heads	Probabilities
HH	2	0.25
HT	1	0.25
TH	1	0.25
TT	0	0.25

The probability that the random variable takes a particular value may be obtained by adding the probabilities for the outcomes which produce that value. The probability of getting two heads is 0.25; of getting one head 0.50; of getting zero heads 0.25. The ordered pairs of possible values for this variable, and the probabilities, are

$$(0, 0.25), \ (1, 0.50), \ (2, 0.25).$$

This set is the *probability function* of the random variable

$$f = \{(0, 0.25), \ (1, 0.50), \ (2, 0.25)\}.$$

Conventionally, the random variable is denoted by a capital letter; for example, X. The lower case x denotes its values, and $f(x_i)$ is the probability that X takes on the values $x_i, \ i = 1,2,3 \ldots n$.

In the preceding illustrations $f(x)$, read "f at x," is the probability that $X = x$, or $P(X = x)$. That is:

$$f(0) = P(X = 0) = 0.25; \ f(1) = P(X = 1) = 0.50; \ \text{etc.}$$

The same probability function is shown in Table 5-3 in the more common tabular form.

Table 5-3

Probability Function in Tabular Form

Number of Heads	Probability
x	$f(x)$
0	0.25
1	0.50
2	0.25

The probability function may also be given as a formula for $f(x)$. Several of the widely used probability functions in this form will be discussed later.

Expected Value. The mean or expected value of a random variable is the sum of the products of each of its values multiplied by its probability. For the illustration of the random variable, daily demand, the probability function is shown in Table 5-4.

Table 5-4

Probability Function for Daily Demand

Number of Units	Probability
x	$f(x)$
4	0.1
5	0.2
6	0.2
7	0.3
8	0.2

The expected value, E, is computed as

$$E = (4 \cdot 0.1) + (5 \cdot 0.2) + (6 \cdot 0.2) + (7 \cdot 0.3) + (8 \cdot 0.2) = 6.3 \text{ units.}$$

The expected value is not one of the outcome values and is not thought of as the value which could occur on any trial. If the experiment is repeated many times, the average number of units demanded per trial (per day) is the expected value, or 6.3 units.

This statistic is analogous to the arithmetic mean with which the student is familiar. While the probability function tells us what values the variable may assume and their probabilities, the expected value is a summary statistic useful when characterizing central tendency or as the measure of the center of the mass of the function. Expected value, as well as measures of the variability of a random variable, will be used when constructing and experimenting with simulation models.

The function in Figure 5-5 may be graphed as shown. But since the random variable takes on only a limited number of isolated values, the function is described as *discrete*. If we convert the graph to a histogram we have the form shown in Figure 5-6.

FIGURE 5-5

Graph of Discrete Random Variable

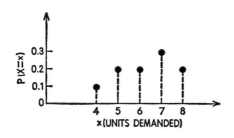

FIGURE 5-6

Histogram of Discrete Random Variable

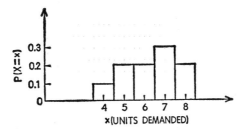

The height of each rectangle represents the probability of the outcome whose value is the midpoint of the base of the rectangle. The enclosed area, the sum of all the rectangles, is equal to 1.

Cumulative Probability Function. The probability function provides the information from which the cumulative probability function can be derived. The cumulative function is used to obtain the probability that the random variable is "equal to or more," or "equal to or less," than a specified value. For the random variable, daily demand, we expressed interest in the events: daily demand is equal to four units *or less,* daily demand is equal to five units *or less,* etc.

From Table 5-4 we can calculate the necessary probabilities for all demand levels (D will denote the random variable).

$$P(D \leq 4) = 0.1$$
$$P(D \leq 5) = 0.1 + 0.2 = 0.3$$
$$P(D \leq 6) = 0.1 + 0.2 + 0.2 = 0.5$$
$$P(D \leq 7) = 0.1 + 0.2 + 0.2 + 0.3 = 0.8$$
$$P(D \leq 8) = 0.1 + 0.2 + 0.2 + 0.3 + 0.2 = 1.0$$

The ordered pairs of these events and their probabilities is the cumulative probability function[3] of the variable. The graph of this function results in a step function shown in Figure 5-7. The function (Table 5-5) can be shown in tabular form as well.

FIGURE 5-7

Graph of Cumulative Probability Function

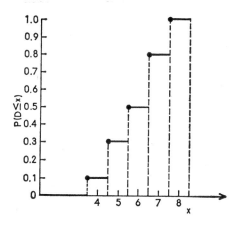

Table 5-5

Tabular Cumulative Probability Function

Number of Units x	Probability $P(X = x)$	Cumulative Probability $P(X \leq x)$
4	0.1	0.1
5	0.2	0.3
6	0.2	0.5
7	0.3	0.8
8	0.2	1.0

[3] The terms *probability function* and *probability distribution function* are used interchangeably, as are *cumulative probability function* and *cumulative probability distribution function.*

For reasons which will be discussed later, we find it generally desirable to work with the cumulative probability distribution.

Mathematically Defined Probability Functions. In the preceding references to the random variable—number of units ordered or demanded—we have said nothing about how the probability measures were selected. Since the outcomes were not given the same probability, it might be reasonable to expect that some information exists concerning the variable and the *frequency* with which the several values occurred in the past. If such information were tabulated and a *relative frequency distribution* computed, the probability measures most likely would be the relative frequencies.

Suppose that data for the variable demand had been recorded for the past 200 days and arranged in tabular form:

Number of Units	Frequency (Number of Days)	Relative Frequency	Probability
4	20	1/10	0.1
5	40	2/10	0.2
6	40	2/10	0.2
7	60	3/10	0.3
8	40	2/10	0.2
	200		

Lacking additional knowledge about the demand process, we would not venture to say that the true nature of the process is different from that of the probability function empirically obtained. Further observation may lead us to alter the probabilities or to assume that the probability function is mathematically defined; that is, that the formula of the function can be written.

THEORETICAL PROBABILITY DISTRIBUTIONS

The foregoing discussion contained illustrations of experiments and processes for which the probability functions could conveniently be expressed as sets of paired numbers or represented by tables. Use will be made of functions in these forms, particularly those obtained from empirical observation presented as frequency distributions. However, a number of theoretical probability functions are available, and it is often assumed that one or another of these represents the true nature of a process under investigation.

Three of the most important theoretical distributions are the normal, binomial, and Poisson distributions. The binomial and Poisson distributions, and their usefulness in simulation studies, are developed in Chapter 8. While it is assumed that the student is familiar with the properties of the normal distribution, a few comments about the standard normal curve are appropriate in our discussion of probability concepts.

The Normal Probability Distributions. When the outcome set of an experiment is finite, the set of possible values of the random variable is finite and its probability distribution is called discrete. The normal probability distribution is, by contrast, *continuous*. The normal random variable takes values which are the real numbers between ± infinity. The requirement that the sum of the probabilities of the outcome set not exceed 1 would be violated if we assigned a probability to each of the outcomes, since they are infinite in number and their sum would be greater than 1 so long as the probabilities are positive—no matter how arbitrarily small.

The normal probability distribution assigns probabilities to *intervals* of values by reference to the *standard normal curve*, which has the equation

$$y = \frac{1}{\sqrt{2\pi}} e^{-x^2/2} .$$

Computing and plotting x and y coordinates with this equation gives us the familiar bell-shaped curve of Figure 5-8.

FIGURE 5-8

Standard Normal Probability Distribution Curve

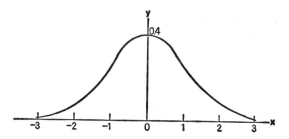

It can be proved that the area enclosed by the curve equals 1.0. From this it follows that the probability that the standard normal variable X takes on a value in a given interval (x_1 to x_2) is equal to the area (enclosed by the normal curve, the x-axis and the vertical lines at x_1 and x_2) represented by the shaded area below.

FIGURE 5-9

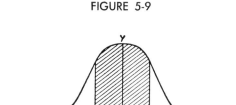

The curve has the property that it is symmetrical about the y-axis. Thus areas from 0 to $+x$ are equal to areas from 0 to $-x$. Areas under the normal curve are usually calculated only for the right side of the curve, and tables of these areas are available. Table 5-6 is an abbreviated form of such a table.

Table 5-6

x	Area	x	Area	x	Area
0.0	.000	1.2	.385	2.4	.492
0.2	.079	1.4	.419	2.6	.495
0.4	.155	1.6	.445	2.8	.497
0.6	.226	1.8	.464	3.0	.499
0.8	.288	2.0	.477		
1.0	.341	2.2	.486		

The probability that the normal random variable takes a value in the interval $x = -1$ to $x = 1$ is two times the area 0 to 1, or $P(-1 \leqq X \leqq 1) = (2)\,(0.341)$, or about 0.68.

$P(0.6 \leqq X \leqq 1.0)$ is obtained by subtracting the areas for the intervals 0 to 1.0 and 0 to 0.6. The probability equals $0.341 - 0.226$, or about 0.115.

The probability, $P(-2.2 \leqq X \leqq 1.4)$, would be equal to the sum of the areas 0 to -2.2 and 0 to 1.4. The area from 0 to -2.2 would be equal to the area 0 to 2.2. Probability is the sum of 0.486 and 0.419, or 0.905.

In any of the preceding, the probability that X does not take a value in the prescribed interval is equal to $(1 - P)$.

From the accompanying table the student can verify the frequently quoted probabilities:

$$P(-1 \leq X \leq 1) = 0.68$$
$$P(-2 \leq X \leq 2) = 0.95$$
$$P(-3 \leq X \leq 3) = 0.99.$$

The *mean* of the standard normal distribution is 0 and the *standard deviation* is 1. Normal distributions which have means $\neq 0$ and standard deviations $\neq 1$ can be "standardized."

The normal distribution is often a good approximation for probabilities of certain non-normal distributions. In addition, many random variables are normally distributed.

MARKOV CHAIN PROCESSES

So far we have restricted our discussion of stochastic processes to those in which successive events are (or are assumed to be) independent. More typically we find the case to be that in which the occurrence of an event depends at most upon the occurrence of the immediately preceding event. A Markov chain process is of this variety, and for each trial or experiment there is a finite number of outcomes or *states*. A probability is assigned to outcome B for any trial, given that outcome A immediately preceded it. Such probability measures are called *transition probabilities*.

To illustrate the process, assume an experiment with three states (outcomes) A, B and C, with transition probabilities, P, given by the matrix:

		A	B	C
	A	0.0	1.0	0.0
P =	B	0.0	0.3	0.7
	C	0.2	0.0	0.8.

The matrix shows the probability of going to successive states, given that we begin in state A *or* B *or* C. For example, the probability of going from state B to state C is 0.7. Each row contains the possible outcomes for a trial, given one of the outcomes as the preceding state. The sum of the probability measures in each row equals 1. Probability 0.0 means that transition between two states is not possible. A transition diagram of the process is shown in Figure 5-10.

FIGURE 5-10

Transition Diagram*

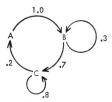

* *Source:* Kemeny, *et al., op. cit.,* p. 194.

If the process is arbitrarily assumed to be in state A, the process through three trials would be represented by the tree diagram of Figure 5-11. The sum of the joint probabilities is 1.

FIGURE 5-11

Tree Diagram through Three Trials
(Assuming process is in state A)

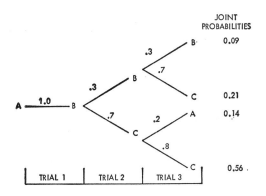

If we assume that the initial state is B, then after three trials we would have the situation of Figure 5-12.

Finally, if state C were assumed to be the initial state, Figure 5-13 would represent the process through three trials.

The matrix below summarizes these probabilities:

$$
P = \begin{array}{c c} & \begin{array}{c c c} A & B & C \end{array} \\ \begin{array}{c} A \\ B \\ C \end{array} & \begin{array}{c c c} .14 & .09 & .77 \\ .15 & .17 & .68 \\ .13 & .22 & .65. \end{array} \end{array}
$$

FIGURE 5-12

Tree Diagram through Three Trials
(Assuming process is in state B)

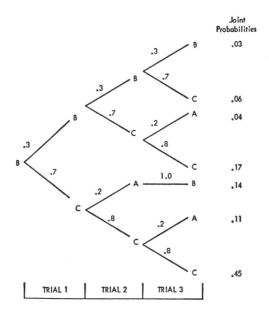

FIGURE 5-13

Tree Diagram through Three States
(Assuming process is in state C)

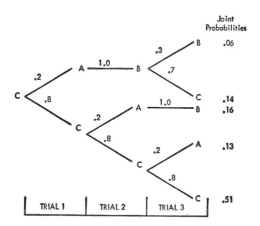

It is understood that these are the probabilities that the process will be in a given state (A, B, or C) after three trials if the initial state has been prescribed. Note that each row in the matrix equals 1 and that, since all the numbers are greater than 0, it is possible, after three trials, to arrive in any state.

Problems for which Markov chain processes apply are growing in number, particularly in the social sciences and business. Brand choices for many products by consumers (coffee, toothpaste, soap, etc.) are frequently Markov processes. Switching from one brand of an item to another can be modeled for the purpose of predicting demand.

The time progress or "aging" of accounts receivable in a department store has been modeled as a Markov process in which process states are successive time periods (months) and in which two states (absorbing states) exist from which transition is not possible: "paid up" and "bad debts." The model is solved to determine what accounts receivable will be paid up, and when; or, more accurately, the probabilities that accounts will be paid up within varying time periods and the probabilities that accounts will end as bad debts.[4]

RANDOM NUMBERS

Reference has been made to the special kind of stochastic process with equally likely outcomes, each of which was one of the set of ten numbers 0 through 9. The results of this kind of process are sequences of numbers called *random numbers,* and the design of processes to generate such numbers is important in simulation work.

The probability that a given number occurs (or is generated) on any trial of the process is 1/10, or 0.1. Since all outcomes are equally likely, the equiprobable measure 0.1 is assigned to each. Repeated trials of the process produce a sequence in which each of the ten numbers occur with the same relative frequency: 1/10. However, the *order* is left to chance. Randomness is well defined and should not imply chaos.

With such a process (or rather its output, the sequence of one-digit random numbers), we can develop sequences of n-digit random numbers. The set of one-digit numbers has ten numbers, and equi-

---

[4] R. M. Cyert, H. J. Davidson, and G. C. Thompson, "Estimations of the Allowance for Doubtful Accounts by Markov Chains," *Management Science,* Vol. 8, No. 3, April, 1962.

probable measure $= 0.1$. The set of two-digit numbers has 100 numbers $\{00,01,02,...,98,99\}$. The probability $1/100$ or 0.01 is assigned to each two-digit number. We could compute the probability measure by considering the two-digit number as the result of the compound event, the generation of two one-digit numbers. Hence the joint probability would be (0.1) $(0.1) = 0.01$.

Generally the set of n-digit numbers has 10^n numbers, each assigned probability $1/10^n$. To illustrate, the set of three-digit numbers has 10^3, or 1,000 numbers, and is $\{000,001,002,...,998,999\}$. The probability $1/10^3$, or $1/1,000$, or 0.001 is used for each of the numbers.

Size of random numbers (number of digits) will be determined by the number of significant digits of the probability measures we use in subsequent problems. If probabilities are written as one-digit numbers, then we will use the set of one-digit random numbers, etc.

The nature of the processes used to generate random numbers is discussed in Chapter 8. In the introduction to the Monte Carlo method below, and in the following chapter where the method is used in simulating an inventory system, we assume that a source of random numbers is available. Most likely, the source would be a table of numbers. Random number tables are readily obtained and numbers of any size may be formed by combining one-digit numbers. The only obvious precaution is that numbers be selected in the order in which they appear.

Monte Carlo

Before we conclude this chapter we will utilize a number of the concepts reviewed to describe a method for modeling and simulating stochastic processes which will be used frequently. The ingredients of the method—called Monte Carlo—are a random variable, its probability distribution function, and a sequence of random numbers.

Assume the random variable X with probability function:

x	$P(X = x)$
4	0.15
5	0.20
6	0.50
7	0.10
8	0.05

and cumulative probability function:

x	$P(X \leqq x)$
4	0.15
5	0.35
6	0.85
7	0.95
8	1.00

Accept for the present that X is exogenous to the system which we wish to analyze through successive time intervals. Thus it is required that we produce values of X in the same way as in the process described by the probability function given above. By this we mean that successive values of X should be determined by chance, but that, if a large number of values were produced, each x would occur with relative frequency equal to its prior probability. For example, if we generate X sequentially 1,000 times, then $x = 4$ should occur 150 times.

A method for doing this involves using a sequence of random numbers. Essentially, we shall employ one kind of process to synthetically produce (simulate) another kind of process. Let us contrast the processes.

The process which produced the random numbers is stochastic, with 100 outcomes (since we want two-digit random numbers), each equally likely. The process which produced X is stochastic, with only five outcomes, which are not equally likely.

What we must do first is to partition the set of random numbers into five subsets, each representing one of the outcomes of the "X process." How many random numbers shall constitute a subset? Here we use the probability measures $(X = x)$; for example, for $n = 4, 0.15 \times 100$—or 15 random numbers—would represent the outcome. Twenty random numbers would be associated with $x = 5$, etc.

The next question is "Which 15 random numbers shall represent outcome, $x = 4$?" It doesn't matter so long as a random number does not belong to any more than *one* subset. For convenience, let us assign the first 15 random numbers to outcome, $x = 4$; i.e., (00,01,....,13,14). Then assign the next 20 random numbers to outcome, $x = 5$, the next 50 to outcome $x = 6$, etc. The entire assignment would be:

x	Random Numbers
4	00–14
5	15–34
6	35–84
7	85–94
8	95–99

To make the assignment, it is convenient to make use of the cumulative distribution given above. Note the relationship between the probability measures and the lower limit of each set of random numbers.

Finally, recall that, given an outcome set of an experiment, an event was defined as a subset of one or more of the outcomes. We said that if any of the outcomes occurred, then the event occurred. In the Monte Carlo method we have really redefined the events of interest as sets of random numbers; outcome $x = 4$ is the set $\{00,01,...,13,14\}$. If any of the numbers of this set occurs, then X takes the value 4.

To "cause" the random numbers to occur, we merely select them from a table. We obtain the first, determine its magnitude, find the subset of which it is a member, and identify the event; i.e., the value of x. This value may be treated or used in whatever manner is required in our analysis. When the next value of x is needed, we take a second random number and repeat the process. Suppose that the first three two-digit random numbers in our list are 37, 56, 21. The first three x values would be 6, 6, 5.

Monte Carlo and Markov Processes

Given the transition matrix of a process and a sequence of random numbers, a sequence of process states can be generated with the Monte Carlo method.

From the illustration used in the discussion of Markov chain processes we had the transition matrix:

$$P = \begin{array}{c} \\ A \\ B \\ C \end{array} \begin{array}{ccc} A & B & C \\ 0.0 & 1.0 & 0.0 \\ 0.0 & 0.3 & 0.7 \\ 0.2 & 0.0 & 0.8 \end{array}$$

Random numbers (one-digit) are assigned to the outcomes according to the probabilities in the matrix rows:

	A	B	C
A	–	0–9	–
B	–	0–2	3–9
C	0–1	–	2–9

The procedure is to specify the initial state, obtain a random number, evaluate it (determine the new state), obtain another random number, and so on. Suppose the initial state is B and the first three random numbers in our list are 7, 4, 1. The process states would then be C, C, A.

SUGGESTIONS FOR FURTHER STUDY

FELLER, W. *An Introduction to Probability: Theory and Its Applications* New York: John Wiley & Sons, 1950.

MOSTELLER, FREDERICK; ROURKE, ROBERT E. K.; AND THOMAS, GEORGE B., JR. *Probability and Statistics.* Reading, Mass.: Addison-Wesley, 1961.

SCHLAIFER, ROBERT. *Probability and Statistics for Business Decisions.* New York: McGraw-Hill, 1959.

WALLIS, W. A., AND ROBERTS, H. V. *Statistics.* Glencoe, Ill.: Free Press, 1956.

CHAPTER 6

Monte Carlo Simulation: The Inventory System Under Uncertainty

Two ASSUMPTIONS in our retailer's inventory model made it somewhat unrealistic: the constant demand rate from one day to the next, and the constant lead time from one order to the next. By assuming these factors to be constant, uncertainties were eliminated, shortages were easily and economically avoided, and the problem became extremely simple—and correspondingly unrealistic.

We will now introduce some uncertainties, which complicate the inventory management problem but which make it more realistic, and in the process we will build an inventory model which has rather general applicability to inventory systems in everyday business. As before, we will develop the model by an example; then we will concern ourselves with a *general model*. Our example will be the inventory system of "Brown Electronics Company."

BROWN ELECTRONICS COMPANY

Brown Company stocks purchased units of Item A, a component used in subsequent assembly. Brown knows that:

1. Each unit of Item A costs $500.
2. The cost of holding Item A in inventory is 20 percent of its cost price per year.
3. The cost of processing an order for any number of units of Item A is $20 per order processed.
4. Brown Company can expect a demand for 365 units during the year.

5. All units of Item A demanded but not available are backordered, and are filled immediately when a new shipment arrives.

But two uncertainties stand out in the case of Brown Electronics Company's operations:

1. Brown is uncertain about the day-to-day demand rate for Item A.
2. Brown is uncertain about lead time.

However, Brown has the records of last year's experience and believes that this year's experience will be the same. Specifically, Brown's records show that the demand rate and lead time last year were as shown in Tables 6-1 and 6-2:

Table 6-1

Demand for Item A during Past Year*

Units Demanded per Day	Frequency of Demand
0	40% of the days
1	30% ” ” ”
2	20% ” ” ”
3	10% ” ” ”
	100%

* It is assumed that there is no seasonal pattern in demand and lead time; and that both are random, with the frequency distributions shown.

Table 6-2

Lead Time for Item A during Past Year

Lead Time (Days)	Frequency of Lead Time
1	25% of the lead time periods
2	50% ” ” ” ” ”
3	25% ” ” ” ” ”
	100%

Brown's problem is: In order to minimize total inventory cost (1) *How many units of Item A should we order at one time?* [reorder quantity, $\hat{Q}$], and (2) *At what point, as the stock level drops, should we place an order?* [reorder point, $\hat{R}$].

In our retailer's inventory problem (Chapter 4) we were not willing to permit a stockout to occur. Also, in our retailer's problem, we were able to determine the optimum reorder point, $\hat{R}$, independently of the optimum order quantity, $\hat{Q}$. In the Brown Electronics Company case, involving an inventory system under uncertainty, we will discover that $\hat{R}$ cannot be determined independently of $\hat{Q}$, but that we must find an optimum combination of $\hat{Q}$ and $\hat{R}$; we will also find that setting R at a level where an occasional stockout is expected is a good policy. We will, however, postpone consideration of *why* this is true until we've advanced a bit further in our study of the nature of Brown's expected demand and lead time experience.

Since permitting an occasional stockout may be desirable for Brown Electronics Company, we need—for planning purposes—to have some notion of the seriousness of the consequences of a stockout. Brown estimates that the monetary measure of the cost of a stockout is $40 per unit of Item A demanded but unavailable at the moment it is needed.

It is helpful to visualize the problem by referring to a graphic representation of the expected inventory experience of the Brown Company. Particular attention should be focused on the period during lead time (see Figure 6-1) since it is only during the lead time period that a stockout can occur.

FIGURE 6-1

A Sample of Brown Company's Inventory Experience*

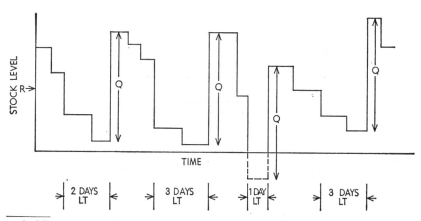

* ←LT→ represents a lead time period; R is the reorder point; and Q represents the reorder quantity.

The magnitude of the shortages that can be expected during the average lead time is dependent upon the reorder point, the various lead times which might be experienced, the various rates of demand which might be experienced during lead times, and the probabilities of these lead times and demand rates occurring *simultaneously*.

In order to determine the optimum values of $\hat{Q}$ and $\hat{R}$, we must know what the *expected shortage* during a lead time period is. And in order to determine the expected shortage during a lead time period, we must determine the expected demand during a lead time period.

In Table 6-1 we have data which tells us the various quantities which might be demanded on any one day and the relative frequency with which these various demands are expected. If we view relative frequency as a measure of probability, Table 6-1 would appear in the form shown in Table 6-3.

Table 6-3

Possible Unit Demand in a Day	Probability of This Demand
0	.40
1	.30
2	.20
3	.10
	1.00

In a similar way, Table 6-2 would become Table 6-4.

Table 6-4

Possible Lead Time in Days	Probability of This Lead Time
1	.25
2	.50
3	.25
	1.00

What we need now is a similar table of data which will tell us the various amounts of Item A which might be demanded during the various lead time periods throughout the year, and also the probability of these various demands. From such a table we could calculate the expected value of stockout per lead time period corresponding to various reorder points; and with this knowledge we could build an inventory model under uncertainty. To construct a table of this sort we might reason as follows:

Demand during lead time could be as high as nine units. This is apparent because lead time could be as long as three days and the demand rate could be as high as three per day on each of the three days. Now, the probability that nine units will be demanded during lead time is the *joint probability* that lead time will be three days and that a demand rate of three per day will occur on three successive days. The joint probability that the demand will be for three units on each of three successive days is $(.10) \times (.10) \times (.10)$. The joint probability of "lead time of three days" *and* "demand for three units on each of three successive days" is $(.25) \times (.10) \times (.10) \times (.10)$, or .00025, which we will round to .0003.

Demand during lead time could also be eight units. This is apparent because lead time could be three days, and on two of these days three units could be demanded each day, followed by a demand for two on the third day. The sequence of these events could, of course, occur three different ways (as shown in Table 6-5, along with their various probabilities of occurrence).

Table 6-5

Probability That Eight Units Will Be Demanded during Lead Time

Ways in which demand for 8 might occur	Probability that this "event" might occur
(1) First day, 3 demanded .... Second day, 3 demanded .... Third day, 2 demanded	$(.25)\ (.10)\ (.10)\ (.20) = .0005$
(2) First day, 3 demanded .... Second day, 2 demanded .... Third day, 3 demanded	$(.25)\ (.10)\ (.20)\ (.10) = .0005$
(3) First day, 2 demanded .... Second day, 3 demanded .... Third day, 3 demanded	$(.25)\ (.20)\ (.10)\ (.10) = .0005$

The combined probability of these events is the *sum* of their individual probabilities of occurrence, or .0015.

Proceeding in this fashion we could develop a table which would give all the possible demands during lead time and the probability of their occurrences. Another way to develop a combined probability distribution—and a more practicable way to deal with complex systems of this sort—is by Monte Carlo simulation.

MONTE CARLO SIMULATION

The possible events described in Table 6-3 could be simulated by a sampling process involving different colored balls. We could place together in a jar 4 white balls, 3 blue balls, 2 yellow balls, and 1 green ball. Then, if we drew a ball at random, recorded its color, replaced it and drew another, recorded its color, replaced it, etc., stirring the balls each time, we would expect that if we continued this sampling process long enough 40 percent of the time we would find ourselves drawing white balls, 30 percent of the time blue balls, 20 percent of the time yellow balls, and 10 percent of the time green balls. To simulate Brown Electronics Company's expected daily demand pattern, we simply consider the "drawing of a ball" to be the "simulation of a day's operation," equating

> *White balls* as demand for *0 units;*
> *Blue balls* as demand for *1 unit;*
> *Yellow balls* as demand for *2 units;*
> *Green balls* as demand for *3 units.*

If a white ball is drawn, we reason that on that simulated "day of operations" 0 units of Item A were demanded; if a blue ball is drawn 1 unit was demanded; if a yellow ball is drawn 2 units were demanded; and if a green ball is drawn 3 units were demanded. Since we have loaded the jar with 4 white balls, 3 blue balls, 2 yellow balls, and 1 green ball, over the long run 0 units will be demanded 40 percent of the days; 1 unit will be demanded 30 percent of the days; 2 units will be demanded 20 percent of the days, and 3 units will be demanded 10 percent of the days. Thus our sampling process will perfectly simulate Brown Electronics' expected daily demand pattern.

In the same way we could simulate Brown's expected lead time pattern. In a *separate* jar 25 white balls might be deposited to represent a lead time of 1 day; 50 blue balls for a lead time of 2 days; and 25 yellow balls for a lead time of 3 days.

Simulating Brown Electronics Company's Demand during Lead Time

Now, to simulate demand during lead time, we would proceed as follows:

1. Draw a ball from jar two (representing Table 6-4):
   a) If a white ball was drawn, we reason that in our first "simulated experience" lead time was one day. Therefore we draw one ball from jar one (representing Table 6-3). If we draw a white ball from jar one, we record "demand zero." If we draw a blue ball, we record "demand 1"; if a yellow ball, "demand 2," etc.
   b) If a blue ball was drawn, we reason that in our first "simulated experience" lead time was two days, so we draw one ball from jar one, record our experience, replace the ball and draw

another ball, record our experience, and add up the resulting "demands" for the two days in order to determine *total* demand during the *two* days of lead time.

    c) If a yellow ball was drawn, we proceed as above, but we draw from jar one *three* times.

2.   Draw a second ball from jar two to simulate a second lead time experience, and proceed as in *a)*, *b)*, and *c)* above.

3.   Draw a third ball from jar two to simulate a third lead time experience, and proceed as in *a)*, *b)*, and *c)* above, etc.

If we continued this simulation process over a large number of trials we would expect to find that a demand during lead time (DDLT) of 9 units would occur 0.03 percent of the time—and that a DDLT of 8 units would occur 0.15 percent of the time—since we have already developed these probabilities analytically.

Where a great number of combinations of demands per day and lead time durations are possible, an analytical solution becomes impracticable, and Monte Carlo simulation is very useful.

In actual practice, however, we do not use colored balls but rather a random number list. From the preceding chapter recall that we expect in a list of two-digit random numbers that each number is as likely to occur next (reading the list from the top down, for example) as any other two-digit number; and we can cause the "reading of a number" to be the equivalent of "drawing a ball" by the following scheme:

Let number 00 through number 39 represent a demand for 0 units
   "   40   69   1 unit
   "   70   89   2 units
   "   90   99   3 units

And

Let number 00 through number 24 represent a lead time of 1 day
   "   25   74   2 days
   "   75   99   3 days

We now "read a number" from our two-digit random number list to determine the number of days in our simulated lead time; and, depending on the outcome, read 1, 2, or 3 numbers to determine total demand during lead time for that simulated lead time experience.

Monte Carlo Simulation on the Computer

This process of reading a number and recording its interpretation in terms of the system being simulated would be cumbersome if we were obliged to do it in the fashion described above. We can cause the computer, by a variety of schemes, to do this for us. We will develop one possible FORTRAN program for doing this, but first we will introduce the READ statement, another important FORTRAN "device."

The READ Statement

The READ statement bears some similarity to the PRINT statement except that where the PRINT statement causes the computer to print out (or output) data, the READ statement causes the computer to read in (to input) data. Recall that the statement   PRINT _____YEAR,S,   in our compound interest program, could be used to cause the values currently stored for the variables   YEAR and S   to be printed out.

The statement   READ_____IRN, DA   could be used to cause the computer to *give to* (store in memory for) the variable   IRN some value, and to give the variable   DA   another value. In a fashion similar to the PRINT statement, the READ statement must refer to a FORMAT statement which will tell the computer the format in which the values to be given to IRN and DA will be found. To make this clear, we must say a word about inputting data into the computer.

Inputting Data

As we have seen thus far, the computer performs various operations on data given to it. We have also seen how data can be given to the computer "from within" the FORTRAN program. Thus in the program:

$$YEAR = 0.0$$
$$P = 10000.00$$
$$R = .04$$
$$N = 1$$
$$DO\ 3\ I = 1,5$$
$$S = P * (1.0 + R) ** N$$
$$YEAR = YEAR + 2.0$$
$$3 \quad PRINT_____,YEAR,S$$
$$STOP$$
$$END$$

the first four statements supply the computer with data to be operated on in the remainder of the program.

Data can also be introduced at the end of the program, *after* the END statement. Data supplied at the end of the program are supplied as purely numerical data. A random number list is data of this type. We can cause the computer to "read" a list of random numbers, from top down, and to conduct our Monte Carlo simulation for us. To cause the computer to read or input data into the computer in this fashion we must prepare a "data deck" of punched cards. On each card we punch one two-digit random number, arranging our deck in the order in which the numbers are encountered in our random number table. Each two-digit number must be punched in the same two columns on its card as all the other numbers.

A FORMAT statement is then added to the "main program" (all that precedes the END statement) in which the computer is advised *where,* on each data card, the random numbers are to be found. Suppose, for example, we wanted to leave the first four columns blank and to punch our two-digit numbers in columns 5 and 6. Our FORMAT statement might appear thus: 15 FORMAT (4X,I2). (Since our random numbers are integers, we use an I rather than an F specification in the FORMAT statement.)

Although we need only one kind of data for our Monte Carlo simulation (i.e., our random numbers list), it should be observed that many data can be read into the computer with one execution of one READ statement. Thus we might provide for reading into the computer two lists of numbers by punching two numbers on each data card. Our data deck, for example, might represent these two lists of numbers:

06	3000.00
71	4000.00
18	5000.00
49	6000.00

Let's assume that the first digit of the numbers in the column on the left is punched in column 5 and the first digit of the numbers in the column on the right is punched in column 15. These lists might be read into the computer by the two statements:

READ 15, IRN, DA
15   FORMAT (4X,I2,8X,F8.2)

The FORMAT statement tells the computer the precise arrangement of the data to be found on each punched card in the data deck.

When the READ statement above is encountered, the first pair of numbers will be read in; that is, the variable IRN will have stored for it the value 06, and the variable DA will have stored for it the value 3000.00. The next time the READ statement is encountered the values previously stored for IRN and DA will be erased, and 71 and 4000.00 will be stored for IRN and DA, respectively.

In punching data cards it should be observed that all 80 columns in a data deck can be used, and that data may be arranged in any fashion to suit the programmer. Thus our two lists could occupy only the first nine columns of the card. This is possible because in inputting data (if no sign is indicated) the computer will assume that the sign is positive, and therefore no space need be left for a sign in inputting data *except* where the data are negative. Our data might therefore be punched in this fashion:

063000.00
714000.00
185000.00
496000.00

and they might be read in by these statements:

READ 16, IRN, DA
16   FORMAT (I2,F7.2)

It is possible to have many different lists compose a complete data deck, with data in each list arranged differently from data in the other lists. Under these circumstances all the individual decks (each corresponding to one list) are simply stacked together in the order in which they are to be read in, and the complete data deck is added to the main program deck following the final END statement. The main program must contain a pair of READ and FORMAT statements for the data deck segment corresponding to each list, and provision must be made in the main program for reading in *all* the data in one list *prior* to reading in any data from the data deck segment which follows it.

(*Note:* By use of input data *tapes,* rather than input data *cards,* this limitation can be avoided and data from a number of different lists can be read in selectively. Since the limitation associated with inputting data via a data deck is no problem to us at this stage, we will concern ourselves only with the data deck as a scheme for reading data into the computer's memory.)

We are now equipped to write a FORTRAN program to cause the computer to READ a two-digit random number list and to conduct a Monte Carlo simulation of Brown Electronics Company's demand during lead time experience. We will compose a list of FORTRAN statements to cause the computer to:

1. Read the first random number (from our input data deck) and interpret the number of days of lead time it represents; then
2. Read as many more random numbers as there are days in the lead time period (in step 1); and
3. Add up the daily demands to get DDLT (demand during lead time).

In Figure 6-2, the steps called for above are diagrammed in flow-

FIGURE 6-2

Monte Carlo Simulation Flow Chart for Simulating Demand during Lead Time for One Lead Time Period

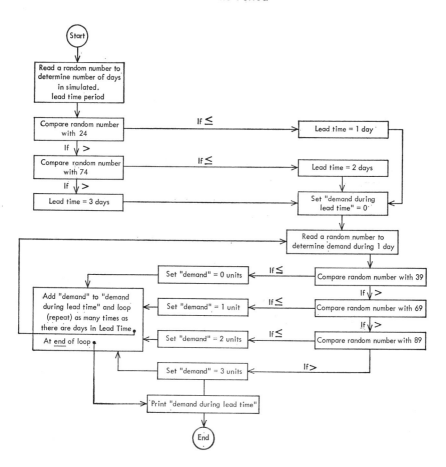

chart form, while Figure 6-3 shows a FORTRAN program segment which should simulate one lead time period.

FIGURE 6-3*

FORTRAN Program Segment Simulating One Lead Time Period

```
2    READ_____,IRN
     IF (IRN − 24)3,3,4
3    LT = 1
     GO TO 7
4    IF (IRN − 74)5,5,6
5    LT = 2
     GO TO 7
6    LT = 3
7    IDDLT = 0
     DO 14 I = 1, LT
     READ_____,IRN
     IF (IRN − 39)8,8,9
8    ID = 0
     GO TO 14
9    IF (IRN − 69)10,10,11
10   ID = 1
     GO TO 14
11   IF (IRN − 89)12,12,13
12   ID = 2
     GO TO 14
13   ID = 3
14   IDDLT = IDDLT + ID
```

----

* LT = lead time, in number of days; IRN is the variable which holds the most recently read-in two-digit random number; ID represents the demand in one *day*, in units; IDDLT represents the demand during lead time. (We add the I's to make these integer variables.)

Note: We have seen that statement numbers in a FORTRAN program do *not* have to be in consecutive order. From this point on, however, we will number statements consecutively, wherever practicable, to facilitate interpretation.

Each time through the program (Figure 6-3), one lead time experience is simulated. The statements preceding the DO statement cause the computer to determine the number of days lead time. The DO statement then causes the statements through 14 to be executed the number of times there are days in the lead time period currently simulated. Each time the computer passes from statements 7 through 13, one day's demand is simulated. In statement 14, the demands for each of the days in the lead time period are summed, so that by the time the DO loop has been completed the variable

IDDLT holds the number of units demanded during the simulated lead time period. This value could be printed out, and the computer could be returned to statement 2 to simulate another lead time experience.

We would, of course, want to go further, and let the computer "keep score" (count up the frequency) of the various demands during lead time which were simulated over an adequate sample, and then calculate and print out for us a probability distribution for demand during lead time. (To do this efficiently we will need to employ an additional FORTRAN device, the "subscripted variable," but it would be best to return to consideration of our inventory model under uncertainty before introducing this added programming convention.) To facilitate interpretation of what is yet to come in the development of our inventory model under uncertainty, Table 6-6 provides the probability distributions which a complete Monte Carlo simulation would yield.

Table 6-6

Brown Electronics Company's (Monte Carlo) Demand during Lead Time
Probability Distributions

Possible Demand during Lead Time (Units) DDLT	Probability of This Demand	Cumulative Probability (Probability Demand Will Be Greater)
0	.1960	.8040
1	.2310	.5730
2	.2260	.3470
3	.1797	.1673
4	.0935	.0738
5	.0477	.0261
6	.0190	.0071
7	.0053	.0018
8	.0015	.0003
9	.0003	.0000

In the last column we have added the probability that demand during a lead time period will be *greater* than DDLT; and the usefulness of this probability will become apparent shortly. The determination of the values in the last column is quite simple: the probability that DDLT > 9 is zero, since (as we saw earlier) 9 is the maximum possible demand during lead time. The only way DDLT can be greater than 8 is for it to be 9. Since the probability of a DDLT of 9 is .0003, clearly, the probability that DDLT > 8 is .0003. The only way in which DDLT can be greater than 7 is for it to be

8 *or* 9. Since these probabilities are additive, the probability of a DDLT > 7 is the sum of the probability of a DDLT of 8 plus the probability of a DDLT of 9, or 0.0018. The other values in the last column of Table 6-6 are calculated in this same way.

The Expected Value of Stockout

We are now equipped to determine the expected (or average) stockout per lead time period, given any particular reorder point, R. In what follows it will be useful to focus attention on the lead time period and to think of R as the beginning inventory during a span of time which is the lead time period. The ending inventory will either be zero or some positive value, depending on R and DDLT.

Table 6-6 makes it apparent that if we place R at 9 units (that is, if we reorder the moment the stock level drops to 9 units) we will never be caught short, since the probability of a DDLT > 9 is zero. But if we place R at 8 units, what is the expectation? Clearly, a stockout can occur, and it is expected to occur .03 percent of the lead time periods since the probability of a DDLT > 8 is .0003. The "expected value of stockout" *per lead time period,* assuming Brown Electronics Company reorders at R $= 8$ units, is $(9 - 8) \times .0003 =$ .0003 units.

To make this more persuasive, consider what would happen in the long run—given a policy of reordering at R $= 8$ units. Assume Brown operates its inventory system, with a policy of reordering at R $= 8$, over 10,000 lead time periods. We would expect that Brown would experience a shortage of one unit $(9 - 8)$ in three of these 10,000 lead time periods (.03 percent of 10,000). A stockout of three units in 10,000 lead time periods is an "average" of .0003 units *per* lead time period.

What if Brown follows a policy of reordering at R $= 7$ units? Over the long run Brown would expect to run short .18 percent of the time, since the probability of DDLT > 7 is 0.0018. But what is Brown's expected or average stockout *per lead time period* under this policy? Over 10,000 lead time periods Brown would expect:

1. A shortage of two units $(9 - 7)$ during three lead time periods, since the probability of nine being demanded is .0003; and
2. A shortage of one unit $(8 - 7)$ during 15 lead time periods, since the probability of eight being demanded is .0015.

Thus Brown's expected total number of units demanded, but unavailable, would be $2 \times 3 + 1 \times 15 = 21$ units in 10,000 lead time periods, or an average of .0021 *per* lead time period.

In a similar way, we could determine the expected value of stockout (expected number of units short) per lead time period if Brown reorders at R = 6 units:

$$
\begin{aligned}
(9 - 6) &\times .0003 = .0009 \\
+ (8 - 6) &\times .0015 = .0030 \\
+ (7 - 6) &\times .0053 = .0053 \\
\hline
&\text{Total} = .0092
\end{aligned}
$$

Under this policy Brown's expected stockout per lead time period is .0092 units. We will label this quantity $E(DDLT > R)$, meaning the expected amount by which DDLT is greater than R (the reorder point), or the expected stockout per lead time period, in units short.

Clearly, Brown will never be caught short .0092 units—or any other fractional part of a unit (review the definition of expected value, Chapter 5)—but for purposes of policy determination the concept of an expected fractional stockout is necessary. The reason for this will become more apparent if we return now to consider why a policy in which an occasional stockout is expected may be a desirable policy under conditions of uncertainty, and why optimum order quantity, $\hat{Q}$, and optimum reorder point, $\hat{R}$, cannot be determined independently of each other. Since the reason for this interdependence of $\hat{Q}$ and $\hat{R}$ under conditions of uncertainty is not readily apparent, a few words about the inventory problem under uncertainty might be appropriate.

The Nature of Conditions of Uncertainty

In our retailer's inventory problem we did not bother to defend our policy of reordering when the stock level dropped to two units—rather than reordering at some point *less* than R = 2. Since one unit was certain to be demanded each day (in our retailer's hypothetical system), and since lead time was two days, we simply assumed that while our retailer would want R to be as low as possible (to keep the average inventory level low), he would not be willing to tolerate a stockout. This policy clearly needs no defense: to lower the reorder point to one, for example, would yield a *certain* stockout of one unit each lead time period. If buying, storing and reselling units of Item A is profitable to our retailer, then the savings in inventory holding cost by reordering at one unit would be *less* than the lost profits from unsatisfied demand. Therefore our retailer would want to set R at the lowest level, but not so low as to permit a stockout of even one unit.

Under conditions of *uncertainty*, however, setting R at a level which makes a stockout a possibility may be very desirable. In our retailer's problem we found that lowering R by one unit *below* two units yielded an "increased stockout," per lead time period, of one unit. In the Brown Electronics case, lowering the reorder point by one unit, from nine to eight units, would yield an "increased stockout" per lead time period of .0003 units. And, by lowering the reorder point from nine to eight units, we can make a very significant contribution to decreased holding costs at practically no increase in stockout costs.

In short, under conditions of uncertainty an inventory policy which makes a stockout impossible is almost certain to cost more than it is worth. Our problem, then, is to balance stockout costs against (1) holding costs and (2) ordering costs, in order to find that policy which minimizes total costs.

The cost of expected stockout *per lead time period* is the expected number of units demanded but not available during a lead time period *times* the cost per stockout. We assumed that the monetary measure of the seriousness of a stockout of one unit is $40.00.[1] The cost of expected stockout per lead time period, then, would be E (DDLT > R) × $40.00.

The cost of expected *annual* stockout is the expected stockout cost per lead time multiplied by the expected number of lead time periods in a year. The expected number of lead time periods is the expected number of units demanded in one year divided by the order quantity, Q, or 365/Q. The expected annual stockout cost for Brown Electronics, therefore, would be E (DDLT > R) × $40 × 365/Q.

We have just seen how the expected annual stockout cost is dependent both upon Q and upon R, and *also* we have seen that the

---

[1] We will assume further that the stockout cost is linear; i.e., the cost of a stockout of two units is twice the cost of a stockout of one unit; the cost of a stockout of three units is three times the cost of a stockout of one unit; etc.

size of R influences average inventory and hence annual holding cost. But inventory holding cost is also dependent upon Q. Therefore $\hat{Q}$ and $\hat{R}$ are interdependent, and we cannot—as in the case of our retailer's problem—solve for one independently of the other. Rather, we must seek an optimum combination of Q and R.

THE INVENTORY MODEL UNDER UNCERTAINTY

We are now equipped to construct our total annual inventory cost model for Brown Electronics Company under conditions of uncertainty. Our total annual cost model for Brown Electronics consists of three parts: (1) annual inventory holding cost, (2) annual ordering cost, and (3) annual stockout cost. We will now develop each of these.

Annual Holding Cost (1)

As we have seen, Brown's average inventory level is dependent upon R as well as Q. To get at Brown's average inventory level, let us examine a *simplified* curve of Brown's expected inventory experience *if no stockouts ever occurred* (Figure 6-4). If no stockouts ever occurred, Brown's *average* inventory pattern would be as depicted

FIGURE 6-4

Brown Electronics Company's Average Inventory Pattern
(Assuming no stockouts occur)

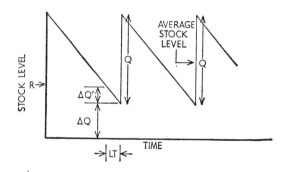

in Figure 6-4. If our assumption that no stockout would ever occur were a valid assumption, then clearly Brown's *average* inventory level would be $Q/2 + \Delta Q$.

It should be apparent from Figure 6-4 that ΔQ is $R - \Delta Q'$, and that $\Delta Q'$ is the expected or average demand during lead time, assuming no stockouts. We can calculate the expected demand during lead time from our demand and lead time distributions (Tables 6-3 and 6-4):

$$
\begin{aligned}
0 \times .40 &= 0.00 \\
+ 1 \times .30 &= 0.30 \\
+ 2 \times .20 &= 0.40 \\
+ 3 \times .10 &= 0.30 \\
\hline
\text{Total} &= 1.00
\end{aligned}
$$

Average daily demand, accordingly, is for one unit. Furthermore:

$$
\begin{aligned}
1 \times .25 &= 0.25 \\
+ 2 \times .50 &= 1.00 \\
+ 3 \times .25 &= 0.75 \\
\hline
\text{Total} &= 2.00
\end{aligned}
$$

and thus average lead time is two days.

If expected or average lead time is two days, and average daily demand is for one unit, then expected or average demand during lead time is for two units.

Referring again to Figure 6-4, $\Delta Q'$ is seen to be two units, and hence $\Delta Q = R - 2$. It therefore follows that average inventory, assuming no stockouts occur, would be $Q/2 + R - 2$.

But we expect an occasional stockout, and hence our analysis (above) would seem to be invalid. If we assume that a stockout *can* occur, then, during those lead time periods when a stockout does occur, the actual withdrawal from inventory—and hence the reduction of the inventory level—will be less than $\Delta Q'$ by an amount equal to the amount demanded but not available. The average ΔQ, therefore, would be greater by the stock demanded but not available, and hence our average inventory level throughout the year would seem to be larger than $Q/2 + R - 2$.

Recall, however, that backordering is permitted in the Brown Electronics Company inventory system, and that unsatisfied demand is satisfied immediately upon receipt of a new shipment. This would mean that, following a lead time period when a stockout occurs, the inventory level falls short of rising to a level equal to the reorder quantity, Q, by an amount equal to the backordered demand. (A second look at Figure 6-1 should substantiate this expectation.)

It develops, therefore, that the errors in our calculation of average inventory level (above) tend to cancel each other, and Brown's average inventory level can be considered to be[2]

$$Q/2 + R - 2. \tag{6-1}$$

Since the cost of holding inventory for one year amounts to 20 percent of its value, Brown's expected annual inventory holding cost will be

$$0.20(\$500)(Q/2 + R - 2). \tag{6-2}$$

Annual Ordering Cost (2)

Annual ordering cost is—as before with our retailer—the cost per order times the number of orders processed per year

$$\$20 \times (365/Q). \tag{6-3}$$

Annual Stockout Cost (3)

Annual stockout cost, as was shown, is

$$\$40 \times E(DDLT > R) \times 365/Q. \tag{6-4}$$

Brown's total annual inventory cost is the sum of **6-2**, **6-3**, and **6-4**, or:

$$\begin{aligned} TAC = {}& 0.20 \ (\$500) \ (Q/2 + R - 2) \\ & + \$20 \ (365/Q) \\ & + \$40 \times E(DDLT > R) \times 365/Q. \end{aligned} \tag{6-5}$$

To deal with **6-5**, we might reason—somewhat as we did with our retailer's model—that if we set our reorder point at 1 (let R = 1) and then vary Q from a small to a very large value, we would get a U-shaped total annual cost curve. As before, we might search this curve for the minimum TAC.

This would give us the minimum TAC for a reorder point of 1, and we have reason to believe that the minimum TAC associated with a reorder point of 2 is lower than the minimum TAC associated with a reorder point of 1 (A look at Table 6-7 will make this apparent). With R = 1 we must expect a stockout of more than one unit each lead time period. If it is profitable to purchase, hold, and then utilize or resell units of Item A, then quite probably the savings

---

[2] *Note:* If backordering is not permitted; i.e., if unsatisfied demand is lost demand, then $Q/2 + R - 2$ does *not* represent the average inventory level precisely. In a great many cases, however, it is a very close approximation, and therefore the general validity of our model is not seriously limited.

in holding cost resulting from ordering at $R = 1$, rather than at $R > 1$, cannot be sufficient to compensate for the loss due to a stock-out per lead-time-period of this magnitude.

We have already seen that the savings in holding cost by reducing R from 9 to 8 (where stockouts are eliminated altogether) is almost certain to be more than enough to compensate for the negligible loss due to expected stockout when $R = 8$.

Our objective, then, is to search among a *family* of U-shaped TAC curves (much like the three curves shown in Figure 6-5) to find the lowest point among them. In fact, there will be nine of these

FIGURE 6-5

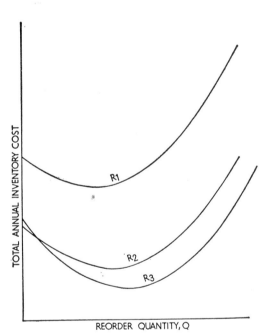

U-shaped curves, corresponding to each of our nine reorder policies. The Q and R combination which yields the lowest TAC among this family of curves is the optimum Q, R combination.

The only difficulty in conducting this search is encountered in dealing with the expression $E (DDLT > R)$ in our TAC model, **6–5**.

If we could determine all the possible values for $E (DDLT > R)$, and then if we could call forth the value for $E (DDLT > R)$ corresponding to the reorder point currently under consideration, as we go through an iterative process searching for the best R, we could write a FORTRAN program which would cause the computer to conduct the search for us. To do this most easily, we must introduce a powerful FORTRAN device called the *subscripted variable*.

The Subscripted Variable

A subscripted variable differs in appearance from a non-subscripted variable in that it has a set of parentheses associated with it. The following could be subscripted variables:

$$AHC(1), \ TAC(3), \ CPU(47)$$

Many constant values can be stored simultaneously for one subscripted variable—in contrast to a non-subscripted variable which can have only one value stored at a time. A subscripted variable might be thought of as a row of "pigeon holes" or positions into each of which a different numerical value can be stored. The number in the parentheses associated with the subscripted variable indicates which position is intended when one of the values stored for the subscripted variable is referred to.

If AHC(1) were encountered on the right side of the equal sign in a FORTRAN algebraic expression, the computer would substitute for AHC(1) the value currently stored for the subscripted variable AHC in position 1. For TAC(3), encountered on the right side of the equal sign in an algebraic expression, the computer would substitute the value currently stored for the subscripted variable TAC in position 3.

In a fashion similar to that of the non-subscripted (sometimes called a "zero dimension subscripted") variable, the computer stores (in the position indicated by the number in parentheses) the value of the expression to the *right* of the equal sign when a subscripted variable is encountered to the *left* of an equal sign in an algebraic statement. Thus, if CPU(47) were encountered to the left of an equal sign, the computer would store in position number 47 (for the subscripted variable CPU) the value of the expression to the right of the equal sign.

The subscripted variable's usefulness is enhanced enormously because it is possible to place a *variable* (but only an integer variable) rather than a constant in the parentheses. Thus, P(N),

COH(MN), AR(KIT)   may also be legitimate subscripted variables. The variable in the parentheses can take any value (within the limits of the computer's memory) so long as it is a positive integer and greater than zero. If the subscripted variable P(N) were encountered to the right of an equal sign in an algebraic statement, P(N) would be replaced by the value currently stored in position N (whatever N happens to be at that moment in the computer's memory) for the subscripted variable P.

The same rules that govern both non-subscripted integer and floating point variables apply to subscripted variables. Thus, if the integer subscripted variable J(8) is given the value 16.23, the two digits to the right of the decimal will be truncated and only the value 16 will be stored in position 8 of the variable J.

In addition to one-dimension subscripted variables, we can also have two- and three-dimension subscripted variables:

P(N,M)   (*two dimension*)
COH(MN,L3T,KD)   (*three dimension*).

The Dimension Statement

Every FORTRAN program which contains a subscripted variable must contain a DIMENSION statement. At the beginning of the program, the DIMENSION statement causes the computer to reserve in memory for the subscripted variable or variables (one DIMENSION statement can be used for a number of different subscripted variables) the number of storage locations required to accommodate the subscripted variable.

Thus, the statement DIMENSION ES(9) could be used to cause the computer to reserve nine storage locations to accommodate the nine values for expected stockout in our program for Brown Electronics Company. (*Note:* The DIMENSION statement must precede all statements in which a variable appears.) Let us, then, return to Brown Electronics Company's inventory problem and see how a subscripted variable might be employed.

We should begin by completing our list of expected stockouts, per lead time period, as R varies from 1 through 9. Proceeding as before, we would find that

TABLE 6-7

Reorder Policies and Associated Expected Stockouts

With a reorder point, R, of:	Expected stockout per lead time period, E(DDLT > R), would be:
1	1.1864
2	0.6234
3	0.2764
4	0.1091
5	0.0353
6	0.0092
7	0.0021
8	0.0003
9	0.0000

We can store this array of values for $E(DDLT) > R$ in computer memory by using a subscripted variable. Recalling that when a *variable* is employed in the parentheses of a subscripted variable it must be an integer variable, let us designate the subscripted variable, into which our values for $E(DDLT > R)$ will be stored, as $ES(IR)$.

Now if we think of IR as not only the position indicator for our subscripted variable, $ES(IR)$, but also as our reorder point, then we would want to store in position $IR = 1$, the expected value of stockout per lead time period when the reorder point is 1. We would want to store in position $IR = 2$, the expected value of stockout per lead time period when the reorder point is 2, and so on, until all our expected values of stockout are stored in the array, $ES(IR)$.

If we now list, after the END statement at the end of a FORTRAN program, all the nine values for $E(DDLT > R)$, and if we compose a suitable READ statement to successively read in these values for $E(DDLT > R)$, we can "load" our subscripted variable, $ES(IR)$. The following statements should do this:

```
      DO 1 IR = 1,9
      READ_____,E
    1 ES(IR) = E
```

The first time through the DO loop the variable E will be given the value of the first $E(DDLT > R)$ in our data list; and then in statement 1 this value will be stored in position 1 of our subscripted variable since, the first time through the DO loop, $IR = 1$. The second time through the DO loop, the variable E will be given the value of the second E (DDLT > R)   in our data list, and this value will be stored in position 2 since, the second time through the DO loop,   IR = 2.[3] After completion of the nine loops called for in the DO statement, all values for E (DDLT > R) will have been stored. All we have to do now to call forth the expected value of stockout per lead time period when R equals any particular value, say 6, is to give the variable IR the value 6, and then employ the subscripted variable ES(IR)   itself.

We can now write a FORTRAN program which will cause the computer to search for the best Q, R combination. We want our computer model to begin with a reorder point of 1, vary Q, search the TAC curve corresponding to R = 1, and store the minimum TAC on this curve in some variable; then increase R to 2, vary Q, search the TAC curve corresponding to R = 2, and compare the minimum TAC on this curve to the lowest TAC corresponding to R = 1 (previously stored); and to continue increasing R until this comparison shows us we have reached the "absolute minimum" TAC. The Q, R combination which yielded this absolute minimum will be the optimum Q, R combination.

We want our computer model to do what appears diagrammatically in the flow chart shown in Figure 6-6. In the flow chart the variable "Big TAC" is used to store (as a standard for comparison) the values of TAC as Q is increased; the variable "Small TAC" is used to store values of TAC as R is increased; and the variable "Absolute Minimum" is used to store the minimum TAC from a previous search. A FORTRAN program which should do this for us is shown in Figure 6-7.

In the final DO statement,   DO 2 IQ = 1,10000,   we provide for many loopings so as to guarantee that we reach the lowest point on the curve prior to completion of the looping process. The IF statement (which precedes statement 2) provides for getting us out of the DO loop as soon as the low point has been found, thereby discontinuing the looping and avoiding waste of computer time.

---

[3] We could also have input these data in the main program by the following statements:

ES(1) = 1.1864	ES(5) = 0.0353
ES(2) = 0.6234	ES(6) = 0.0092
ES(3) = 0.2764	ES(7) = 0.0021
ES(4) = 0.1091	ES(8) = 0.0003

FIGURE 6-6

Optimum Inventory Policy—Flow Diagram for Determining Optimum Order
Quantity (Q̂), Optimum Reorder Point (R̂), and Corresponding Least
Total Annual Inventory Cost (TAC)

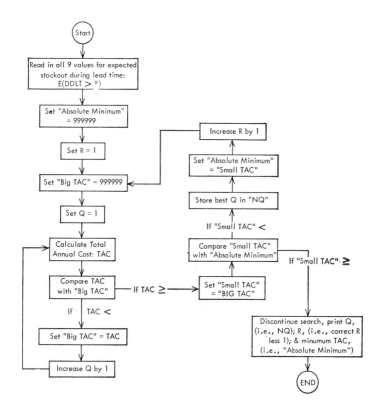

The Optimum Inventory Policy

It develops that Brown Electronics Company will experience a
minimum total annual inventory cost of $1,534 with a $\hat{Q}$ of 13 units
and an $\hat{R}$ of 4 units. Brown's *decision rule* for minimizing total annual inventory cost is: "When stock level in Item A drops to four
units, order a new shipment of thirteen units."

Our expectation that $\hat{Q}$ and $\hat{R}$ are interdependent is confirmed by
the observation that if Brown should elect to order ten or fewer
units with each order placed, then the most economical reorder point
becomes five rather than four.

FIGURE 6-7

FORTRAN Program for Brown's Optimum Inventory Policy

```
    DIMENSION ES(9)
    DO 1 IR = 1,9
    READ_____,E
1   ES(IR) = E
    ABSMIN = 999999.9
    DO 5 IR = 1,9
    R = IR
    BIGTAC = 999999.9
    DO 2 IQ = 1,10000
    Q = IQ
    TAC = 0.2*500.0*(Q/2.0 + R − 2.0) + 20.0*365.0/Q + 40.0*ES
       (IR)*365.0/Q
    IF (TAC − BIGTAC)2,3,3
2   BIGTAC = TAC
3   SMTAC = BIGTAC
    IF (SMTAC − ABSMIN)4,6,6
4   NQ = IQ − 1
5   ABSMIN = SMTAC
6   IR = IR − 1
    PRINT_____,NQ,IR,ABSMIN
    STOP
    END
```

Frequency of Stockouts

Referring to Table 6-6, we see that with a reorder point of four units the probability of Brown's being caught short in a lead time period is 0.0738. That is, 7.38 percent of the lead time periods Brown Electronics Company can expect to experience a shortage of some magnitude. If the reorder quantity is 13 units, Brown can expect 28 lead time periods per year (365/13). Clearly, then, Brown can expect stockouts of some magnitude about two times a year (7.38 percent of 28).

Sensitivity Analysis

In any inventory system we are probably as interested in knowing about the sensitivity of the system as we are in knowing the optimum policy for minimizing costs. We are interested in two kinds of sensitivity:

1. Sensitivity in terms of the behavior of the cost of operating the
    system if we deviate from the optimum policy, and
2. Sensitivity of the optimum policy to changes in various system
    parameters.

Sensitivity of Total Annual Cost to Policy Change. Our computer model for determining optimum inventory policy for Brown
Electronics Company's inventory system was designed to search
each of a family of U-shaped TAC curves for the Q, R combination
corresponding to the lowest possible TAC. If we had made provision in our computer program for printing out all values of Q, R
and TAC, we would have obtained data which would enable us to
plot only the left "half" of the U in each of our family of curves.
From these curves we could get some notion of the consequences in
increased total annual cost from adopting a policy of reordering *less*
than 14 units; but we would also like to know about the consequences of ordering 14 or more units.

We can get the required data with a few alterations in our computer model. In Figure 6-8, Brown's total annual inventory cost
curves are shown for reorder policies in which R varies from 3 units
through 6 units, and Q varies from 10 through 18 units. From these
curves it is apparent that within the range $11 \leqq Q \leqq 16$ and
$3 \leqq R \leqq 6$ total annual inventory cost varies only about 10 percent from the minimum possible cost.

Under these circumstances, Brown might be tempted to increase
R from the optimum of 4 and thereby reduce expected stockout frequency to less than 2 per year. By reordering at $R = 6$ rather than
at $R = 4$, stockouts could be reduced to about one every five years.
This is deduced from Table 6-6 where, with a reorder point of 6,
the probability of a stockout in one lead time period is 0.0071; and
$0.0071 \times 28 = 0.199$.

By adopting a policy of ordering 12 units when the stock level
drops to six units, Brown's expected stockout rate goes from two
stockouts per year to one every five years, and total annual inventory cost goes from \$1,534 to \$1,619, an increase of only about 5
percent.

In spite of the apparent attractiveness of this policy change, the
change would in fact be undesirable unless Brown has inaccurately
estimated the monetary value of the consequence of being caught
short. This brings us to the question "How sensitive is Brown's in-

FIGURE 6-8

Brown Electronics Company's Inventory Cost Curves

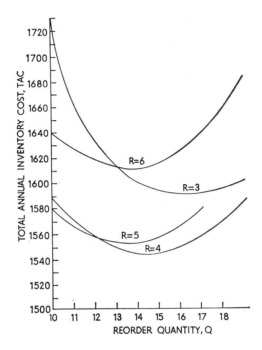

ventory system to variations, and hence to inaccuracies in estimating stockout (and other) costs?"

Sensitivity of Optimum Policy to Changes in System Parameters.
Additional alterations in our computer model would enable us to obtain data on which to evaluate the effect on the optimum inventory policy when the per unit stockout cost is varied.

In Table 6-8 the optimum inventory policies associated with varying per unit stockout costs are tabulated. Also shown are the minimum total annual inventory costs corresponding to the optimum policy in each case. In the next-to-last column are shown total annual inventory costs which Brown Electronics would actually incur if it based its inventory policy on a belief that stockout cost was $40 per unit of stockout (leading to a policy of Q = 13 and R = 4)—when *in fact* stockout cost was as shown in column 1.

Clearly, the Brown Electronics inventory model is not highly sensitive to miscalculations in stockout cost. If Brown bases its inventory policy on a belief that stockout cost is $40 per unit stockout, when *actual* stockout cost is anywhere from $10 to $80, the consequences in increased annual costs attributable to imperfect information are not serious.

Table 6-8

Optimum Inventory Policies and Varying per Unit Stockout Costs

Stockout Cost (per unit)	Corresponding Optimum Inventory Policy $\hat{Q}$	$\hat{R}$	Minimum Total Annual Cost (Based on Optimum Policy)	Total Annual Cost (If Policy Is Based on *Estimated* Stockout Cost of $40 Unit)	Added Inventory Cost (Attributable to Ignorance of *Actual* Stockout Cost)
$10 14		2	$1,384	$1,442	5.6%
20 14		3	1,466	1,473	0.5
30 13		4	1,503	1,503	0.0
40 13		4	1,534	1,534	0.0
50 13		5	1,561	1,564	0.2
60 13		5	1,571	1,595	1.5
70 13		5	1,581	1,625	2.8
80 13		5	1,591	1,657	4.2

A similar analysis might be made of other parameters: holding-cost and its components, and ordering costs. We could also enrich our model to account for non-linearity in parameters; that is, to account for the fact that the cost of being caught short two units is not exactly *twice* the cost of being caught short one unit. Similarly, we could deal with the case where the cost of holding 20 units in inventory is not exactly twice the cost of holding ten units. Furthermore, with a few additional statements, we could read into the computer's memory an array representing a delivered cost schedule and cause the computer to search this schedule—once what is believed to be an optimum Q has been determined—to discover if unit cost-discounts, arising out of larger orders, might justify altering the reorder policy.

A General Inventory Model Under Uncertainty

The model that we developed above may have general validity in a wide variety of cases—where some sort of discrete demand and lead time distributions can be estimated with some confidence.

By substituting *variables* in the Brown Electronics Company model (where we have employed *constants*), we get the following *general model* which Brown might use during periodic reviews, and as various costs associated with its inventory system change, to determine when a change in policy is appropriate (Figure 6-9).

FIGURE 6-9

Computer Program for a General Inventory
Model under Uncertainty

```
C GENERAL INVENTORY MODEL UNDER UNCERTAINTY
C PARAMETERS
C N = NUMBER OF POSITIONS IN THE ARRAY REPRE-
       SENTING THE EXPECTED VALUES OF STOCKOUT
       'SCHEDULE'
C UHC = ANNUAL UNIT HOLDING COST AS A PERCENT OF
       THE COST PRICE PER UNIT
C CPU = COST PRICE PER UNIT
C EDDLT = EXPECTED DEMAND DURING LEAD TIME
C CPO = ORDERING COST PER ORDER PROCESSED
C DPY = DEMAND PER YEAR
C STKCOS = STOCKOUT COST PER UNIT STOCKOUT
C ES(IR) HOLDS THE EXPECTED STOCKOUT SCHEDULE
       DIMENSION ES( )
       N =
       UHC =
       CPU =
       EDDLT =
       CPO =
       DPY =
       STKCOS =
       DO 1 IR = 1,N
       READ_____,E
   1   ES(IR) = E
       ABSMIN = 999999.9
       DO 5 IR = 1,N
       R = IR
       BIGTAC = 999999.9
       DO 2 IQ = 1,10000
       Q = IQ
       TAC = UHC *CPU*(Q/2.0 + R − EDDLT) + CPO*
       (DPY/Q) + STKCOS*ES(IR)*DPY/Q
       IF (TAC − BIGTAC)2,3,3
   2   BIGTAC = TAC
   3   SMTAC = BIGTAC
       IF (SMTAC − ABSMIN)4,6,6
   4   NQ = IQ − 1
   5   ABSMIN = SMTAC
   6   IR = IR − 1
       PRINT_____, NQ,IR,ABSMIN
       STOP
       END
```

Values for the system parameters; i.e., N, UHC, CPU, EDDLT, CPO, DPY, STKCOS and the array ES(IR), as defined in the comment statements (Figure 6-9) should be initialized at the beginning of the program, and a data deck containing the expected values of stockout schedule (expected number of units short per lead time period, corresponding to various reorder points) should be read in as provided for in the first DO loop of the program. The program provides for printing out the optimum reorder quantity, $\hat{Q}$, the optimum reorder point, $\hat{R}$, and the minimum total annual inventory cost associated with these values, TAC.

Completing Our Monte Carlo Simulation Model

In building our inventory model under uncertainty, we became acquainted with the subscripted variable. We are now equipped to explore how the subscripted variable could be used to "keep score" in our Monte Carlo simulation and to print out a probability distribution for our demand during lead time pattern.

Referring to Figure 6-3, we developed a program which would simulate Brown Company's lead time periods and would give the variable IDDLT, following one pass through the program, a value corresponding to the number of units of Item A demanded during the lead time period just simulated.

Let us let SCORE(I) be a subscripted variable in which we store our number of times various demands during lead time are experienced. We will need ten positions in our array, SCORE(I), one for each of the ten possible demands during lead time.

We should empty the SCORE(I) array by equating all ten positions to zero prior to statement 2 in Figure 6-3. We might do this with the statements

$$\text{DO } 1 \text{ I} = 1,10$$
$$1 \quad \text{SCORE(I)} = 0.0$$

Now, immediately following statement 14—in which a new IDDLT is determined in our program (Figure 6-3)—we should place the following statement:[4]

$$15 \quad \text{SCORE(IDDLT} + 1) = \text{SCORE(IDDLT} + 1) + 1.0.$$

---

[4] *Note:* Simple algebraic expressions *can* be employed inside the subscript; thus: SCORE(IDDLT + 1). The complexity of the algebra permitted inside the parentheses varies with the FORTRAN compiler.

As a result of statement 15, the score of the appropriate demand—of our ten possible demands during lead time—is increased by 1, following the simulation of each new lead time period.

Demand during lead time in our model can be zero, and hence IDDLT will sometimes be zero. It will be recalled, however, that the subscript in a subscripted variable must be a positive, non-zero integer. Therefore we are obliged to let the position IDDLT + 1 in our array, SCORE(I), hold the score for the demand during lead time, represented by the current value of the variable IDDLT. Thus when IDDLT = 0, position 1 in our array will have 1 added to its current score.

```
        DIMENSION SCORE(10)
        DO 15 K = 1,1000
 2      READ_____,IRN
        IF (IRN − 24)3,3,4
 3      LT = 1
        GO TO 7
 4      IF (IRN − 74)5,5,6
 5      LT = 2
        GO TO 7
 6      LT = 3
 7      IDDLT = 0
        DO 14 I = 1, LT
        READ_____,IRN
        IF (IRN − 39)8,8,9
 8      ID = 0
        GO TO 14
 9      IF (IRN − 69)10,10,11
10      ID = 1
        GO TO 14
11      IF (IRN − 89)12,12,13
12      ID = 2
        GO TO 14
13      ID = 3
14      IDDLT = IDDLT + ID
15      SCORE(IDDLT + 1) = SCORE(IDDLT + 1) + 1.0
```

By the time this loop is completed, our score for 1,000 simulated lead time experiences has been stored in the 10 positions of the SCORE(I) array. To convert these scores to probabilities and print them out, we might add the statements:

```
        DO 16 J = 1,10
        PROB = SCORE (J)/1000.0
        K = J − 1
```

```
16   PRINT 17, K, PROB
17   FORMAT (1HO,28HPROBABILITY OF A DEMAND
        FOR ,I2,2X,20HDURING LEAD TIME IS ,F12.10)
```

The complete Monte Carlo program for generating and printing out the data required for the first two columns in Table 6-6 becomes Model 6-1 (but without the FORMAT statement referred to in the 2 READD statements, and without the input random number list).

MODEL 6-1

Monte Carlo Program

```
     DIMENSION SCORE(10)
     DO 1 I = 1,10
1    SCORE(I) = 0.0
     DO 15 K = 1,1000
2    READ_____, IRN
     IF (IRN − 24)3,3,4
3    LT = 1
     GO TO 7
4    IF (IRN − 74)5,5,6
5    LT = 2
     GO TO 7
6    LT = 3
7    IDDLT = 0
     DO 14 I = 1, LT
     READ_____, IRN
     IF (IRN − 39)8,8,9
8    ID = 0
     GO TO 14
9    IF (IRN − 69)10,10,11
10   ID = 1
     GO TO 14
11   IF (IRN − 89)12,12,13
12   ID = 2
     GO TO 14
13   ID = 3
14   IDDLT = IDDLT + ID
15   SCORE(IDDLT + 1) = SCORE(IDDLT + 1) + 1.0
     DO 16 J = 1,10
     PROB = SCORE(J)/1000.0
     K = J − 1
16   PRINT 17, K, PROB
17   FORMAT (1HO,28HPROBABILITY OF A DEMAND
        FOR ,I2,2X,20HDURING LEAD TIME IS ,F12.10)
     STOP
     END
```

SUGGESTIONS FOR FURTHER STUDY

BUCHAN, JOSEPH, AND KOENIGSBERG, ERNEST. *Scientific Inventory Management*. New York: Prentice-Hall, 1963.

FETTER, ROBERT B., AND DALLECK, WINSTON C. *Decision Models for Inventory Management*. Homewood, Ill.: Richard D. Irwin, Inc., 1961.

GALLER, BERNARD A. *The Language of Computers*. New York: McGraw-Hill, 1962.

SCHLAIFER, ROBERT. *Probability and Statistics for Business Decisions*. New York: McGraw-Hill, 1959 (chapters 4 and 15).

STARR, MARTIN K., AND MILLER, DAVID W. *Inventory Control: Theory and Practice*. New York: Prentice-Hall, 1962.

EXERCISES

(Begin each of the following problems by composing a flow diagram.)

1. A retailer forecasts demand per day for an item (which he buys and resells) according to the following distribution:

Possible Demand	Probability
0	0.05
1	0.10
2	0.25
3	0.30
4	0.20
5	0.10
	1.00

Compose a FORTRAN program which will read these data into memory from a data deck, and which will calculate the retailer's average or expected daily demand.

2. Assume that the retailer in Problem 1 must pay $1 for the item, that he resells them at $5 each, and that items stocked one day but unsold that day are a total loss due to perishability.

Compose a FORTRAN program which will interpret the retailer's payoff matrix and which will determine and print out the number of units of this item which the retailer should stock each day in order to maximize his expected profit.

3. ABC, Inc., anticipates a demand pattern during the coming year with the following distribution:

Weekly Demand	Probability
11	0.10
12	0.40
13	0.25
14	0.15
15	0.07
16	0.03
	1.00

Past experience suggests that lead time for replenishing stock will be distributed as follows:

Weeks of Lead Time	Probability
2	0.15
3	0.45
4	0.20
5	0.15
6	0.05
	1.00

If the demand and lead time patterns which ABC, Inc., anticipates materialize, what sort of distribution should ABC expect for demand during lead time?

Write a FORTRAN program which will determine the expected demand during lead time distribution through Monte Carlo simulation.

4. In regression analysis,

$$Y - \bar{Y} = b(X - \bar{X})$$

is a straight line which crosses the Y axis at $\bar{Y} - b\bar{X}$, and crosses the X axis at

$$\frac{b\bar{X} - \bar{Y}}{b} \text{ ; where:}$$

$$\bar{X} = \frac{1}{n} \sum_{i=1}^{n} X_i$$

$$\bar{Y} = \frac{1}{n} \sum_{i=1}^{n} Y_i$$

$$b = \frac{\sum_{i=1}^{n} (X_i - \bar{X})(Y_i - \bar{Y})}{\sum_{i=1}^{n} (X_i - \bar{X})^2} \quad ;$$

X and Y being the coordinates of a set of points. (X_1, Y_1), (X_2, Y_2), ... (X_n, Y_n).

From a data deck of not over 1,000 cards, each containing three data fields in the form:　FORMAT (F8.4,F8.4,I1),　we want to determine a regression line. The first two fields on each data card contain values for X and Y, respectively. The third data field contains a zero in every card in the data deck except the last card. The last card is a 'dummy' card with zeros in the first two data fields and a 1 in the third data field.

Compose a FORTRAN program which will:

a) Read a data deck consisting of up to 1,000 cards and then calculate and print out the statement:　REGRESSION LINE IS $Y - BARY = B(X - BARX)$,　substituting in this statement for BARY, BARX and B the values calculated for these quantities in the program.

b) Ignore the last card *except* as an indication that the deck has been completed, whereupon it will terminate the program.

5. In the Brown Electronics Co. problem (Chapter 6) annual inventory holding cost was assumed to be 20 percent of the delivered cost of the items in inventory. If inventory holding cost is assumed to be related to the size of the average inventory in a non-linear fashion, specifically:

$$AHC = \$400 + \$120 \text{ (average inventory)}^{1.2},$$

per unit holding cost clearly varies with the size of the order quantity, Q.

Assume that annual inventory holding cost is represented by the function expressed above, and write a FORTRAN program which will determine and print out Brown Electronics Company's optimum order quantity, reorder point, and corresponding total annual inventory cost, all other parameters of the model remaining as described in Chapter 6.

6. Aikens Company expects a demand during lead time pattern precisely like that of Brown Electronics Company (Chapter 6) for each of its three principal inventory items: Item X, Item Y, and Item Z. Costs and other data associated with each of these three items are shown below:

	Item X	Item Y	Item Z
Unit holding cost (UHC)	0.12	0.20	0.32
Cost per unit (CPU)	$120	$380	$813
Cost per order processed (CPO)	$ 20	$ 20	$ 30
Demand per year (DPY)	365	365	365
Stockout cost (STKCOS)	$ 14	$125	$ 56

Employ a modified version of the general inventory model of Figure 6-9 to determine and print out $\hat{Q}$, $\hat{R}$, and the corresponding TAC for each of these three items in Aikens' inventory.

7. Blackstone Manufacturing Company wants to determine $\hat{Q}$, $\hat{R}$ and minimum TAC for each of four products employed in the manufacture of its electronic control gear: Product 1, Product 2, Product 3, and

Product 4. Costs and other data associated with these products are shown in the two tables below:

	Product 1	Product 2	Product 3	Product 4
UHC	0.20	0.20	0.20	0.20
CPU	$500	$ 35	$210	$ 16
CPO	$ 25	$ 25	$ 25	$ 25
DPY	400	350	285	300
STKCOS	$ 48	$ 72	$ 14	$110

Assume that expected demand during lead time (EDDLT) for each of the four products is 2.0 (a bit unrealistic for Products 2 and 4, but acceptable for our purposes).

With a reorder point, R, of:	Expected stockout (units short) per reorder period E(DDLT > R)			
	Product 1	Product 2	Product 3	Product 4
1	1.172	2.416	1.911	3.912
2	0.612	2.121	0.701	3.701
3	0.256	1.800	0.301	3.201
4	0.100	0.702	0.191	2.719
5	0.090	0.500	0.070	2.408
6	0.070	0.312	0.050	2.176
7	0.040	0.191	0.020	1.615
8	0.012	0.050	0.004	1.298
9	0.005	0.010	0.000	0.898
10	0.000	0.000	0.000	0.000

Employ a modified version of the general model of Figure 6-9 to determine and print out Q, R and minimum TAC for each of these four products, whose inventory management is of current concern to Blackstone Manufacturing Company.

8. Employing the Brown Electronics Company model that was described in Chapter 6, determine whether total annual inventory cost is more sensitive to EQUAL PERCENTAGE changes in (1) delivered price per unit, or (2) stockout cost per unit.

9. It was found that with a cost price per unit of $500, Brown Electronics Company's optimum inventory policy was $\hat{Q} = 13$ units and $\hat{R} = 4$ units. Assume that the Brown Company is given the following delivered price schedule by its supplier:

Size of Order (Units)	Cost Price Per Unit
1 through 20	$500
21 through 40	490
41 & over	489

Modify the general model of Figure 6-9 to cause the computer to consider quantity discounts in determining optimum inventory policy, and cause the computer to calculate and print out $\hat{Q}$, $\hat{R}$ and associated TAC, assuming the above delivered price schedule is quoted by Brown's supplier.

10-1. Assume that 20 integers, each consisting of 4 digits or less (which occupy 20 fields of 4 columns each on one data card), represent the 20 possible demands during lead time.

Assume that 20 fractions, each consisting of 3 digits plus the decimal point (which occupy 20 fields of 4 columns each on another data card), represent the 20 probabilities associated with the various possible demands mentioned in the preceding paragraph.

Compose a FORTRAN program segment which will:

a) Read into the one dimension subscripted variable, DEMAND (M), the data representing the 20 possible demands during lead time from the first data card;

b) Read into the one dimension subscripted variable, PROB(M), the data representing the 20 probabilities associated with these various possible demands;

c) Calculate, from the data in the array DEMAND(M) and the array PROB(M): (1) average or expected demand during lead time, EDDLT; and (2) a schedule of 20 expected stockouts per lead time period, $E(DDLT > R)$, corresponding to each of the demands in DEMAND(M) viewed as reorder points. Cause the computer to store the schedule of the 20 expected stockout quantities in the one-dimension subscripted variable, STKOUT(M).

Assume that 5 floating point numbers, each occupying one field of 15 columns on one data card, constitute (respectively) the following data associated with an inventory system, reading the data card from left to right:

> Unit holding cost (UHC)
> Cost per unit (CPU)
> Cost per order processed (CPO)
> Demand per year (DPY)
> Stockout cost per unit stockout (STKCOS)

compose a FORTRAN statement which will read these data and store them in the variable names shown above.

10-2. Tempo, Ltd., purchases, stocks, and uses—or resells—320,000 different items. A clerk keeps records concerning each of these items. These records contain the information required for punching the three data cards described in Part A above.

A master inventory file consists of four cards on each of the 320,000 items. The first of the four cards contains only 2 data: one to identify the stock number of the item; the other to indicate whether any of the data in the remaining three cards (those described in Part A, above) have changed, and hence whether the reorder policy bears review. The first data field on this card consists of the first column on this card. If the inventory policy applicable to the item demands review, the first field of the first card contains a 1. If the inventory policy applicable to the item does not require review, the first field of the first card contains a zero.

The second field of the first card consists of columns 11 through 30, and contains the stock number of the item to which the four cards apply, punched as an integer of 20 or fewer digits.

When the inventory clerk is provided with new data for updating the master file, she punches new cards where necessary, and thus prepares the master file for periodic review.

Write a FORTRAN program which will incorporate the essential elements of the general inventory model of Figure 6-9, plus the three program segments called for in Part A, and which will serve to read, as input data, the complete master file of Tempo's inventory, and which will (upon encountering a 4-card group pertaining to an item which bears review) recalculate the optimum order quantity and optimum reorder point, and print out these data in association with the stock number of the item to which they pertain.

11. If one is to review inventory policy periodically, and if review involves re-examination of several thousand records, each requiring a search for the optimum Q, R combination, then computer time becomes a rather significant cost item.

If expected demand during lead time is in the range of several hundred units for a particular item carried in inventory, then our general model depicted in Figure 6-9 would not be efficient. It would almost certainly be better, under this condition, to initialize R and Q at some value greater than 1 and to increase them, as the search for $\hat{Q}$ and $\hat{R}$ is conducted, by an increment larger than 1.

Add to the general model of Figure 6-9 to cause the computer to inquire about the size of the expected demand during lead time, and to conduct a search involving *unit* increases in Q and R only after approximating optimum Q and optimum R through a *gross* search.

Suggestion:

a) If $1 \leqq \text{EDDLT} < 100$, initialize Q and R at 1 and increase by increments of 1.

b) If $100 \leqq \text{EDDLT} < 1000$, initialize Q and R at 10 and increase by increments of 10, then proceed as in (*a*) after $\hat{Q}$ and $\hat{R}$ have been grossly approximated.

c) If $1000 \leqq \text{EDDLT} < 10,000$, initialize Q and R at 50 and increase by increments of 50, then proceed as in (*b*) after $\hat{Q}$ and $\hat{R}$ have been grossly approximated.

12. On the morning of November 1, Raintree County found that 116,472 hunters had applied for grouse licenses. As each application was received, a number (starting with 1) was placed opposite the name of the applicant in a log book. The final applicant was given the number 116,472.

To protect the grouse population it has been decided to issue only 36,000 licenses. Compose a FORTRAN program which will select at random 36,000 applicants to whom licenses should be issued and will also print out the numbers (i.e., from 1 to 116,472 inclusive) assigned to those applicants.

13. Assume that Brown Electronics Company (Chapter 6) insists on a service level of 99.726 percent. That is, Brown Company does not want to lose more than 0.274 percent of its expected annual demand of 365 units, due to stockouts. What order quantity and reorder point combination will yield the lowest total annual inventory cost while maintaining a service level of 99.726 percent? How much added total annual inventory cost would Brown Company incur per year by insisting on maintaining a service level of 99.726 percent?

14. The commercial loan officer of the Mercantile Trust Bank follows the following procedure (in a somewhat deliberate fashion) in deciding whether to lend money to the bank's industrial customers, how much to lend, and at what interest rate:

If the client's ratio of current assets to current liabilities is 1.5 or higher, if his cash on hand is at least 9 percent of his total assets, and if his average profit during the past 3 years has been 12 percent or higher, then the loan officer will approve the loan (up to an amount equal to 3 times the client's current cash position) at a rate of interest equal to 3 percentage points higher than the current U.S. Treasury bond rate.

Use the following *input* data:

$$CA = \text{client's current assets}$$
$$CL = \text{client's current liabilities}$$
$$TA = \text{client's total assets}$$
$$CSH = \text{client's cash on hand (cash position)}$$
$$P3 = \text{client's profit 3 years ago}$$
$$P2 = \text{client's profit 2 years ago}$$
$$P1 = \text{client's profit last year}$$
$$TR = \text{current U.S. Treasury bond rate}$$

and write a FORTRAN program that will cause the computer to make the loan officer's future decisions for him and that will print out the amount of money any client may obtain and the interest rate he will have to pay.

15. On the X-Bar-X hog ranch the production of pork is stimulated by adding hormone-treated water to the hog swill. Each day one gallon of hormone-treated water is withdrawn from a 1,000-gallon tank and is added to the swill. Immediately after the gallon of hormone-treated water is withdrawn, a faucet is turned on and a gallon of fresh water is added to fill the tank again.

On January 1 the hormone concentrate in the 1,000-gallon tank stands at 250 pounds per 1,000 gallons (i.e., there are 250 lbs. of hormone concentrate dissolved in the 1,000 gallons of water).

When the level of hormone concentrate drops to 162 pounds per 1,000 gallons of water it becomes necessary to add more concentrate to increase the strength of the solution.

Write a FORTRAN program that will simulate this daily hormone diluting process and will print out the number of days which will elapse before additional hormone concentrate will have to be added.

16. We can compose computer programs which can cause the computer to study a collection of data and to pose and test a variety of hypotheses about that data, thus doing much of the "hack work" associated with quantitative data in research. A simple example will show how this is possible:

A data deck contains 100 cards, each of which has 3 integers punched on it. The third integer bears some relationship to the first and second integers. Specifically, the third integer is either:

1. the product of the first and the second integers,
2. the sum of the first and the second integers,
3. the largest common denominator of the first and second integers (i.e., the largest integer which can be divided into *both* the first and the second integers a whole number of times).

One and only one of these three possible relationships is "operative" in the full 100-card deck. However, at least two of the three relationships *could* apply to some of the cards. Thus to the set:

First:	Second:	Third:
2	2	4

relationships (1) and (2) could apply. And to the set:

First:	Second:	Third:
−16	20	4

relationships (2) and (3) could apply.

A FORTRAN program is desired which will "pose and test" each of the above relationships as a hypothesis, and will print out an answer to the question, "Which of the three possible relationships is operative in the full 100-card deck?"

Compose such a "hypothesis-testing" program. Assume that the statement: READ 1, I, J, K will cause the first number on a data card to be stored in the variable I, the second in the variable J, and the third in the variable K.

CHAPTER 7

Basic Queuing Concepts

THE UNCERTAINTIES associated with queuing phenomena are attributable to randomness—or what seems to be randomness—in certain system parameters. To illustrate this fact, let us consider Pete's Two-Minute Auto Wash.

Pete's Two-Minute Auto Wash

Two minutes are required for washing each car in Pete's facility. There is only one wash facility and it can accommodate only one auto at a time.

If customers arrived exactly at two-minute intervals there would be no uncertainties associated with the operation of Pete's auto wash. If "the system" (i.e., the wash facility plus any customers waiting to enter the wash facility) began operations with six customers in it, there would always be exactly 6 customers in the system:

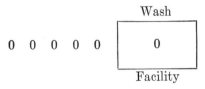

If the system began operations empty, there would always be one customer in the system and zero customers in the queue. In either case the wash facility would be busy continually, and whatever state (queue length) prevailed at the beginning of operations would continue.

However, Pete's customers do not arrive at exact two-minute

intervals. Customers average two minutes between arrivals, but the arrival pattern is random with the following distribution:

Time between Arrivals (Minutes)	Relative Frequency
1	40%
2	30
3	20
4	10
	100%

On the morning of June 1, there were no customers in Pete's auto wash system when it opened for business at 9:00. Pete's first customer arrived one minute after time zero; i.e., one minute after 9:00 A.M., when operations began. The arrival times of the first and the succeeding five customers are shown in Table 7-1.

Table 7-1

Time Data of First Six Customers at Pete's Auto Wash

Customer Number	Time of Arrival	Time since Previous Arrival	Time Entered Wash Facility	Time Departed Wash Facility	Total Time in System (Minutes)
1	9:01	–	9:01	9:03	2
2	9:04	3	9:04	9:06	2
3	9:06	2	9:06	9:08	2
4	9:09	3	9:09	9:11	2
5	9:10	1	9:11	9:13	3
6	9:11	1	9:13	9:15	4

It is apparent from Table 7-1 that the first four customers entered the wash facility the moment they arrived. When customers 5 and 6 arrived the wash facility was occupied and they were obliged to wait. During the first 15 minutes of operations the wash facility had been idle 3 minutes, and the average customer had spent 2½ minutes in the system.

During the first 15 minutes of operation the average time between arrivals was 2 minutes. Thus, in spite of the fact that customers arrived at the same average rate at which the wash facility could service them, customers waited (queues existed) 20 percent of the time, the wash facility was idle 20 percent of the time, and the average customer spent 2½ minutes in the system.

The randomness of one or more parameters in a queue system is responsible for the uncertainties associated with it. In business and economic systems the queuing phenomenon is omnipresent. At times machines are idle; at other times customers must wait. At times inventories are excessive, and stock sits idle; at other times needs go unsatisfied. At times an industry operates at half-capacity, workers are unemployed, and capital is idle. At other times capacity is taxed, labor is critically short, and suppliers have large files of unfilled orders (backorder queues).

Neither extreme is desirable, and a basic management decision involves a balance between the costs of idle men, facilities, and materials on the one hand, and the costs associated with a low level of service on the other hand. To make decisions of this type, management must know something about the behavior of a given queue system; that is, given some knowledge of the pattern of demand on a service facility (if the capacity of the facility to provide service is varied), management must know how the following are affected:

1. Queue lengths.
2. Percent utilization of the capacity of the service facility.
3. Total service time (time spent waiting plus service time).

Management needs to know the expected or average data concerning the system attributes, but it also needs to know *more*. The following two waiting lines have the same average length (15 customers) but their differences are of considerable significance:

Waiting Line No. 1		Waiting Line No. 2	
Length	Relative Frequency	Length	Relative Frequency
5	10%	5	1%
10	20	10	10
15	40	15	78
20	20	20	10
25	10	25	1

In view of the prevalence of queuing phenomena, and the importance of an understanding of these phenomena for the analysis of complex systems, it is appropriate that we pursue some of the theory associated with queuing.

THE BINOMIAL PROBABILITY DISTRIBUTION

To understand queuing theory it is useful to develop analytically the single channel queue model with a customer arrival pattern having a Poisson distribution. And to develop an understanding of the

Poisson distribution, it is useful to begin with the binomial distribution. Since the binomial distribution is generated by a Bernoulli process, we also would do well to understand, at the outset, the Bernoulli process.

Many processes encountered in business can be described in terms of a number of distinct trials, each of which has only two possible outcomes. The toss of a coin exemplifies the process; or the inspection of parts, each of which is determined to be either good or bad; or examination of accounts to determine if budgeted expenses were exceeded or not; or inquiry into a program of activities to determine if the programmed deadline of each component event was met or not; etc.

A process of this character is said to be a Bernoulli process if, as with the toss of a coin,

1. There is no "pattern" to the occurrence of one or the other event—giving us no reason to believe that trials early in the day, for example, will differ from those late in the day; in short, the events occur in a truly random fashion.
2. The long-run outcome is known; thus, in an infinite number of trials, heads will be tossed half the time.

The throw of a die can be a Bernoulli process. If we chose to designate the toss of "snake eyes" as "success" and the toss of anything *other than* a snake eyes as "failure," then the process is clearly Bernoulli.

We know that the probability of a snake eyes in one toss (or "trial," as it is generally called) is 1/6. But suppose we want to know more. Specifically, suppose we would like to know the probability of 2 successes in 6 Bernoulli trials, given that the probability of success in one trial is 1/6. In our die experiment we would be asking, specifically, "What is the probability of tossing 2 snake eyes in 6 consecutive tosses of 1 die?"

Let us let S = snake eyes and N = not snake eyes; that is, anything except a snake eyes. We might, in 6 tosses, get 2 snake eyes in the following order: SSNNNN. From our knowledge of joint probabilities we know that the probability of tossing this particular pattern in 6 tosses of 1 die is:

$$(1/6) \, (1/6) \, (5/6) \, (5/6) \, (5/6) \, (5/6) = 625/46656.$$

However, we might also get 2 snake eyes in the order: SNSNNN; and the probability of tossing this pattern is:

$$(1/6) \, (5/6) \, (1/6) \, (5/6) \, (5/6) \, (5/6) = 625/46656.$$

It is evident, therefore, that the probability of getting 2 snake eyes in any one particular pattern is 625/46656.

A quick survey will show that it is possible to get 2 snake eyes in 6 tosses in 15 different patterns:

SSNNNN	NSSNNN	NNSNSN
SNSNNN	NSNSNN	NNSNNS
SNNSNN	NSNNSN	NNNSSN
SNNNSN	NSNNNS	NNNSNS
SNNNNS	NNSSNN	NNNNSS

Since each pattern is equally likely (we infer this since we have no reason to believe otherwise), the probability of tossing 2 snake eyes in 6 tosses of 1 die, without regard to the pattern or order in which the 2 snake eyes occur, is: $(625/46656) \times (15)$.

We can now develop a general model. We will let:

p = probability of "success" on 1 trial (then $1 - p$ = probability of "failure" on 1 trial);

n = number of trials;

r = the number of successes whose probability we want to determine.

Then we would have, as in our snake eyes experiment,

$$(p \times p \times p \times \ldots \ldots p) \times (1 - p)(1 - p)(1 - p) \ldots (1 - p)$$

Now also, as in our snake eyes experiment, we will have r of the p's in the left-hand expression, and $n - r$ of the $(1 - p)$'s in the right-hand expression. Therefore the above expression becomes: $p^r \times (1 - p)^{n-r}$.

This gives us the probability of r successes in n trials, given that all the successes come at the first of the series of n trials. To get at the probability of r successes in n successive trials *without regard to the order in which the successes come,* we must multiply the above expression (as we did in our snake eyes experiment) by the number of ways in which r successes can occur in n trials. From our knowledge of permutations and combinations we know that this number

is: $\dfrac{n!}{r!(n-r)!}$ (in our snake eyes experiment this was 15).

Our general model[1] then becomes:

---

[1] $p(r)$ means: the probability of r successes in n successive Bernoulli *trials,* given that the probability of success in one trial is p. Note that 0! is defined as 1.

$$p(r) = p^r(1-p)^{n-r} \times \frac{n!}{r!\,(n-r)!} .$$

This is known as the binomial probability distribution, and with this distribution model we can determine the probability of various numbers of successes in a given number of trials, knowing the probability of success in one trial.[2]

Referring once again to our die experiment, we might determine—using our binomial model—the probability of various numbers of snake eyes in 6 tosses of one die. We might portray these probabilities graphically in a histogram like that shown in Figure 7-1.

FIGURE 7-1

Binomial Distribution

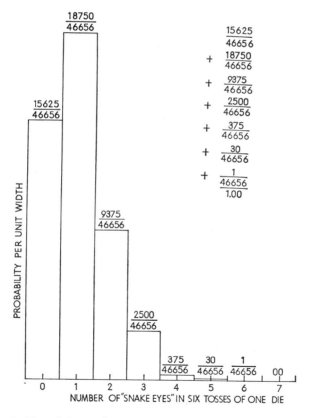

NUMBER OF "SNAKE EYES" IN SIX TOSSES OF ONE DIE

PROBABILITY PER UNIT WIDTH

---

[2] This sort of knowledge can be extremely useful to us in quality control, enabling us to determine the probability of r defects in a batch of n products, given some knowledge of the expected number of defects in a "universe."

THE POISSON DISTRIBUTION

The binomial distribution is not applicable to the queuing system; it applies to a Bernoulli process. In queuing systems we are interested not in the number of "successes" in a number of discrete *trials*, but rather in the number of *arrivals* or *departures* in a period of time. Time, unlike the toss of a die, cannot be viewed as being made up of discrete units, or trials; time is *continuous*.

What is required for queuing systems is a model which will enable us to determine the probability of a certain number of arrivals in a given period of time. To get at this, let us envisage a machine producing insulated wire in which defects are found to occur at random, but to average 1,000 defects per 1,000 feet of wire—or one defect per foot as a mean or expected number of defects per foot of wire.

We will try to develop a model to determine the probability of 2 defects in 1 foot of wire. To do this, let us imagine that we cut a 1-foot piece of the wire into 6 equal segments, each segment 2 inches long. Now the expected number of defects in all 6 pieces is 1. Yet, of course, we view 2 defects as a possibility, and we want to know what the probability of 2 defects is.

If we could be sure that one, but no more than one, defect could occur in *each* of our 6 pieces, we could then view the experiment as a Bernoulli process, corresponding precisely to our experiment with the die. In that experiment we knew that the expected number of snake eyes in 6 tosses was 1; and that the probability of a snake eyes in one toss was 1/6. Similarly, with our 6 small pieces of wire, the expected number of defects in all 6 pieces together is 1, and the probability of a defect in any one piece is 1/6.

By dividing our 1-foot length of wire into 6 equal pieces, and by assuming that not more than 1 defect in any one piece is possible, we make our wire-inspecting experiment a Bernoulli process, precisely like the experiment with the toss of a die. In the case of the toss of the die we knew that the expected number of snake eyes in 6 tosses was 1. Similarly, the expected number of defects in our 6 pieces of wire is 1.

In the case of the die we knew that 2 snake eyes in 6 tosses is possible; that 3 snake eyes is possible—or 4, 5, or 6—but no more. In the die experiment a toss of the die was a "trial"; in the case of the wire, inspection of one piece is a "trial." In the case of the die, snake eyes was "success" in a trial; in the wire experiment, encountering a defect is "success." And, as in the die experiment, we know that 2 defects might be encountered among our 6 pieces of wire; 3 might be encountered; or 4, 5, or 6; but no more than 6 (since we've assumed that more than one defect in any one of our 2-inch pieces is impossible).

Thus by assuming that no more than one defect can occur in any one of the 6 pieces, we have made a Bernoulli process out of our inspection of the wire. The binomial distribution governs, and we can calculate the probabilities of various numbers of defects easily. Thus the probability of 2 defects in the 6 pieces is:

$$p(2) = (1/6)^2(5/6)^{6-2} \times \frac{6\ !}{2\ !\ (6-2)\ !}.$$

Clearly, however, the above is only an approximation of the real probability of encountering 2 defects in our 1-foot piece of wire because of our assumption about each 2-inch piece having no more than one defect. It should occur to us, however, that if instead of dividing our 1-foot piece of wire into 6 pieces we divide it into 60 pieces, then each piece is smaller, and hence our assumption that the process is a Bernoulli process becomes more nearly valid. If we do this, and then employ the binomial distribution to determine the probability of 2 defects in our 1-foot piece, we have:

$$p(2) = (1/60)^2(59/60)^{60-2} \times \frac{60\ !}{2\ !\ (60-2)\ !}.$$

(Note that when we divide the 1-foot piece of wire into 60 rather than 6 pieces, we no longer have a process precisely like that of the toss of the die. Whereas in 60 tosses of the die we can expect 10 snake eyes, in our 60 pieces of wire the expected number of defects is still only 1. The probability of any of our 60 pieces having a defect is therefore 1/60, and the probability of any one piece not having a defect is 59/60. However, the process is still thoroughly Bernoulli, and this is all that matters: our binomial distribution still governs, and we can use it to calculate the probabilities of various numbers of defects in our 1-foot length of wire, the maximum possible now being 60.)

If 60 pieces is a better basis for approximation, then it must occur to us that if we could divide the 1-foot piece of wire into *still smaller* pieces we would approach the point where more than 1 defect in any one of the pieces is so unlikely that we could, with impunity, assume it to be impossible. Then our model would give us the real probability of 2 defects in a 1-foot piece of wire. Pursuing this logic, we would ask our selves what value $p(2)$ approaches as n approaches infinity in the expression:

$$p(2) = \left[\frac{1}{n}\right]^2 \left[\frac{n-1}{n}\right]^{n-2} \times \frac{n!}{2!(n-2)!}.$$

It develops that as n approaches infinity, the limit of this expression (and hence the probability of our encountering 2 defects in our 1-foot piece of wire) is:

$$p(2) = \frac{e^{-1}(1)^2}{2!},$$

where e is the base of natural logarithms and equals (approximately) 2.718. The 1's in the above expression represent the average or the expected number of defects in a unit of length of wire (1 in our model), and so for the more general model we can write:

$$p(2) = \frac{e^{-\lambda}(\lambda)^2}{2!},$$

where λ = the average number of defects *per unit* of length.

In *our* model we were looking for the probability of two defects or "successes"; for a more general model we can write:

$$p(r) = \frac{e^{-\lambda}(\lambda)^r}{r!}. \tag{7-1}$$

Equation 7-1 is the Poisson distribution, and with it we can determine the probabilities of various numbers of defects, r, in a foot of wire—for example—given that the average number of defects in a foot of wire is λ. Such a distribution is shown in Figure 7-2.

We can also use the Poisson distribution to determine the probability of various numbers of arrivals at a service facility in a unit of time, given the expected or average number per unit of time. Thus Figure 7-2 might be viewed as giving us the probability of 1, 2, 3, etc., customers arriving at our service facility in one hour, given that the average or expected rate of arrival is 1, 2, 3, or 4 customers per hour. We can go further, using this model, and determine the probabilities of various numbers of customers arriving in *any* period of

FIGURE 7-2

Poisson Distributions

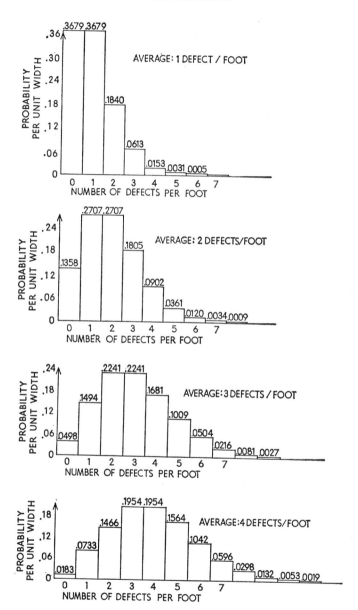

time, the expected number of customers during any period of time, and the like.

This is predicated, of course, on the assumption that arrivals occur in a fashion which is characterized by the Poisson distribution. (Customers might arrive in some pattern other than Poisson. The fact is, however, that in a number of real situations, arrivals tend to approximate Poisson, and the Poisson distribution therefore is useful for other than purely theoretical purposes.)

THE SINGLE CHANNEL QUEUE SYSTEM WITH POISSON ARRIVALS AND NEGATIVE EXPONENTIAL SERVICE TIME

Let us now develop a model for a queue system by introducing a service facility. We will employ the same methodology as was employed in the development of the Poisson distribution so that our model will embody the behavioral attributes of a queue system with a Poisson arrival pattern—and a queue system in which service time is also negative-exponentially distributed.

We will assume that the service facility can accommodate only one customer at a time (single channel) and that arrivals are serviced on a first-come-first-served basis (the "queue discipline"). From time to time queues will form before the service facility, and at times the service facility will be idle. We would like to develop a model to predict:

1. The probability of various numbers of customers (arrivals) in the *system* (either in the queue or in the service facility) at any given moment.
2. The expected or average time a customer will spend in the system.
3. The probability that the service facility will be idle, or the portion of time that it will be idle.

Let us begin by assuming that the service facility is so equipped that it *can* service, on the average, μ customers per unit of time. If the service facility is servicing μ customers per unit of time, on the average, then μ is also the expected number of departures from the service facility during each unit of time. (Observe that μ represents the average number of customers the service facility can service per unit of time, *assuming that the service facility is kept busy, and is not idle*. That is, the service facility could service, say, 15 customers per hour if the moment it completes service on one customer another customer is immediately introduced into the facility. Clearly, if the facility can service 15/hour but only 3 show up during an hour, it will not service 15 during that hour.)

We are now going to think of t as a *moment* in time. Perhaps t is 8:00 in the morning, tomorrow morning. We begin observing our queue system at time t. We would like to develop a model for determining the probability of various numbers of customers *in* the system at this moment in time.

To do this, let us think beyond time t by a *fractional* part of one unit of time. This second "moment in time" with which we are going to concern ourselves is Δt, a fraction of one unit of time, *after* time t. Therefore, this second *moment* in time is $t + \Delta t$.

Now let us assume, as we did in developing our Poisson model, that Δt is so small that, while one arrival or one departure during interval of time Δt is possible, *more* than one arrival or departure during this fractional part of one unit of time is impossible.

Let us now designate p_n as the probability of n customers in the *system* at some moment in time, *n being equal to or greater than 1*. We make this restriction so that we can use μ with confidence; since n is not 0, the system (and hence the service facility) is not empty. Now, so long as the service facility always has a customer in it, we can assume that it will, in fact, average μ customers serviced per unit of time.

To get at the problem, let us first ask ourselves what the probability is that there will be n customers in the system at time $t + \Delta t$; that is: $p_n(t + \Delta t)$.

Now, n customers in the system at time $(t + \Delta t)$ can occur in four different mutually exclusive and collectively exhaustive ways.

Way One. We could have n customers in the system at time t; 0 arrivals during interval of time Δt; and 0 departures during interval of time Δt.

Assuming for the moment that $p_n(t)$ is the probability of n in the system at time t, the probability of n in the system at time $t + \Delta t$ can be got at by the following logic: We have assumed that no more than 1 arrival during interval Δt is possible. Therefore, we will have, during time interval Δt, either 1 arrival or 0 arrivals. The probability of 0 arrivals is 1 minus the probability of 1 arrival. The probability of 1 arrival is $\lambda \Delta t$.

Recall that in our wire experiment $\lambda = 1$; that is, the expected number of defects/unit length of wire was 1, and in our wire experiment Δt was 1/6 when we divided our 1 foot of wire into 6 pieces. The probability of 1 defect in Δt in our wire experiment was, therefore, $(1) \times (1/6)$. It would follow, in a similar way, that the probability of 1 arrival in Δt is $\lambda \Delta t$, and the probability of 0 arrivals during time interval Δt is $(1 - \lambda \Delta t)$.

Now if μ is the expected number of customers serviced by the service facility during a unit of time—assuming that the facility is not idle—then μ is also the expected number of departures from the facility during a unit of time. Recall that *more* than 1 departure during Δt has been ruled out.

Therefore, as above, the probability of 1 departure from the system (and therefore from the service facility) during time interval Δt is $\mu \Delta t$. And the probability of 0 departures is $(1 - \mu \Delta t)$. The probability of Way One, then, is: $p_n(t)(1 - \lambda \Delta t)(1 - \mu \Delta t)$.

Way Two. We could have $n - 1$ in the system at moment of time t; 1 arrival during interval of time Δt; and 0 departures during interval of time Δt. Reasoning as above, the probability of Way Two is: $p_{n-1}(t)\ (\lambda \Delta t)\ (1 - \mu \Delta t)$.

Way Three. We could have $n + 1$ in the system at moment of time t; 0 arrivals during interval of time Δt; and 1 departure during interval of time Δt. Reasoning as above, the probability of Way Three is: $p_{n+1}(t)(1 - \lambda \Delta t)(\mu \Delta t)$.

Way Four. We could have n in the system at time t; and 1 arrival and 1 departure during interval of time Δt. The probability of this is: $p_n(t)(\lambda \Delta t)(\mu \Delta t)$.

Now, the probability of n in the system at moment of time $t + \Delta t$ is the sum of the probabilities of the four individual ways in which it might occur; or:

$$p_n(t + \Delta t) = p_n(t)(1 - \lambda \Delta t)(1 - \mu\ \Delta t) + p_{n-1}(t)\ (\lambda \Delta t)\ (1 - \mu \Delta t) + \left.\begin{array}{c} \\ \end{array}\right\}$$
$$p_{n+1}(t)(1 - \lambda \Delta t)\ (\mu \Delta t) + p_n(t)\ (\lambda \Delta t)(\mu \Delta t).\Big\}$$

Expanding and collecting terms above, transposing $p_n(t)$ to the left side of the equation, dropping infinites of the order $(\Delta t)^2$, and dividing by Δt, we have:

$$\frac{p_n(t + \Delta t) - p_n(t)}{\Delta t} = p_n(t)\,(-\lambda - \mu) + \lambda p_{n-1}(t) + \mu p_{n+1}(t).$$

Now recall that the above "provisional model" is somewhat invalid because we assumed that no more than one arrival or departure could occur during the interval of time Δt. Clearly, if as before we make Δt smaller, then our assumption becomes more tenable and our model improves in validity. Specifically, if we allow Δt to approach zero as a limit, the above expression becomes the differential equation:

$$\frac{dp_n(t)}{dt} = -(\lambda + \mu)p_n(t) + \lambda p_{n-1}(t) + \mu p_{n+1}(t). \qquad (7\text{-}2)$$

And now recall that the development above applies to the case where $n \geq 1$. To determine the special case in which $n = 0$, we simply reflect that when $n = 0$ the probability of $n - 1$ is 0, since less than zero customers in the system is impossible. Replacing $p_{n-1}(t)$ by 0 in **7-2** above, we have:

$$\frac{dp_0(t)}{dt} = -\lambda p_0(t) - \mu p_0(t) + \mu p_1(t).$$

Note that the second term on the right, $-\mu p_0(t)$, has to do with the expected number of departures from the system. This can be checked by following through once again our calculation of the probability of n being encountered in the system. If $n = 0$ the system is empty and there can be no departures. The second term, therefore, drops out, and our differential equation for the special case where $n = 0$ becomes:

$$\frac{dp_0(t)}{dt} = -\lambda p_0(t) + \mu p_1(t). \qquad (7\text{-}3)$$

Observe the sense of **7-2** and **7-3**. Since the left side is the derivative of the probability of various numbers of customers in the system, and since the derivative is (as shown on the right side of the equal sign) a function of time (i.e., t), it must follow that the probabilities of various numbers of customers in the system changes with time.

This might be expected. If we began our queue system empty at 8:00 tomorrow morning, it is less likely that there would be 10 customers in it at 8:01 than that there would be 10 customers in it at noon. We might further expect that, after some time has elapsed (assuming the system continues to operate without interruption for, say, 5 days), the system would stabilize, so that the probability of finding n in the system at 8:00 A.M. on the fifth day is about the same as the probability of finding n in the system at 8:00 A.M. on the fourth day.

While the system is settling down to this stable condition it is said to be in the *transient state*. Once it has settled down, it is said to be in the *steady state*.

In many cases the transient state is very important. In many cases the steady state is very important, and the transient state is rather unimportant. For the moment we will concern ourselves with the steady state only.

By manipulating **7–2** and **7–3** we can develop the model toward which we set out at the beginning. Note first that if we concern ourselves only with the steady state, then the derivative (i.e., the rate of change through time) of the probability of various numbers of customers in the system is zero, and **7–2** and **7–3** become:[3]

$$(\lambda + \mu)p_n = \lambda p_{n-1} + \mu p_{n+1};$$
(7-4)

and for $n = 0$:

$$\lambda p_0 = \mu p_1.$$
(7-5)

From **7–5** it is apparent that:

$$p_1 = [\lambda/\mu]p_0.$$
(7-6)

Solving **7–4** for p_{n+1}, we find:

$$p_{n+1} = \left[\frac{\lambda + \mu}{\mu}\right] p_n - \left[\frac{\lambda}{\mu}\right] p_{n-1}.$$
(7-7)

Now we let $n = 1$; from **7–7** it follows that:

$$p_2 = \left[\frac{\lambda + \mu}{\mu}\right] p_1 - \left[\frac{\lambda}{\mu}\right] p_0.$$
(7-8)

Substituting in this expression our value for p_1 (from **7–6**), we have:

$$p_2 = \left[\frac{\lambda + \mu}{\mu}\right]\left[\frac{\lambda}{\mu}\right] p_0 - \left[\frac{\lambda}{\mu}\right] p_0 = \left[\frac{\lambda}{\mu}\right]^2 p_0.$$

Now we let $n = 2$; again (from **7–7**), it follows that:

$$p_3 = \left[\frac{\lambda + \mu}{\mu}\right] p_2 - \left[\frac{\lambda}{\mu}\right] p_1.$$

From our knowledge of p_1 and p_2 (from **7–6** and **7–8**), we can manipulate the above to yield:

[3] Since the probability is now independent of time we can drop the subscript t; and p_n now means the probability of n customers in the system at any time *in the steady state*.

$$p_3 = [\lambda/\mu]^3 p_0.$$

If we continue, we will find that:

$$p_4 = [\lambda/\mu]^4 p_0$$

$$p_5 = [\lambda/\mu]^5 p_0,$$

and by induction we infer that:

$$p_n = [\lambda/\mu]^n p_0. \tag{7-9}$$

Now, from our knowledge of probabilities, we know that as n increases without limit,

$$p_0 + p_1 + p_2 + p_3 \ldots + p_n = 1.$$

Therefore:

$$p_0 + [\lambda/\mu] p_0 + [\lambda/\mu]^2 p_0 \ldots + [\lambda/\mu]^n p_0 = 1,$$

and

$$p_0 = \frac{1}{1 + [\lambda/\mu] + [\lambda/\mu]^2 + [\lambda/\mu]^3 + \ldots + [\lambda/\mu]^n}.$$

The denominator (above) is an infinite geometric series of the form: $a, ar, ar^2, ar^3 \ldots$ where $a = 1$ and $r = \lambda/\mu$; and for all values of $r < 1$ the series converges, and its sum is: $s = \dfrac{a}{1-r}$.

Therefore our expression for p_0 (assuming that $\lambda/\mu < 1$) becomes:

$$p_0 = \frac{1}{\dfrac{1}{1 - [\lambda/\mu]}} = 1 - \lambda/\mu.$$

Now, having a value for p_0, we can solve for p_n from **7–9**:

$$p_n = [1 - \lambda/\mu] \ [\lambda/\mu]^n. \tag{7-10}$$

In **7–10** we have a general model for determining the probability of n customers in a single channel queue system in the steady state wherein the mean arrival rate (i.e., λ) is less than the mean service rate (i.e., μ). The model we have developed is frequently referred to as: *The single channel queue system, having a Poisson input and a negative exponential service time distribution, in the steady state.*

Notice that the probability that we will find n customers in the system at any time is dependent *only* upon the average or expected number of arrivals per unit of time, λ, *and* upon the average time required to service one customer, $1/\mu$.

Notice, too, that if $\lambda/\mu = 1$, then **7–10** becomes zero. This makes little sense. And when $\lambda/\mu > 1$? Then, for all values of n, p_n is negative ! Nor does this make much sense. It should be remembered that our model is restricted to the case where $\lambda/\mu < 1$. We will consider the case where $\lambda/\mu > 1$ shortly.

ANALYSIS OF THE SINGLE CHANNEL
QUEUE SYSTEM MODEL

We can understand more fully the behavior of our single channel queue system, with Poisson arrivals, if we develop several other expressions to describe certain characteristics we are interested in.

Percent Idle Time and Percent Utilization

What portion of the time will the service facility be empty, and the system therefore idle? This would be simply the probability that there will be zero customers in the system. From **7–10** we have:

$$p_0 = [1 - \lambda/\mu] \ [\lambda/\mu]^0 = 1 - \lambda/\mu.$$

And if the probability that the system is idle is: $1 - \lambda/\mu$, it follows that the fractional utilization of the full capacity of the service facility is:

$$1 - [1 - \lambda/\mu] = \lambda/\mu. \tag{7–11}$$

Expected Number in the System

What is the expected number of customers in the system? This would be, simply, the probability of 1 in the system times 1, plus the probability of 2 in the system times 2, plus the probability of 3 in the system times 3, etc.; or:

$$
\begin{array}{llll}
& \text{For 1 in the system:} & [1 - \lambda/\mu] \ [\lambda/\mu] & \times 1 \\
+ & \text{'' } 2 \text{ '' '' } \text{''} & + [1 - \lambda/\mu] \ [\lambda/\mu]^2 \times 2 \\
+ & \text{'' } 3 \text{ '' '' } \text{''} & + [1 - \lambda/\mu] \ [\lambda/\mu]^3 \times 3 \\
+ & \text{'' '' '' '' } \text{''} & + \text{'' } \text{'' } \text{''} \\
+ & \text{'' '' '' '' } \text{''} & + \text{'' } \text{'' } \text{''} \\
+ & \text{'' '' '' '' } \text{''} & + \text{'' } \text{'' } \text{''} \\
+ & \text{'' } n \text{ '' '' } \text{''} & + [1 - \lambda/\mu] \ [\lambda/\mu]^n \times n \\
& \ldots \text{ as } n \to \infty
\end{array}
$$

This proves to be an infinite series of the form: $ar + 2\,ar^2 + 3ar^3 + \ldots nar^n$, in which a corresponds to $1 - \lambda/\mu$ and r corresponds to λ/μ. The sum of the series proves to be: $\quad [a] \times \left[\dfrac{r}{(1-r)^2} \right].$

Therefore the sum of our series, and hence the expected number of customers in the system, is:

$$[1 - \lambda/\mu] \left[\frac{\lambda/\mu}{(1 - \lambda/\mu)^2} \right] = \frac{\lambda}{\mu - \lambda}. \qquad (7\text{--}12)$$

Expected Number in the Queue

What is the expected number of customers waiting for service?

Since the average or expected number in the system is the expected number in the service facility plus the expected number in the queue waiting for service, we reason that the expected number in the queue is the expected number in the system minus the expected number in the service facility.

But what is the expected number in the service facility? This, simply, would be:

1. The number in the service facility when it is busy times the probability that it is busy; plus
2. The number in the service facility when it is idle times the probability that it is idle.

Having already determined the probability that the system is busy and the probability that it is idle, we can write:

1. $\quad 1 \times (\lambda/\mu) = \lambda/\mu$

2. $\quad \dfrac{+\, 0 \times (1 - \lambda/\mu) = 0}{\text{Sum} \quad\quad = \lambda/\mu}.$

Now, since the expected number in the system (7–12) is: $\dfrac{\lambda}{\mu - \lambda}$, the expected number in the queue waiting for service is:

$$\frac{\lambda}{\mu - \lambda} - \frac{\lambda}{\mu} = \frac{\lambda^2}{\mu(\mu - \lambda)}. \qquad (7\text{--}13)$$

Expected Time in the System

How much time will the average customer have to spend in the system; that is, waiting in line and being serviced? A moment's reflection will make it apparent that the expected number in the system is λ times the expected time in the system. Thus if five customers are arriving each hour on the average, and if each customer spends two hours in the system on the average, then there will be ten customers in the system on the average. The expected time in the system, then, is the expected number in the system divided by λ, or:

$$\frac{\frac{\lambda}{\mu - \lambda}}{\lambda} = \frac{1}{\mu - \lambda}. \tag{7-14}$$

Expected Waiting Time

How much time will the average customer have to spend waiting in line for service? This would be simply the expected total time in the system less the expected time in the service facility. Since the expected time in the service facility is $1/\mu$, we have:

$$\frac{1}{\mu - \lambda} - \frac{1}{\mu} = \frac{\lambda}{\mu(\mu - \lambda)}. \tag{7-15}$$

Probability of N in the Queue

The probability of n in the queue is simply the probability of $n + 1$ in the system. If there are n customers in the queue, there are $n + 1$ in the system—one being in the service facility. (*Note:* This would apply only where $n > 0$; the probability of 0 in the queue is the probability of 0 in the system *plus* the probability of one in the system.)

We are now equipped to make some observations about the behavior of the single channel queue system with Poisson arrivals. Let us explore what happens to the following attributes as the rate of customer arrivals approaches the rate at which the service facilities can accommodate them: (1) The expected time in the system, (2) The portion of time the system is idle, and (3) The probability of various numbers in the system.

We will assume that when the facility is busy our service facility is equipped to service customers at an average rate of 100 per hour ($\mu = 100$). Let us plot curves of the three system attributes (above) as the average rate of arrivals (λ) varies from 0 to 99 customers per hour.

As we should expect (see Figure 7-3) the probability of our en-

FIGURE 7-3

Mean Service Rate ($\mu = 100$ Units per Hour)

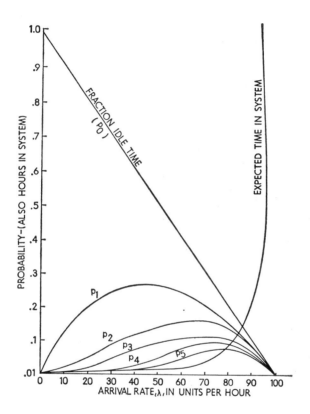

countering 1, 2, 3, 4, or any other number except zero in the system, varies, reaching a peak as the hourly arrival rate, λ, increases from zero, and then decreases as λ approaches the mean service rate, μ.

The time we can expect the system to be idle (i.e., the probability of zero in the system) is a straight line, being 1.0 at $\lambda = 0$ and becoming quite small as λ approaches μ.

Since the probabilities of various numbers in the system sum to unity, at any point on the X axis the distance from the X axis to a corresponding point on the "Fraction Idle Time curve," plus the distances to each of the probability curves, will add to 1.0. The expected time in the system increases rapidly as λ approaches 99.

THE TRANSIENT STATE AND TRUNCATION

In developing our model for the single channel queue system, we restricted ourselves to the steady state and developed a model in which the expected number of customers in the system at any time is constant.

In some situations the transient state is of more interest than the steady state: the opening of a new facility, the annual model change-over in the automobile industry, and so on. Some systems can never be expected to operate long enough to achieve a steady state.

So far, we have spoken of the case where the arrival rate is less than the rate at which customers could be served if the service facility were kept busy. What about the case where customers arrive at an average rate faster than the average rate at which they can be serviced? It is easy to conceive of a system wherein $\lambda > \mu$, and to perceive that in theory the system would have only a transient state, since over time the number of customers in the system would grow indefinitely.

In practice, systems in which $\lambda > \mu$ do not grow indefinitely. As the waiting line—and hence the required time in the system—grow larger, customers become impatient and will not wait. Or, perhaps, accommodating a longer line becomes costly, and the queue is not allowed to grow beyond a certain limit.

In this way systems in which $\lambda > \mu$ get truncated at some queue length, and we find that even with $\lambda > \mu$, queue systems *can* have a steady state.

OPTIMUM SYSTEM DESIGN

In our study of the inventory system we observed that the randomness of demand on the system forces us to seek an optimum service capability in which an occasional stockout can be expected. The cost of maintaining this capability is the cost of holding in readiness—idle and on the shelf—an inventory of stock.

The queue system poses the same problem when the economics of the system are considered. If demand on the system were constant, our problem would be simple; and obliging customers to wait could be easily avoided. Randomness, however, forces us to seek an optimum service capability in which *some* waiting can be expected.

The cost of maintaining this capability is the cost of holding—ready to serve but idle part of the time—a service facility.

Most queue systems are a great deal more complex than the single-channel system for which we have developed an analytical model. Service may not be on a first-come-first-served basis; we may have multiple channels, when a waiting line gets too long, arrivals may be shunted to a separate facility, etc.

Queue systems can become extremely complex, and attempting to develop practicable, analytical models for predicting their behavior becomes all but impossible. With the computer, however, we can build models with which we can simulate, and thus study, the behavior of extremely complex queue systems. In Chapter 9 we will explore how this might be done. First, however, we must equip ourselves to simulate a number of processes which are approximated in real queuing systems.

SUGGESTIONS FOR FURTHER STUDY

MORRIS, WILLIAM T. *Analysis for Materials Handling Management.* Homewood, Ill.: Richard D. Irwin, Inc., 1962.

SAATY, THOMAS L. *Elements of Queuing Theory.* New York: McGraw-Hill, 1961.

SCHLAIFFER, ROBERT. *Probability and Statistics for Business Decisions.* New York: McGraw-Hill, 1959 (chapters 10 and 13).

EXERCISES

(Where a computer program is called for in any of the following problems, begin with a flow diagram.)

1. Compose a FORTRAN program which will determine the value of:

$$\frac{N!}{R!(N-R)!}$$

for positive integer values of N and R less than 1,000. (*Note:* Do not fail to consider the limitations of the computer in dealing with extremely large or extremely small numbers.)

2. The base of Napierian or natural logarithms, designated e in mathematics, is defined as the limit of the expression $(1 + X)^{1/X}$, as X gets smaller and smaller and approaches zero.

We can discern something about the nature of this expression by giving X several values and determining the corresponding value of the above expression, thus:

$$\text{when } X = 2: \ (1 + X)^{1/X} = 1.73$$
$$\text{''} \quad X = 1: \quad \text{''} \qquad = 2.00$$
$$\text{''} \quad X = \tfrac{1}{2}: \quad \text{''} \qquad = 2.25$$

It is apparent that as we let X take a value equal to $\frac{1}{2}$ the value it had previously, the expression $(1 + X)^{1/X}$ becomes larger, but by smaller increments.

Write a FORTRAN program which will cause the computer to continue this process, printing out the values of this expression and the corresponding values for X, with each value of X equal to $\frac{1}{2}$ the preceding value of X, through $X = 1/2048$.

3. Compose a FORTRAN program which will provide data for plotting a curve of the expected number of customers in a single channel queue system with Poisson arrivals and negative exponential service-time (i.e., employing the model 7-12 of Chapter 7) with a mean service rate, μ, of 1,000 units per hour, as the mean arrival rate, λ, varies from zero units per hour through 999 units per hour. Plot the curve.

In what way does your curve differ from that of Figure 7-3?

4. The Youngstown Company produces a line of widgets in a two-stage process. Widgets emerge from the first stage in a fashion which is Poisson distributed, at a mean rate of 10.1 per hour (i.e., $\lambda = 10.1$). The second stage is capable of handling the output from the first stage at a mean rate of 10.4 per hour (i.e., $\mu = 10.4$).

a) If the first stage is shut down whenever the production bank between the two stages reaches 4 widgets, what is the expected downtime for the first stage?

b) Assume now that there is no limit to the size of the bank allowed, that the cost associated with a bank of semifinished widgets between the two stages is $3 per widget per hour, and that idle time in stage 2 costs $250 per hour. Determine the optimum rate of production (λ) for stage 1; i.e., the rate which minimizes total cost.

5. On each trial a particular Zippo either lights or it does not light. Whether it lights on a trial is independent of whether it lit on the previous trial. In the long run it lights 90 percent of the time. Do successive efforts to light this Zippo constitute a Bernoulli process?

6. Given a single-channel queue system with an average of λ arrivals per hour and an average service rate of μ per hour,

a) When λ is smaller than μ, queues will or will not form?

b) When λ equals μ, a queue will or will not form and grow indefinitely?

c) When λ is greater than μ, there is no steady state?

7. In a queue system like that described in Chapter 7, if the probability of encountering ten customers in the system is 0.45, what is the probability of encountering nine in the queue?

8. Write a FORTRAN program which will determine as economically as possible and as accurately as possible the sum of the series: $1/x + 2/x^2 + 3/x^3 + 4/x^4. \ldots n/x^n$, as n approaches infinity. (Assume that x is greater than 10 and that the computer will interpret any number smaller than 10^{-37} as 0.0.)

CHAPTER 8

Process Generators

IN CHAPTER 6 we saw how, by Monte Carlo simulation, one could cause the computer to read a random number list and interpret the meaning of the numbers it read in such a way as to simulate a stochastic process. By Monte Carlo simulation, one can gain insight into the behavior of a system which cannot be gained in any practicable way by purely analytical mathematical methods.

However, in spite of the power of Monte Carlo simulation (of the variety demonstrated in Chapter 6) two aspects of that model pose limitations within which we are not content to restrict ourselves. One has to do with the means for getting random numbers, and the other with the discrete character of the probability distributions with which we dealt.

In this chapter we will deal with these limitations and we will equip ourselves to handle more complex systems simulation problems.

GENERATION OF RANDOM NUMBERS

In Chapter 6 we read random numbers into a main computer program for the purpose of interpreting a "simulated experience" by use of a READ statement and a data deck. Each card in our data deck contained one two-digit number, and the deck itself was in effect a random number list.

Under this arrangement 1,000 data cards would have been required for the Monte Carlo program described at the end of Chapter 6. We could have reduced the size of our data deck by placing 40 two-digit numbers across the 80 columns of each card. By employing a more flexible version of the FORTRAN READ statement (shown

146

below) we could cause 40 numbers to be stored in the array J(M) with each encounter of the READ statement:

READ 1, (J(M), M = 1,40)
1   FORMAT (40(I2))

With a modification in our program we could cause the computer to "draw" numbers from storage in the array J(M), until 40 numbers have been drawn, at which point a new set of 40 numbers could be read into J(M). This scheme would have reduced our data deck from 1,000 to 25 cards.

In some cases a scheme of this sort is appropriate. But in many cases, especially where a larger number of random numbers is desired and where we would like larger than two-digit numbers, we would find simulation of stochastic processes a somewhat agonizing business if all random numbers had to be read into computer memory from an input data deck or tape.

To deal with this problem, considerable effort has been devoted to random number generation. Some effort has been devoted to using physical processes, such as random signals from a source of electrical noise, emissions from radioactive materials, and the like, which might be converted to random numbers. But reliance on these physical processes has never become widespread.

The idea that random numbers might be generated by an arithmetic process seems to have been first suggested about 17 years ago. First employed was a "middle square" method in which one might begin with any integer, square it, drop the extreme left-most and right-most digits resulting from squaring (to obtain a new integer with the same number of digits as the original number), then repeat the process. The "middle digits" thus generated are both the new random number and the "root" from which to obtain the next random number.

To illustrate, suppose we wanted a generator which would give us a new four-digit random integer each time we called for one. We would select, arbitrarily, a four-digit integer root to initialize our generator, perhaps the number 3147. This number is both our first random number and the root for determining the next random number. To generate the next number we first square 3147: $3147^2 =$ 9903609. And our next random number is the middle four digits of 9903609: 9036.

We could cause the computer to generate numbers by this process through a few simple FORTRAN statements. At the beginning of the program in which we expect to have need for random numbers, we would initialize our generator with the statement: $M = 3147$. Then each time a new random number is needed we cause the computer to execute the following group of statements:

$$N = M ** 2/100$$
$$K = N/10000$$
$$M = N - K * 10000$$

The first of the three statements squares the previous value of M and truncates the two right-most digits; and the second and third statements drop the left-most digits, storing for M the four middle digits.

Were we to use this generator, it would be convenient to be able simply to call for execution of the above program segment from any number of different positions in the complete computer model as need for a new random number arises. And to make this possible, we might exploit an additional FORTRAN convention of great convenience: the subroutine.

The Subroutine

A FORTRAN subroutine consists of a group of statements which are, in a sense, isolated from the rest of the program. By "calling" on the subroutine from any part of the "main" program, we can cause those statements which make up the subroutine to be executed and then cause control to be transferred back to the position in the main program from which the subroutine was called. The advantages of this will soon become apparent.

The subroutine has the form:

SUBROUTINE _____ (____,____,____ . . . . . . ____)
and the executable statements   RETURN   and   END

A FORTRAN program may have a number of subroutines. In order to identify the subroutine being called, each is given a different name, which appears immediately after the word SUBROUTINE at the beginning of the subroutine (indicated in the example above by the blank space.) Any acceptable FORTRAN variable (non-subscripted) may be employed as a subroutine name.

As the example above would indicate, the subroutine name is also followed by other data (indicated by the blank spaces in parentheses). The computer ordinarily views variables and statement numbers *inside* a subroutine as different and distinct from variables and statement numbers *outside* a subroutine. Thus the variables TAC, J(M), and M12 might be used inside *and* outside a subroutine, and, in the absence of a provision specifying otherwise, the computer would assume that the variables TAC, J(M), and M12 inside and outside the subroutine (i.e., elsewhere, in the main program or in other subroutines) are *not* the same variables in spite of the fact that they have the same names. Thus two or more values might be stored simultaneously for variables having the same name, one arising from computations within the main program and the other(s) arising from computations in one or more subroutines.

While this arrangement has advantages, provision must be made for getting around it; otherwise we would have no means for transferring a value from a subroutine to a main program, and vice versa; and therefore "calling" a subroutine would be valueless.

We provide for transferring values in and out of a subroutine by identifying—in the blanks inside the parentheses to the right of the subroutine name, separated by commas—a set of variables; thus:

SUBROUTINE SALES (TAC,J,M12)

We "call" a subroutine by a CALL statement; and we identify the specific subroutine we want to call by stating its name in the CALL statement. Then, for every variable appearing in the parentheses to the right of the subroutine name, we must have a variable in parentheses to the right of the subroutine which we name in the CALL statement. Thus, with the statement, CALL SALES (TAC,J,M12), we could "call" the subroutine: SUBROUTINE SALES (TAC,J,M12).

The computer will associate the variables named in the CALL statement with the variables named in the SUBROUTINE statement. The computer will regard the variables TAC, J(M), and M12 as being "common" to both the subroutine and the main program. In this way, the *values* which these three variables get as a consequence of computation (which we have caused to be executed by "calling" the subroutine) will also be given to these same variables in the main program.

A useful flexibility is added by the fact that the computer associates the variables in the SUBROUTINE statement and the variables in the CALL statement by the order in which they appear rather than by their names. For example, we might have written the CALL statement: CALL SALES (R,LPT,M7R),   and the SUBROUTINE statement: SUBROUTINE SALES (TAC,J,-M12).

The computer would associate R with TAC, LPT(M) with J(M), and M7R with M12. Whatever value the variables TAC, J(M), and M12 received (as a consequence of the execution of the statements in the subroutine) would also be given, respectively, to the variables R,LPT(M) and M7R, in the main program. (By now it will have been observed that we do not include the subscript where a subscripted variable is referred to either in the CALL statement or in the SUBROUTINE statement.)

One more rule merits attention: *When values for subscripted variables are to be transferred from inside out, or from the outside in, there must be a* DIMENSION *statement inside the subroutine specifying the space reserved for that variable.* The DIMENSION statement should follow the SUBROUTINE statement.

Our generator might be employed as a subroutine in this way:

```
SUBROUTINE RANDOM (M)
N = M ** 2/100
K = N/10000
M = N − K * 10000
RETURN
END
```

The punched cards which make up the subroutine should follow the END statement in the main program and must precede the data deck (if any). To use our generator we would have to initialize, in our main program, $M = 3147$,   and each time we need a new four-digit random number we simply employ the statement: CALL RANDOM (M).

Each time the computer encounters the above statement, it interrupts the main program, proceeds to execute the instructions called for in SUBROUTINE RANDOM (giving the variable M a new four-digit random number value), then returns to the statement which follows the statement CALL RANDOM.

Should we desire to obtain a new random number at several places in our main program, we simply insert CALL RANDOM at each place.

Should we wish to repeat a random number list, we simply call into play the initial or "root" value for M (i.e., 3147), and our generator starts over again.

The generation of random numbers by arithmetic processes can be a troublesome business, and it must occur to us that our middle square generator above would break down if it ever generates a number consisting of four zeros.

We might lessen this possibility by using a ten-digit root rather than a four-digit root, dropping all but the middle ten digits after each squaring. Then, to get a two-digit number or a number of any size less than ten digits, we simply truncate the unwanted digits, while preserving our ten-digit root in preparation for the next generation.

Even with this improvement our middle square generator, as designed above, has serious flaws (the reader can verify this by testing the action of the generator after it has generated *any* very small number). Some of these flaws could be dealt with by adding a few refinements, but even then it has shortcomings. Clearly, in 10 digits there are only 10^{10} possible numbers, and our generator is certain to cycle or repeat itself once it generates its initial root.

In fact, all arithmetic generators cycle eventually, and since any number generated by an arithmetic generator is the product of its predecessor number, one may argue that arithmetic generators are deterministic and not random at all.[1]

For purposes of simulation, this problem does not really bother us. We are content with "the appearance of randomness," and while our numbers might better be called pseudo-random numbers, they do nicely for our purposes.

A great deal of effort has been devoted to the design of ever-better arithmetic random number generators since the advent of the computer. This effort has centered around the search for a generator with a large cycle, and one which is also efficient, in terms of computer computation time.[2]

In systems simulation we have such frequent use for random numbers that we sometimes become dissatisfied with the need to

---

[1] For that matter, random numbers produced by card shuffling and ball drawing are deterministic in the sense of Newtonian mechanics, and "randomness" itself is an illusion.

[2] For a rather complete discussion of generator theory, a number of good generators, and an extensive bibliography of literature on this subject, see T. E. Hull and A. R. Dobell, "Random Number Generators," *SIAM Review,* Vol. 4, No. 3, July, 1962, pp. 230–54.

include a subroutine in our program as a means of generating numbers, and we find ourselves seeking even greater convenience.

We would like to be able to get a random number even more easily, and we can achieve greater convenience by equipping our compiler with a random number generating "function." FORTRAN compilers, it will be recalled, are themselves programs which accept FORTRAN programs and translate them into machine language for execution. FORTRAN compilers almost always come equipped with a number of "functions," or sub-programs, which are brought into play as they are required.

Thus, when we use the FORTRAN statement, SQRTF(   ), to cause the computer to take the square root of a number, we are asking the computer to call into play a program segment (in the compiler) which is so composed as to cause the square root of the number in the parentheses to be computed and then to cause the expression SQRTF(   ) to be replaced by the result of that computation.

Other common FORTRAN compiler functions are:

LOGF(   )   which replaces itself with the natural logarithm of the expression in the parentheses.

ABSF(   )   which replaces itself with the *absolute value* of the expression in parentheses.

COSF(   )   which replaces itself with the cosine of the angle, in radians, represented by the expression in parentheses.

"Maintenance" of a compiler involves adding to it and refining it as the state of the computer arts advances and as needs arise. The addition of a random number generating function would be an addition of this character. Henceforth in this text we will assume that our FORTRAN compiler is equipped with such a function, and that any time the computer encounters (to the right of the equal sign in one of our algebraic statements) the expression RANDOMF(X), the computer will replace the expression with a new random number whose magnitude is less than 1 and equal to or greater than zero.

Thus the random number we get when we employ this function will be a decimal fraction. If we want a two-digit random integer, we simply move the decimal point to the right two places, truncate via a statement such as   M = RANDOMF(X)*100.0,   and the variable M has our two-digit random integer stored for it.

We will still have occasion, from time to time, to employ a subroutine in our FORTRAN programs for generating random numbers. Depending on the design of the generator built into the compiler, we may have no convenient way of returning to our initial "root," and therefore no way of contriving to duplicate precisely (through a looping process) the same sequence of random numbers that we used before. Where duplicating the same sequence of random numbers becomes desirable, we could do our random-number generating in a subroutine of our FORTRAN program; and each time we want to repeat a random number sequence employed before, we would simply re-initialize the generator with our original root.

Random Numbers Uniformly Distributed

Thus far in our discussion of random number generation, we have concerned ourselves only with generating uniformly distributed random numbers. Thus we assume—and indeed we hope—that if we employ the function RANDOMF(X) and use it to get two-digit random numbers, the likelihood of our getting a certain two-digit number is the same as the likelihood of our getting any other two-digit number. We can portray this sort of generator graphically through the "rectangular distribution" of Figure 8-1. As the probability scale on the vertical axis indicates, the probability of our generating each of our 100 possible two-digit numbers is exactly the same, namely 0.01.

FIGURE 8-1

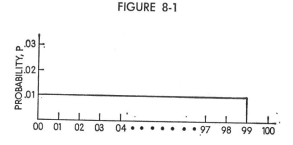

Generating Random Numbers with a Specified Distribution

In Chapter 6 we dealt with two non-uniform probability distributions. We employed a list of uniformly distributed random numbers to simulate these two distributions and thus to develop a combined distribution of demand during lead time in an inventory problem.

Having seen how we can oblige the computer to generate uniformly distributed random numbers by arithmetic means, it must occur to us that it might be possible to oblige the computer to go further, and generate—arithmetically—a sequence of random numbers with some other specified distribution. For example, it would be convenient if we could oblige the computer to generate a sequence of numbers corresponding to the time between arrivals, given that

1. The arrival pattern is Poisson-distributed;
2. The mean arrival rate is a specified value.

A POISSON VARIABLE GENERATOR

To see how we might develop a Poisson generator, refer again to Figure 7-2. Figure 7-2 is a histogram that shows us the probability of zero or more defects per foot of wire, given that:

1. Defects per foot of wire are Poisson-distributed;
2. The average or expected number of defects per foot of wire is 1, 2, 3, or 4.

The Figure 7-2 histogram might also be thought of as the number of arrivals per unit of time, given that:

1. Arrivals per unit of time are Poisson-distributed;
2. The average or expected number of arrivals per unit of time is 1, 2, 3, or 4.

The data shown in the histogram in Figure 7-2 was developed from the Poisson probability distribution:

$$p_n = \frac{\lambda^n e^{-\lambda}}{n!},$$

which tells us the probability of n arrivals per unit of time, n being zero or any positive integer.

We would expect that the probability of a specific number of arrivals in a unit of time on the one hand (the Poisson distribution), and the probability of a specific amount of time between arrivals on the other hand (the exponential distribution), would be related. This is, of course, true, and from our knowledge of the Poisson process we could go further and develop the cumulative probability distribution function:

$$F(t) = e^{-\lambda t}, \tag{8--1}$$

which tells us the probability of more than t units of time between arrivals. In designing a Poisson generator we are more interested in the time between arrivals than the number of arrivals per unit of time, and **8–1** tells us a good deal about the distribution of time between arrivals.

A curve of this distribution is shown in Figure 8-2 for the special

FIGURE 8-2

Cumulative Exponential Distribution for the
Probability that Time between Arrivals Exceeds *t* Units of Time
when Mean Arrival RATE = 1/Unit of Time

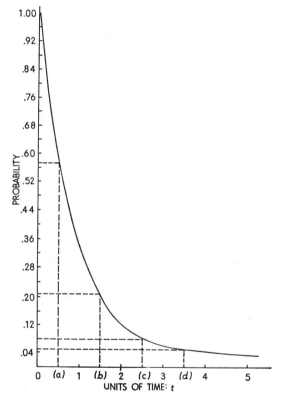

case where the average or expected arrival rate, λ, is 1 arrival per unit of time. As we would expect, the probability of 1 or more units of time between arrivals is greater than the probability of 3 or more units of time between arrivals.

Notice how one might, by viewing the distance on the vertical axis in Figure 8-2 as a weighting factor, associate a possible value of t and its probability. Thus the distance on the vertical axis corresponding to the range of values for t between a and b (in Figure 8-2) measures 36 units (57–21). The distance on the vertical axis corresponding to the range of values for t between c and d measures only 3 units (08–05).

We can use this quality of the function **8–1** to read off the horizontal axis values for t in a random fashion, but with the smaller values of t occurring more frequently. In fact, we can do this with each of all possible values of t occurring in direct proportion to its probability of occurrence in a Poisson process in which $\lambda = 1/\text{unit}$ of time.

We can do this by simply viewing the vertical axis as a list of uniformly distributed random numbers. If we select numbers from this list at random, and if we associate every number we select with the value for t which corresponds to it on the vertical axis, we would find that approximately 36 percent of the values of t which we "generate" by this process will fall between a and b, and approximately 3 percent will fall between c and d.

If we narrow the horizontal distances a to b and c to d, and if we let them approach two specific values for t rather than two *ranges* of values, we expect that our weighting scheme would continue to be operative.

To generate exponential distributed values for the time between arrivals, then, all we need to do is read a random fraction and determine the value for t (in the function **8–1**) which corresponds to it.

When we employ this process we are, in effect, asking ourselves: "Given a value for the function $e^{-\lambda t}$, and a value for λ, what is the value of t?" That is, "What is t in terms of e and λ?" Solving for t in **8–1**, we have:

$$t = -\frac{1}{\lambda} \times \log_e F(t).$$

For generating purposes, $F(t)$ is our uniformly distributed random variable. Therefore, for a group of FORTRAN statements which will generate exponential-distributed time-between-arrivals, we can employ the instructions:

```
R = RANDOMF(X)
T = (−1.0/TLMBDA) * LOGF(R),
```

in which TLMBDA is the mean arrival rate of the Poisson process, in customers per unit of time. This might also be written:

$$T = (-1.0/\text{TLMBDA}) * \text{LOGF}(\text{RANDOMF}(X)). \qquad (8\text{--}2)$$

A NORMALLY DISTRIBUTED VARIABLE GENERATOR

To equip ourselves for efficient systems simulation, we also need a normal generator. Many processes, especially in business and economic systems, approximate the normal distribution, and to study the behavior of these processes we find ourselves in frequent need of a normal generator.

We could develop a normal generator by the same means employed to develop the Poisson generator. However, the problem is a bit more difficult. The probability density function for the normal process is:

$$f(x) = \frac{1}{\sigma\sqrt{2\pi}} \, e^{-\frac{1}{2}\left[\frac{x-m}{\sigma}\right]^2}, \qquad (8\text{--}3)$$

in which m is the mean, σ is the standard deviation, and x is the random variable.

We can translate expression **8–3** into the *cumulative density function* for the normal distribution (to get it in the form of **8–1**—but solving for x in terms of the *cumulative probability* is quite another thing. Therefore, we cannot design a normal generator as easily as we designed our Poisson generator.

Using Simpson's rule (discussed more fully in the exercises at the end of this chapter), we could approximate the cumulative probabilities of a sample "x or more" as x varies over, perhaps, $m \pm 3\sigma$. For use in a computer program, we might then store these probabilities as a "table" of values in an array, and we might devise a scheme for calling for values of x by a random selection from the table. Through this means we could build a rather satisfactory normal generator, but this is a bit complicated; and storing our table may consume a good deal of memory space.

A number of schemes have been employed to design an arithmetic function which would (approximately) generate normally distributed variables. A rather widely used generator of this sort will be presented—but without elaboration on why the variables it generates approximate the normal distribution.

This generator requires two different, uniformly distributed random fractions to generate one normal variable.[3] With two uniformly distributed fractions, R1 and R2, one generates a variable, V, which is normally distributed about a mean of zero, with a standard deviation of 1, thus:

$$V = (-2 \log_e R1)^{1/2} \times \text{COS} 2\pi R2.$$

To convert V to a variable V1, which is normally distributed about a mean of TMU, with a standard deviation SD, we simply exploit the relationship:

$$V1 = (V)SD + TMU.$$

Four FORTRAN statements suitable for generating a normally distributed variable, V1, about mean TMU, with standard deviation SD, would be:

```
R1 = RANDOMF(X)
R2 = RANDOMF(X)
V  = (-2.0 * LOGF(R1)) ** 0.5 * COSF(6.283 * R2)
V1 = V * SD + TMU
```

or, more briefly:

$$V1 = (-2.0 * \text{LOGF}(\text{RANDOMF}(X))) ** 0.5 * \text{COSF}(6.283 * \text{RANDOMF}(X)) * SD + TMU \qquad (8\text{--}4)$$

THE GAMMA DISTRIBUTION

In simulation studies we will find ourselves in need of another generator; specifically, a gamma generator. While many real processes in business and economics approximate the normal process, many other processes do not. The normal process becomes particularly inappropriate when the ratio of the standard deviation to the mean of the process we want to simulate is larger than about 1/3.

Suppose, for example, that we had reason to believe demand for a particular product was fluctuating about a mean of 50 units per week with a standard deviation of 50, giving us a value of 1 for the standard deviation to mean ratio. We know that about 68 percent of the variables generated by a normal process will fall between the mean minus one standard deviation, and the mean plus one standard

---

[3] For a discussion of this generator and how it *can* be used to generate two normal variables from two uniformly distributed variables, see Box and Muller, "A Note on the Generation of Normal Deviates," *Annals of Mathematical Statistics,* Vol. 28, 1958, pp. 610–11.

deviation; and thus within the range from 0 to 100 for a normal process with mean of 50 and standard deviation of 50.

If we assume that the process generating our demand is normal, then we must assume that about 32 percent of the variables generated by our demand-generating process should fall outside the range 0 to 100. Furthermore, we would expect that half of these variables would fall short of this range, and thus that about 16 percent would be less than 0.

In most real business systems, a negative demand does not occur. Where the ratio of the standard deviation to the mean is less than 1/3, the actual demand generating process may, in many real systems, approximate the normal distribution rather closely. But where this ratio is much larger than 1/3 the normal distribution is not likely to be a good approximation of the real process.

The Poisson distribution may, in some cases, be a better approximation. The Poisson process has the virtue of generating no negative variables. However, the mean and the variance in the Poisson distribution are always equal. Clearly, this restricts the usefulness of the Poisson distribution to those processes which have not only the Poisson curve form but also to those processes in which the ratio of the standard deviation to the mean is precisely the reciprocal of the square root of the mean.

The gamma distribution combines virtues of both the normal and Poisson distributions for processes which do not generate negative values. The probability density function of the gamma distribution is:

$$f(x) = \frac{\lambda^r x^{r-1} e^{-\lambda x}}{(r-1)!}.$$

The development of the gamma distribution somewhat parallels the development of the Poisson distribution. The Poisson distribution resulted from an effort to determine the probability of n successes (defects in our wire experiment) per unit length, given a mean of λ successes per unit of length. The exponential distribution results from an effort to determine the probability of x units of length from 1 success to the next in a Poisson process. The gamma distribution results from an effort to determine the probability of x units of length between one success and the rth succeeding success.

The gamma distribution has two parameters: r and λ, in a Poisson process. The mean and the standard deviation of a gamma process are related to these two parameters as follows:

$$\text{Mean} = r/\lambda$$
$$\text{Standard deviation} = \sqrt{r}/\lambda.$$

From these relationships it follows that:

$$r = \text{mean}^2/\text{standard deviation}^2$$
$$\lambda = \text{mean}/\text{standard deviation}^2.$$

Therefore a gamma distribution, like a normal distribution, can be uniquely specified by its mean and its standard deviation.

Figure 8-3 shows gamma probability distributions for the special case in which $\lambda = 1$, and the mean varies from 1 through 5. In the gamma distribution the ratio of the standard deviation to the mean is the reciprocal of the square root of r. When this ratio is 1/3 or smaller (i.e., when r is 9 or greater), the gamma distribution closely approximates a normal distribution with the same mean and standard deviation.

A GAMMA GENERATOR

Designing a gamma generator poses even greater complexity than designing a normal generator. The added complexity is attributable principally to the presence of the term $(r - 1)!$ in the denominator of the density function, coupled with the fact that the term $r - 1$ will generally be a mixed number rather than an integer.

A scheme for generating gamma distributed variables, in the form of a FORTRAN subroutine, will be presented without elaborating on why the variables it generates approximate the gamma distribution (see Figure 8-4). Variables common to the subroutine and to the main program are TMU and SD, representing the mean and the standard deviation, respectively. Each time the subroutine is called, G gets a new value. These values will be gamma distributed with mean TMU and standard deviation SD. As in the case of our normal generator, a uniformly distributed random fraction generator is called into play to generate gamma distributed variables.

In the subroutine of Figure 8–4 when the computer encounters the function EXPF(E), it replaces it with the base of the natural logarithm, e, raised to the power E, which in this case is 1.0.

FIGURE 8-3

Gamma Probability Distribution for the Special Case where $\lambda = 1$

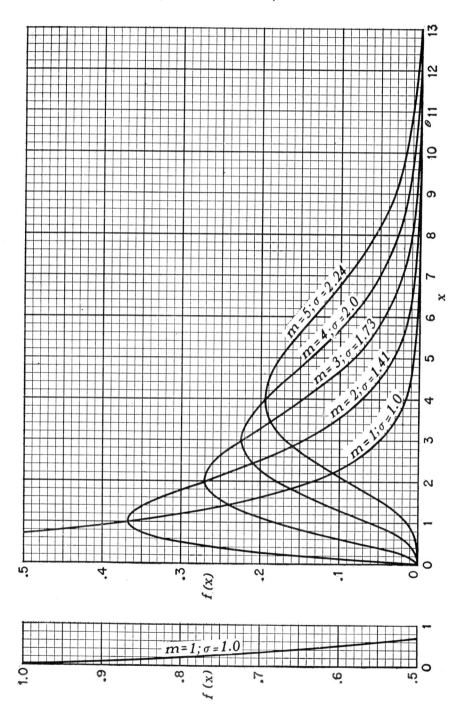

FIGURE 8-4

A Subroutine for Generating Gamma Distributed Variables

```
      SUBROUTINE GAMMA (TMU, SD, G)
      E = 1.0
      A = 0.0
      R = TMU ** 2/SD ** 2
      TLMBDA = TMU/SD ** 2
      I = R
      R1 = I
      R2 = R - R1
      DO 1 K = 1, I
    1 A = A + (-1.0/TLMBDA) * LOGF (RANDOMF (X))
      IF (R2) 2,2,3
    2 X = 0.0
      GO TO 8
    3 V = RANDOMF (X)
      V1 = RANDOMF (X)
      V2 = RANDOMF (X)
      IF (V - EXPF (E)/(EXPF (E) + R2) 4,4,6
    4 IF (LOGF (V1) + V2 ** (1.0/R2)) 5,5,3
    5 Y = (1.0/TLMBDA) * (V2 ** (1.0/R2))
      GO TO 8
    6 IF (V1 - 1.0 * (-LOGF (V2/EXPF (E)))) ** (R2 - 1.0)) 7,7,3
    7 Y = (-1.0/TLMBDA) * LOGF (V2/EXPF (E))
    8 G = X + Y
      RETURN
      END
```

Other Generators

A convenient negative exponential generator, the great majority of whose generated variables, V, fall between 0 and 5 times the mean, TMU, is:

$$V = |TMU \times LOG_e R|$$

where R is a uniformly distributed random fraction and the vertical lines mean "absolute value;" i.e., "without regard to sign."

Two FORTRAN statements suitable for this might be:

$$R = RANDOMF (X)$$
$$V = ABSF (TMU * LOGF (R))$$

or, more briefly:

$$V = ABSF (TMU * LOGF (RANDOMF (X))) \qquad (8\text{--}5)$$

By adding a statement to **8–4**, we can construct a "log-normal" generator:

$$V2 = 2.718 ** V1 \tag{8–6}$$

In **8–6** the natural logarithm base, *e*, is raised to powers which are normally distributed, but the distribution of V2 is skewed, with a mean of: $e^{(\text{TMU}+\frac{1}{2}\text{SD}^2)}$ and a standard deviation of: $e^{(2\text{TMU}+2\text{SD}^2)} - e^{(2\text{TMU}-\text{SD}^2)}$.

Discrete versus Continuous Distributions

In some systems-simulation problems we are obliged to use discrete distributions (like those employed in Chapter 6). In some systems, however, stochastic processes can be approximated with sufficient accuracy by a variety of generators (like those described above) to enable us to employ these more flexible and more efficient continuous process simulators.

SUGGESTIONS FOR FURTHER STUDY

GALLER, BERNARD A. *The Language of Computers.* New York: McGraw-Hill, 1962.

GREEN, BERT. *Digital Computers in Research: An Introduction for Behavioral and Social Scientists.* New York: McGraw-Hill, 1963.

SCHLAIFFER, ROBERT. *Probability and Statistics for Business Decisions.* New York: McGraw-Hill, 1963 (chapters 10, 13, 14 and 17).

EXERCISES

(Where a computer program is called for, begin with a flow diagram.)

1. A "Fibonacci sequence" results when we begin with a number, N; add to it N + 1, yielding N1; then add to N + 1, N1 yielding N2; then add to N1, N2 yielding N3; then add to N3, N2 yielding N4; etc., thus:

2	N
3	N + 1
5	N1
8	N2
13	N3
21	N4, etc.

The numbers 121393 and 414229 are two successive numbers in a Fibonacci sequence. We might design a random number generator, based on a Fibonacci sequence, beginning with these two numbers. To more nearly guarantee randomness, we might select as our random numbers (assuming we want a two-digit random number list) the third and fourth digits, counting from right to left.

Thus our first random number would be 56: (121393 + 414229 = 535622, and we drop all but the third and fourth digits, counting from the right).

Our second random number would be 98: (414229 + 535622 = 989851, and we drop all but the third and fourth digits, counting from the right.)

Write a FORTRAN program which will enable us to get a two-digit random integer based on a Fibonacci sequence, beginning with 121393 and 414229, by calling SUBROUTINE FIBONA.

2. One widely employed scheme for approximating the area under a curve corresponding to the function $Y = f(x)$ is Simpson's Rule, expressed by the model:

$$\int_{x_0}^{x_0 + h} f(x)\,dX \approx h/6[f(x_0) + 4(x_0 + h/2) + f(x_0 + h)]$$

where X_0 is the lower limit of the area to be determined and h is the range (on the X axis) of the area to be determined (see illustration).

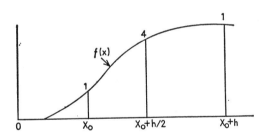

Write a FORTRAN program which will employ Simpson's Rule to determine the area between $x_0 = 4$ and $x_0 + h = 32$, under the curve represented by the function:

$$f(x) = (1/8\sqrt{2\pi})e^{-\frac{1}{2}\left[\frac{x-47}{8}\right]^2}.$$

The function above is the probability density function of the normal distribution with mean of 47 and standard deviation of 8. Therefore the area called for above is the probability of a sample between 4 and 32, given a normal process whose mean is 47 and whose standard deviation is 8.

3. Using the system function associated with your computer for generating uniformly distributed random fractions, compose a FOR-

TRAN program which will generate 4,000 two-digit random integers, and will keep a record and print out the frequency with which each of the various two-digit numbers generated appeared.

4. Using the normal generator described in Chapter 8,

a) Compose a FORTRAN program which will generate 4,000 three-digit integers, randomly distributed about a mean of 163 with standard deviation of 40, and which will keep a record and print out the frequency with which the various three-digit integers appeared.

b) Repeat the above, using the Poisson generator described in Chapter 8, with a mean of 103.

c) Repeat the above, using the log-normal generator described in Chapter 8 and the normal parameters specified in *(a)* above.

d) Plot curves of the distributions generated in *(a)*, *(b)*, and *(c)*.

5. Employ the normal generator described in Chapter 8, using a mean of 67 and a standard deviation of 20, to generate 4,000, three-digit integers. Compose a FORTRAN program which will determine the mean of the 4,000 integers thus generated, and their variance.

CHAPTER 9

Simulation of Queuing Systems

Now that we have equipped ourselves with a variety of process generators, we are in a position to study the behavior of rather complex systems in which processes similar to these seem to be operative. To see how these generators might be employed, let us address ourselves to the design of a computer model for simulating queuing systems. Once again we will begin by designing a rather elementary model, one involving a single channel and a single service facility. However, we will take pains to design the model in a rather particular manner so that it can be applied, with minor modifications, to quite complex queuing systems. We will design our model around a specific queue system, and then move to the more general model.

SINGLE-CHANNEL QUEUE SYSTEM SIMULATION

In this single channel queue system, arrivals are Poisson distributed with a mean arrival rate of 1.42 customers per hour. Arrivals are serviced on a first-come-first-served basis in a service facility which can accommodate only one customer at a time. Average service time is 0.34 hours per customer, and service time is normally distributed with a standard deviation of 0.08.

We wish to determine the behavior of the system by simulating experience with 1,000 customers, beginning at time zero with the system empty.

Two events can occur which change the "state" of the system:

1. Customers arrive in the system; and
2. Customers whose service has been completed depart from the service facility.

To simulate the system's performance, let us employ two subroutines in a FORTRAN program. We will make a comparison, in the main program, between (1) the *time* after time zero when the next arriving customer is "destined to arrive," and (2) the *time* after time zero when the next departure is "destined to occur." The earlier of the two events will determine which of the two subroutines will be "called" for determining the new state of the system.

Data will be accumulated during the simulation to determine:

1. The percent utilization of the service facility (the percent of the total time the facility is busy).
2. The probabilities of queues of varying lengths forming before the service facility.
3. The average or expected time in the system per customer.

Variables employed in the FORTRAN program will be as follows:

TIME: always has the value of the hour of the most recent change in the state or status of the system.
TNARV: has the value of the hour of the next arrival.
TNDPR: has the value of the hour of the next departure.
QUE: has a value equal to the length of the queue.
STATUS: indicates the state of the service facility. When STATUS is 0.0, the facility is empty; when STATUS is 1.0, the facility is occupied.
CUMUTL: has a value equal to the total number of hours since "time zero" that the service facility has been busy (cumulative utilization).
CUSERV: has the value of the number of customers who have been served and have departed from the service facility since time zero.
CUMQUE: is a one-dimension subscripted variable which holds the cumulative record of hours during which the queue has been of various length. Thus: CUMQUE(1) holds the number of hours the queue has had 0 customers in it since time zero; CUMQUE(2) holds the number of hours the queue has had 1 customer in it since time zero; CUMQUE(3) holds the number of hours the queue has had 2 customers in it since time zero; CUMQUE(19) holds the number of hours the queue has had 18 customers in it since time zero (assume that the queue will never exceed 18).

Figure 9-1 is a flow diagram for a computer program which could be employed to simulate the system using the variables defined. The main program is in the center and the two subroutines are on either side.

Notice that in initializing the system we make TNDPR very large so as to assure that the first status-disturbing event is an arrival (a

FIGURE 9-1

Flow Diagram for Single Channel Queue System

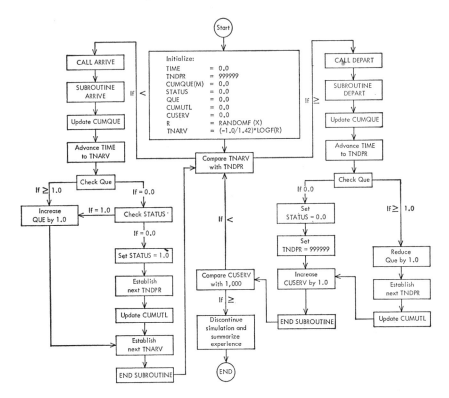

departure being impossible, since the system begins empty). Let us design a subroutine to interpret and record the effect of an arrival on the system.

The Arrival Subroutine

Since an arrival, like a departure, is a status-disturbing event, we should begin by "updating" the variable, CUMQUE. Recalling the use of the variable TIME, we know that—whatever the status of the queue *prior* to our current arrival—it has had that status since TIME, or for TNARV minus TIME hours. Updating CUMQUE means that we must add this increment of time to that cumulative record of time during which the queue has had length QUE. We can do this with the following statements:

M = QUE
CUMQUE(M + 1) = CUMQUE(M + 1) + TNARV − TIME

Now we can reset TIME to reflect the hour of our most recent status-disturbing event: TIME = TNARV.

Next, we would do well to determine whether our new arrival enters the service facility or the queue. Recalling that the variable, STATUS, has a value of zero if the facility is empty and a value of 1.0 if it is occupied, we can determine whether our arrival enters the queue or the facility by two IF statements:

IF (QUE − 1.0)1,3,3
1 IF (STATUS − 1.0)2,3,3.

If, as a result of these two statements, control passes to statement 2, it means that the queue had length zero and the service facility was empty. Under these conditions, our new arrival would enter the facility immediately upon arriving, and we would want to add a statement to indicate that the facility is now occupied: 2 STATUS = 1.0.

Since a customer just entered the facility (at hour TIME), the stage is set for a departure to occur at some future hour. Since service time is known to be normally distributed, with a mean of 0.34 hours and a standard deviation of 0.08, we can use our normal generator to determine the increment of time, T, which will be required to service the customer who just entered the facility. With the following statements we can determine T and calculate the hour this customer is "destined to depart" from the facility, TNDPR:

T = (−2.0 * LOGF(RANDOMF(X))) ** 0.5 * COSF(6.283 *
RANDOMF(X)) * 0.08 + 0.34
TNDPR = TIME + T.

Knowing the magnitude of this added increment of time T with which the facility is "destined" to be occupied, we can update CUMUTL, our cumulative record of the hours the facility is utilized: CUMUTL = CUMUTL + T.

We must now make provision for the event: "Our current arrival arrived to find the service facility occupied." In this event our two IF statements, toward the beginning of our arrive subroutine, would send control to statement 3. We should add a statement to increase the length of QUE: 3 QUE = QUE + 1.0.

Finally, we must set the stage for our next arrival by giving the variable, TNARV, a new value. Knowing that the arrival pattern is Poisson distributed, with a mean of 1.42 customers per hour, we can use our Poisson generator to determine the increment of time "destined to elapse" before our next arrival and determine his hour of arrival, TNARV , by the statement:

4   TNARV $= -1.0/1.42 * \mathrm{LOGF\,(RANDOMF\,(X))} + \mathrm{TIME}.$

Our arrive subroutine would appear as follows:

```
      SUBROUTINE ARRIVE  (QUE,STATUS,TNDPR,
         CUMUTL,TNARV,CUMQUE,TIME)
      DIMENSION  CUMQUE(20)
      M = QUE
      CUMQUE(M + 1) = CUMQUE(M + 1) + TNARV −TIME
      TIME = TNARV
      IF  (QUE − 1.0)1,3,3
    1 IF  (STATUS − 1.0)2,3,3
    2 STATUS = 1.0
      T = (−2.0 * LOGF(RANDOMF(X))) ** 0.5 * COSF
         (6.283 * RANDOMF(X))  *0.08 + 0.34
      TNDPR = TIME + T
      CUMUTL = CUMUTL + T
      GO TO 4
    3 QUE = QUE + 1.0
    4 TNARV = −1.0/1.42 * LOGF(RANDOMF(X)) + TIME
      RETURN
      END
```

The Depart Subroutine

As with our arrive subroutine, we should begin by updating CUMQUE and by resetting TIME:

```
      M = QUE
      CUMQUE(M + 1) = CUMQUE(M + 1) + TNDPR − TIME
      TIME = TNDPR.
```

Next, let us make provision for the event: "A customer departs from the service facility at a time when the queue is zero":

```
      IF  (QUE − 1.0)1,2,2
    1 STATUS = 0.0
      TNDPR = 999999.0
```

In the program segment above we set STATUS at zero, since the service facility is now empty, and we give the variable TNDPR a very large value to assure that the next status-disturbing is *not* a departure (now an impossibility).

Now let us deal with the case where the departure which caused our depart subroutine to be called occurs when the queue is not zero. Clearly, the departure will reduce the queue by one: 2 QUE = QUE − 1.0.

Since a new customer has just entered the service facility, we would do well to determine how long an increment of time, T, this customer will be in the facility, and to use this information to update CUMUTL and to determine the time of our next departure, TNDPR:

```
T = (−2.0*LOGF(RANDOMF(X)))**0.5*COSF
   (6.283*RANDOMF(X))*0.08 + 0.34
TNDPR = TIME + T
CUMUTL = CUMUTL + T
```

Having just serviced an additional customer, we should update CUSERV:

```
3   CUSERV = CUSERV + 1.0
```

Our depart subroutine would appear as follows:

```
    SUBROUTINE DEPART  (QUE,STATUS,TNDPR,
       CUMUTL,CUMQUE,TIME,CUSERV)
    DIMENSION  CUMQUE(20)
    M = QUE
    CUMQUE(M + 1) = CUMQUE(M + 1) +
       TNDPR − TIME
    TIME = TNDPR
    IF  (QUE − 1.0)1,2,2
1   STATUS = 0.0
    TNDPR = 999999.0
    GO TO 3
2   QUE = QUE − 1.0
    T = (−2.0*LOGF(RANDOMF(X)))**0.5*COSF
       (6.283*RANDOMF(X))  *0.08 + 0.34
    TNDPR = TIME + T
    CUMUTL = CUMUTL + T
3   CUSERV = CUSERV + 1.0
    RETURN
    END
```

The Main Program

Our main program will consist of: (1) Initializing statements, (2) Our calling routine, and (3) Some procedure for summarizing and printing out results of our simulated experience.

Let us turn first to the calling routine. Our calling routine must compare TNARV and TNDPR, and call the subroutine which interprets the effect on the system of whichever of these two status-disturbing events occurs earlier. These statements should meet our needs:

```
2   IF (TNARV − TNDPR)3,4,4
3   CALL ARRIVE (QUE,STATUS,TNDPR,CUMUTL,
        TNARV,CUMQUE,TIME)
    GO TO 2
4   CALL DEPART (QUE,STATUS,TNDPR,CUMUTL,
        CUMQUE,TIME,CUSERV)
    IF (CUSERV − 1000.0)2,5,5
```

By the addition of the final statement in the above program segment, we provide for terminating the operating routine when the servicing of 1,000 arrivals has been simulated.

Let us assume that 1,000 arrivals have been serviced and that we are ready to interpret the results of our simulation. The variable, TIME, holds the hour of departure of the 1,000th customer, and hence the total simulated time. The percent utilization of the service facility can be determined by 5 PCUTIL = (CUMUTL/TIME)*100.

To find the average time a customer spent in the system, we could divide the total number of customer-hours spent in the system by 1,000. Total customer-hours in the system would be total customer-hours spent in queues plus total customer-hours spent in the service facility. Total customer-hours spent in queues would be:

> 1 × total hours the queue length was 1
> + 2 × total hours the queue length was 2
> + 3 × total hours the queue length was 3, etc.

We could calculate total customer-hours in queues thus:

```
    HRSNQ = 0.0
    DO 6 M = 1,19
    H = M
6   HRSNQ = HRSNQ + H*CUMQUE(M + 1)
```

And total customer-hours spent in the service facility is simply CUMUTL.

Average time in the system would therefore be: AVTIS = (HRSNQ + CUMUTL)/1000.0.

Since we are interested in the probabilities of queues of varying lengths, we might convert the contents of the array CUMQUE to probabilities in this way:

```
        DO 7 M = 1,20
     7  CUMQUE(M) = CUMQUE(M)/TIME
```

With suitable PRINT and FORMAT statements we can provide for printing out the desired data:

```
     PRINT 8, PCUTIL,AVTIS
   8 FORMAT(1H0,42HPERCENT  UTILIZATION  OF  SERVICE
     FACILITY = ,F10.6,2X,43HAND  AVERAGE  TIME  IN
     SYSTEM PER  CUSTOMER = ,F10.2)
     DO 10  M = 1,19
     L = M − 1
     PRINT 9, L, CUMQUE(M)
   9 FORMAT(1H0,15HPROBABILITY OF ,I2, 2X,
     21HCUSTOMERS  IN  QUEUE = ,F10.8)
```

Our total program, with the initializing statements added and with comment statements interspersed to facilitate interpretation, would appear as shown in Figure 9-2.

Our print-out from this program provides the following data:[1]

1. Percent utilization of the service facility = **48.7** percent
2. Average time in the system per customer = **0.51** hours
3. Probability of 0 customers in queue = 0.832
   Probability of 1 customers in queue = 0.116
   Probability of 2 customers in queue = 0.038
   Probability of 3 customers in queue = 0.010
   Probability of 4 customers in queue = 0.001
   Probability of 5 customers in queue = 0.000
   Probability of 6 customers in queue = 0.000
   Probability of 7 customers in queue = 0.000
   Probability of 8 customers in queue = 0.000
   Probability of 9 customers in queue = 0.000
   Probability of 10 customers in queue = 0.000
   Probability of 11 customers in queue = 0.000
   Probability of 12 customers in queue = 0.000
   Probability of 13 customers in queue = 0.000
   Probability of 14 customers in queue = 0.000
   Probability of 15 customers in queue = 0.000
   Probability of 16 customers in queue = 0.000
   Probability of 17 customers in queue = 0.000
   Probability of 18 customers in queue = 0.000

---

[1] This output is the result of a particular random number generator. Since the sample is not large, other generators can be expected to yield slightly different results.

This single channel queue system appears to be a rather elementary system. Most queue systems in business and economics consist of multiple facilities, multiple channels, and multiple queues. The queue discipline may vary from channel to channel; the service times, arrival patterns, and other parameters of each of the individual subcomponent queue systems may vary. However, in a very real sense, most complex systems may be thought of as many com-

FIGURE 9-2

```
      DIMENSION CUMQUE(20)
C INITIALIZE SYSTEM AT TIME ZERO
      TIME = 0.0
      TNDPR = 999999.9
      DO 1 M = 1,20
    1 CUMQUE(M) = 0.0
      STATUS = 0.0
      QUE = 0.0
      CUMUTL = 0.0
      CUSERV = 0.0
      R = RANDOMF(X)
      TNARV = -1.0/1.42 *LOGF(R)
C CALL UPON TIMING ROUTINE
    2 IF(TNARV - TNDPR)3,4,4
    3 CALL ARRIVE (QUE,STATUS,TNDPR,CUMUTL,TNARV,CUMQUE,TIME)
      GO TO 2
    4 CALL DEPART (QUE,STATUS,TNDPR,CUMUTL,CUMQUE,TIME,CUSERV)
C TERMINATE SIMULATION IF ONE THOUSAND ARRIVALS HAVE BEEN SERVICED
      IF (CUSERV - 1000.0)2,5,5
C DETERMINE PERCENT UTILIZATION OF SERVICE FACILITY
    5 PCUTIL = CUMUTL/TIME*100.
C DETERMINE FROM CUMQUE CUSTOMER-HOURS SPENT IN QUEUES
      HRSNQ = 0.0
      DO 6 M = 1,19
      H = M
    6 HRSNQ = HRSNQ + H*CUMQUE(M+1)
C ADD CUSTOMER-HOURS IN FACILITY AND DETERMINE AVERAGE TIME IN SYSTEM
      AVTIS = (HRSNQ+CUMUTL)/1000.0
C CONVERT CONTENTS OF CUMQUE TO PROBABILITIES
      DO 7 M= 1,20
    7 CUMQUE(M) = CUMQUE(M)/TIME
C PRINT PCUTIL AND AVTIS
      PRINT 8, PCUTIL,AVTIS
    8 FORMAT(1H0,42HPERCENT UTILIZATION OF SERVICE FACILITY = ,F10.6,2X,
     142HAND AVERAGE TIME IN SYSTEM PER CUSTOMER = ,F4.2)
C PRINT PROBABILITIES OF QUEUES OF VARYING LENGTHS
      DO 10 M = 1,19
      L = M-1
      PRINT 9,L,CUMQUE(M)
    9 FORMAT(1H0,15HPROBABILITY OF ,I2,2X,21HCUSTOMERS IN QUEUE = ,F10.8
     1)
   10 CONTINUE
      STOP
      END
      SUBROUTINE ARRIVE (QUE,STATUS,TNDPR,CUMUTL,TNARV,CUMQUE,TIME)
      DIMENSION CUMQUE(20)
C UPDATE CUMQUE,RESET TIME
      M = QUE
      CUMQUE(M+1) = CUMQUE(M+1)+TNARV - TIME
```

FIGURE 9-2 (Continued)

```
      TIME = TNARV
C CHECK QUE LENGTH AND STATE OF SERVICE FACILITY
      IF(QUE - 1.0)1,3,3
    1 IF(STATUS - 1.0)2,3,3
    2 STATUS = 1.0
C ESTABLISH TIME IN SERVICE FACILITY AND TIME OF NEXT DEPARTURE
      T = (-2.0*LOGF(RANDOMF(X)))**0.5*COSF(6.283*RANDOMF(X))  *0.08 +
      10.34
      TNDPR = TIME + T
C UPDATE CUMUTL
      CUMUTL = CUMUTL + T
      GO TO 4
C INCREASE QUE LENGTH
    3 QUE = QUE + 1.0
C ESTABLISH TIME OF NEXT ARRIVAL
    4TNARV = -1.0/1.42 *LOGF(RANDOMF(X)) + TIME
      RETURN
      END
      SUBROUTINE DEPART (QUE,STATUS,TNDPR,CUMUTL,CUMQUE,TIME,CUSERV)
      DIMENSION CUMQUE(20)
C UPDATE CUMQUE,RESET TIME
      M = QUE
      CUMQUE(M + 1) = CUMQUE(M + 1) + TNDPR - TIME
      TIME = TNDPR
C CHECK QUE LENGTH
      IF (QUE - 1.0)1,2,2
    1 STATUS = 0.0
      TNDPR = 999999.9
      GO TO 3
C DECREASE QUEUE LENGTH
    2 QUE = QUE - 1.0
C ESTABLISH TIME IN SERVICE FACILITY AND TIME OF NEXT DEPARTURE
      T = (-2.0*LOGF(RANDOMF(X)))**0.5*COSF(6.283*RANDOMF(X))  *0.08 +
      10.34
      TNDPR = TIME + T
C UPDATE CUMUTL AND CUSERV
      CUMUTL = CUMUTL + T
    3 CUSERV = CUSERV + 1.0
      RETURN
      END
      END
```

ponent subsystems, each of which bears some similarity to the others. By virtue of this basic uniformity we can use the construct of Figure 9-2 to simulate and to study the behavior of highly complex systems that are composed of many different component subsystems, each with different attributes.

We can do this by using one-, two-, and three-dimension subscripted variables to store attributes of the component subsystems where we used zero dimension subscripted variables in Figure 9-2. Thus the variables, TIME, TNDPR, STATUS, QUE, CUMUTL, CUSERV, and TNARV might be converted to one-dimension subscripted variables. Position 1 in each of these subscripted variables could refer to component queue system 1; position 2 in each of these subscripted variables could refer to component system 2; etc.

The main program, then, would serve not simply to inquire which occurs next, "an arrival" or "a departure," but rather "which of many possible arrivals and many possible departures occurs next?" When the component queue system (involved with the event which is "destined" to occur next) is identified, the appropriate position in our set of arrays would be called into play. Execution of the statements in either the arrival subroutine or the departure subroutine would then involve interpreting the effect of an arrival or a departure on the particular component subsystem for which some status-disturbing event just occurred.

In this scheme the variable, CUMQUE, could be made a two-dimension subscripted variable to hold records of all queues.

MULTIPLE SERVICE FACILITIES

Let us suppose that we have a single channel queue system with three rather than one service facilities—as portrayed in Figure 9-3.

FIGURE 9-3

As before, let's assume that arrivals at service facility 1 are Poisson-distributed, with a mean arrival rate of 1.42 customers per hour, and that service time in each of the three service facilities is normally distributed with a mean service time of 0.34 hours per customer and a standard deviation of 0.08 hours.

We can think of this system as three component subsystems, each consisting of a service facility and its queue of customers waiting for service. The status of each subsystem is disturbed, as before, by either of two possible events: an arrival or a departure. Clearly, however, a departure from subsystem 1 is an arrival at subsystem 2, and a departure from subsystem 2 is an arrival at subsystem 3. Therefore, the moment TNDPR for subsystem 1 is determined, TNARV for subsystem 2 is established, and, similarly, the moment TNDPR for subsystem 2 is determined, TNARV for subsystem 3 is established.

Under these circumstances we are obliged to call on our Poisson generator only for establishing the time of the next arrival at subsystem 1. This special characteristic of our multiple service facility system would require only a few modifications in the program of Figure 9-2.

Variables for the model of Figure 9-2 could be redefined, enabling us to simulate the multiple facility model of Figure 9-3 as follows:

TIME(1) . . . always has the value of the hour of the most recent change in the status of subsystem 1.

TIME(2) . . . always has the value of the hour of the most recent change in the status of subsystem 2.

TIME(3) . . . always has the value of the hour of the most recent change in the status of subsystem 3.

TNARV(1) . . . has the value of the hour of the next arrival in subsystem 1.

TNARV(2) . . . has the value of the hour of the next arrival in subsystem 2.

TNARV(3) . . . has the value of the hour of the next arrival in subsystem 3.

TNDPR(1) . . . has the value of the hour of the next departure from subsystem 1.

TNDPR(2) . . . has the value of the hour of the next departure from subsystem 2.

TNDPR(3) . . . has the value of the hour of the next departure from subsystem 3.

QUE(1) . . . has a value equal to the length of the queue of subsystem 1.

QUE(2) . . . has a value equal to the length of the queue of subsystem 2.

QUE(3) . . . has a value equal to the length of the queue of subsystem 3.

STATUS(1) . . . indicates the state of the service facility in subsystem 1.

STATUS(2) . . . indicates the state of the service facility in subsystem 2.

STATUS(3) . . . indicates the state of the service facility in subsystem 3.

CUMUTL(1) . . . has a value equal to the total number of hours since time zero that the service facility of subsystem 1 has been busy.

CUMUTL(2) . . . has a value equal to the total number of hours since time zero that the service facility of subsystem 2 has been busy.

CUMUTL(3) . . . has a value equal to the total number of hours since time zero that the service facility of subsystem 3 has been busy.

CUMQUE(1,1) . . . holds the number of hours the queue of subsystem 1 has had 0 customers in it since time zero.

CUMQUE(1,2) . . . holds the number of hours the queue of subsystem 1 has had 1 customer in it since time zero.

CUMQUE(2,1) . . . holds the number of hours the queue of subsystem 2 has had 0 customers in it since time zero.

CUMQUE(2,2) . . . holds the number of hours the queue of subsystem 2 has had 1 customer in it since time zero.

.
.
.

etc.

We might think of our computer model as consisting of three *sets* of subroutines, one set pertaining to each of the three subsystems. Associated with each set is a separate clock (the various positions of TIME(N)) and means for keeping a cumulative record of the operations of the subsystem to which each subroutine set pertains.

Our timing mechanism in the main program will now be obliged to search (for the smallest value) the time stored in the N positions of the variables TNARV(N) and TNDPR(N).

MULTIPLE CHANNELS

Suppose we have a system like that of Figure 9-4.

FIGURE 9-4

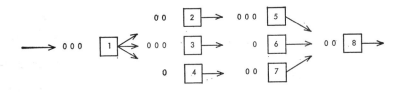

Let us assume that customers departing from subsystem 1 enter subsystems 2, 3, or 4, and that the distribution between these three subsystems is random, with equal probabilities. That is: 1/3 go to subsystem 2, 1/3 go to subsystem 3, and 1/3 go to subsystem 4.

We can employ a slightly modified version of the model of Figure 9-2 here also. We envision a two-subroutine set for each of the eight subsystems, with a clock and an operating experience recording routine for each subsystem. The only innovation required is some scheme for determining whether a departure from subsystem 1 is an arrival at subsystem 2, at subsystem 3, or at subsystem 4. This we could do easily with a suitably designed generator.

Our previous examples have been rather simple in that service times at the various service facilities all have had the same distribution parameters. Suppose service times are all normally distributed but that other parameters of the distributions are different. We might deal with this problem rather easily also. We could introduce a second subscripted variable, which we might call PARAM(M,N) —to hold the means and the standard deviations of the various distributions—with

PARAM(1,1) . . . holding the mean of the service time distribution of subsystem 1.

PARAM(1,2) . . . holding the standard deviation of the service time distribution of subsystem 1.

PARAM(2,1) . . . holding the mean of the service time distribution of subsystem 2.

PARAM(2,2) . . . holding the standard deviation of the service time distribution of subsystem 2.

But what if the service time at one service facility is normally distributed while the service time distribution at another service facility is constant, or perhaps Poisson- or Gamma-distributed?

One way to deal with this added complexity would be to provide a set of special service-time generating subroutines, with one subroutine for each different class of service-time distributions. Thus we might have a service-time generating subroutine for all facilities whose service-time distribution is normal, another for those whose service-time distribution is Poisson, etc. We could also construct a special subroutine for a facility whose service-time was constant, or perhaps one which was characterized by a discrete distribution of some unique form.

With such a general arrangement, we might do our service-time calculating in the main program rather than in a subroutine (as called for in Figure 9-2). Once the subsystem for which a departure has just occurred has been identified, we could cause the appropriate service-time generating subroutine to be called for determining the time of departure of the next customer in that service facility.

In trying to conceptualize the requirements for adapting our model of Figure 9-2 to the systems portrayed in Figures 9-3 and 9-4, we found ourselves thinking of subsystem service facilities and their associated queues. Focusing our attention on a subsystem, we found that we could simulate its behavior by a few modifications of the model of Figure 9-2; that we could relate that subsystem to the other subsystems in the total system; and that we could accumulate records of data relating to the operating experience of each subsystem by specifying:

a)   The distribution of service time in the subsystem's service facility, and

b)   The position of the subsystem in the flow of customers.

The initial subsystem and the final subsystem are unique, however. The time of the next arrival for the initial subsystem is not determined by the time of departure from a predecessor subsystem; rather, customers arriving from outside the total system are generated by some specified process. Also, the time of departure of a customer from the final subsystem does not determine the time of arrival at a succeeding subsystem but rather signals permanent departure of the customer from the total system.

Our conceptual scheme, therefore, involves:

1.   Generation of customers from outside the system,

2.   A flow of customers through a specified sequence of subsystems, each of which involves a service facility and a queue, and

3.   Departure of customers from the system.

THE GENERAL PURPOSE SYSTEMS SIMULATOR

The General Purpose Systems Simulator (GPSS) is one of a variety of programming languages designed specifically for modeling queuing systems. GPSS bears some similarity to FORTRAN in that its statements include a number of English verbs, such as GENERATE, HOLD, QUEUE, ADVANCE, PICK, TERMINATE, etc.

However, GPSS has a logic structure that is all its own. Its structure, and the composition of a GPSS program, are best understood by reference to a GPSS block diagram. GPSS programs are constructed by the use of block diagrams in which a unique GPSS symbol system is employed to designate the complete structure of the queuing system being modeled. The blocks in the diagram are connected by lines which indicate the flow of customers (called "transactions" in GPSS) through the system.

By GPSS convention our single-channel, single-service system might be portrayed as shown in Figure 9-5.

FIGURE 9-5

GPSS Single-Channel, Single-Service System

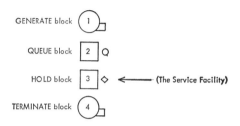

In GPSS the queue subsystem—which we have viewed thus far as a single unit consisting of a service facility and a queue—is viewed as two interconnected facilities: a service facility (the HOLD block) and a queue facility (the QUEUE block).

In the computer program which is composed from a GPSS block diagram, one block corresponds to one statement, and one statement is punched on one card.

Each block, and hence each statement in the program, has a number. To specify the path of flow of customers through the system one includes, as part of the data punched on the card pertaining to each block in the diagram, the number of the block to which customers pass upon departing from that block.

As indicated above, there is one card (and one statement) for each block in the diagram. GPSS-punched cards are all divided into the same 11 fields. The number of the block is punched in the *first* field. The name of the class of the block is punched in the *second* field (thus: GENERATE, HOLD, QUEUE, etc.). The number of the block to which departing customers go is specified in the *seventh* field. In the remaining fields one can specify—in accordance with strict GPSS convention—such requirements as the distribution of time between arrivals in the GENERATE block, the distribution of service time in the HOLD block, and the like.

GPSS has a rich block dictionary, one that provides the model builder with considerable flexibility. Our model of Figure 9-4, written in GPSS block-diagram form, might appear as shown in Figure 9-6.

FIGURE 9-6

Model of Figure 9-4 Written in GPSS Block-Diagram Form

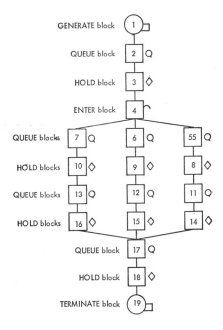

The ENTER block uses whatever selection process the programmar wishes to specify (random or otherwise) to send customers to a number of possible queues.

In Chapter 3, mention was made of the *compiler,* a computer program itself, which translates FORTRAN statements into machine language for subsequent execution. Single FORTRAN statements translate into a rather large number of machine-language instructions. In this sense, FORTRAN is a kind of programming shorthand.

In a similar way, GPSS is also a kind of shorthand. When, for example, the timing mechanism in GPSS sends control to a QUEUE block, the GPSS compiler interprets the single QUEUE statement to mean:

a) Compute and record the number of time units the queue has been at its current length [analogous to updating CUMQUE in the model of Figure 9-2].

b) Change the status of the queue to reflect the event which just occurred.

Similarly, the compiler interprets the single HOLD statement to mean:

a)   Compute and record the number of customers currently served [analogous to updating CUSERV in the model of Figure 9-2].
b)   Compute and record the number of time units the service facility has been utilized [analogous to updating CUMUTL in 9-2].

The process is analogous to calling subroutines as a means of bringing into play a whole sequence of instructions. In GPSS the subroutines, the timing mechanism, and parts of the arrival pattern and service time generators are built into the compiler as system functions.

Equipped with a GPSS compiler, one can construct very complex queue system simulation models with a small number of statements.[1]

SIMSCRIPT

Another simulation language is SIMSCRIPT.[2] Like GPSS, SIMSCRIPT is another kind of shorthand. Many data manipulations required in simulating the effect on a system of a status-disturbing event can be called into play by only one, or a few, SIMSCRIPT statements.

SIMSCRIPT is a FORTRAN-base language, but it has its own logic structure and its own set of programming conventions. Like GPSS, SIMSCRIPT emphasizes the status of the system and the events which modify that status. SIMSCRIPT defines a system's status in terms of its "entities," their "attributes," and the "sets" to which they belong (or which they "own").

There are two kinds of entities in SIMSCRIPT: temporary and permanent entities. Temporary entities might correspond to "customers," as we have employed the term in this text (to "transactions" in GPSS). Permanent entities might correspond to our use of the term "service facilities."

---

[1] For a full description of GPSS, the symbol dictionary, programming conventions and deck organization, see the *IBM Reference Manual for General Purpose Systems Simulator II*, 1963.

[2] A programming manual for SIMSCRIPT was published by Prentice-Hall (Englewood Cliffs, N.J.) in 1963: SIMSCRIPT: *A Simulation Programming Language*, by Harry N. Markowitz, Bernard Hauser, and Herbert W. Karr.

Thus in a machine shop, a machine group or a department through which work orders flow might be a "permanent entity," and orders themselves might be "temporary entities."

In the machine shop setting, an "attribute" of a department might be service time in that department; an order might be a temporary entity; and attributes of an order might include the date of the order or its sequence (routing) through the shop.

In a typical machine shop a work order may also be part of a "set" of work orders. Thus, work orders No. 2071, No. 34, and No. 056 might be the three jobs required for processing customer order No. A-274-6.

SIMSCRIPT provides for defining "entities" (temporary and permanent) by both their "attributes" and the "sets" to which they belong or which they "own." Customer order No. A-274-6 "owns" work orders 2071, 34, and 056. Similarly, a department might "own" a queue.

A SIMSCRIPT program is divided into a number of segments. An initial segment is the "definition" segment, in which the various kinds of temporary and permanent entities, their attributes, and "sets" are identified.

Events in SIMSCRIPT occur *within* the system (*endogenous events,* as when a work order is completed and departs from a department) or from *without* the system (*exogenous events,* as when a customer order arrives after having been "generated" by the market process). Events in SIMSCRIPT are status-disturbing incidents—and in the same sense as we have used the term in this text.

In addition to the definition segment of a SIMSCRIPT program, one also employs a variety of routines. Thus we may have a routine for describing the effect on the system of the receipt of a customer's order; another routine for describing the arrival of a work order at a particular department; and another for describing the effect on the system of a departure from the system itself. These routines are analogous to the subroutines of our model in Figure 9-2.

Another SIMSCRIPT program segment is the report-generator. This segment provides for summarizing results of the simulation and printing them out.

Like GPSS, SIMSCRIPT has a variety of functions built into its compiler which simplify the job of the programmer. For simulating complex queuing systems, SIMSCRIPT, like GPSS, has many advantages over FORTRAN. The most noteworthy advantages are simplicity and flexibility for the programmer in accommodating varied flow patterns and queue disciplines, and the more efficient conservation of computer memory space.

SUGGESTIONS FOR FURTHER STUDY

IBM Reference Manual for General Purpose Systems Simulator II (1963).

MARKOWITZ, HARRY N.; HAUSER, BERNARD; AND KARR, HERBERT W. *Simscript: A Simulation Programming Language.* Englewood Cliffs, N.J.: Prentice-Hall, 1963.

EXERCISES

1. Employ the model in Figure 9-2 to determine the maximum mean arrival rate which could be tolerated without a queue length of 19 or more customers occurring more than 10 percent of the time. Assume that all other parameters of the model remain as shown in Figure 9-2.

2. Super Service, Inc., operates a truck-fleet maintenance and repair service. Arriving trucks enter one of eight service areas, depending on the service they require. Service is on a first-come-first-served basis, and only one truck can be accommodated in each service area at a time.

Each service area operates independently of the others, although arriving trucks are occasionally obliged, upon departing from one service area (after having been repaired), to enter another, before leaving Super Service's facilities entirely.

In spite of this "re-entry" characteristic, arrivals at all service areas are Poisson-distributed. Service time at all service areas is normally distributed. Currently, the mean arrival rate at the service area is as follows:

Service Areas	Mean Arrival Rate
1	.43 hour
2	.16 "
3	.14 "
4	.10 "
5	.09 "
6	.08 "
7	.05 "
8	.05 "

The mean service time at the service areas, and the associated standard deviations, are as follows:

Service Areas	Service Time	
	Mean	Standard Deviation
1	2.0 hours	1.1
2	5.8 "	3.1
3	6.2 "	2.7
4	6.1 "	4.1
5	10.9 "	5.2
6	11.2 "	6.9
7	9.0 "	5.8
8	18.7 "	13.0

Compose a model along the pattern of Figure 9-2 for simulating the behavior of the Super Service system.

Super Service management anticipates that demand on the system will increase in the months ahead and is interested in forecasting when their present space facilities will become inadequate.

Super Service can accommodate *occasional* overloads by renting space in adjoining properties to accommodate trucks waiting for service. Management feels, however, that it is time to expand when demand reaches a level at which their own space facilities are inadequate more than 20 percent of the time.

Super Service is presently equipped to accommodate 85 trucks while they wait for service. If, as management forecasts, the mean arrival rate at each of the eight service areas increases 0.24 percent per week, how many weeks does Super Service have to prepare additional storage space?

(Suggestion: Employ a modified version of the model in Figure 9-2, but use subscripted variables. For example:

QUE(1):   holds the length of the queue before service area 1.
QUE(2):   holds the length of the queue before service area 2, etc.

TMU(1):   holds the mean service time at service area 1.
SD(1):   holds the standard deviation associated with TMU(1).

CUMQUE(1,1):   holds the cumulative hours that the queue before service area 1 has had 0 trucks in it.
CUMQUE(1,2):   holds the cumulative hours that the queue before service area 1 has had 1 truck in it, etc.
CUMQUE(2,1):   holds the cumulative hours that the queue before service area 2 has had 0 trucks in it.
CUMQUE(2,2):   holds the cumulative hours that the queue before service area 2 has had 1 truck in it, etc.

3.   Stored in the N positions of subscripted variables, TNARV(N) and TNDPR(N) are floating-point numbers representing hours after

time zero in which the next status-disturbing event at each of N subsystems in a queue system are destined to occur. Compose a program segment which will cause the computer to search these two arrays, and identify the variable and the position of that variable in which the smallest number is stored.

4-1. Construct a program, using a modified version of the model in Figure 9-2, for simulating the multiple service facility system portrayed in Figure 9-3 and described in the paragraph which succeeds it.

Simulate operations during the processing of 500 customers. Arrange to have printed out:

a) Percent utilization of each of the three service facilities.

b) Average time in each subsystem, per customer.

c) The probabilities (based on this sample of 500) of encountering 0 through 18 customers in each of the three queues.

4-2. Repeat what is called for in part 1 above, but cause the service time at service facility 2 to be normally distributed with a mean of 0.21 hours per customer and a standard deviation of 0.06.

4-3. Repeat what is called for in part 2 above, but cause the service time at service facility 1 to be constant at 0.5 hours per customer, and service time at service facility 3 to be uniformly distributed between 0.18 and 0.58 hours per customer (with a mean, therefore, of 0.38 hours per customer).

4-4. If mean service time in service facility 2 should increase, the behavior of subsystem 1 would not be affected, but how might subsystem 3 be influenced? Employ the model used in 4–3, above, to study the effect of an increase in service time at service facility 2. Cause the mean service time in service facility 2 to increase from 0.21 hours per customer to 0.61 by increments of 0.1. How does an increase in service time in subsystem 2 influence the operating experience of subsystem 3?

5. Construct a program, using a modified version of the model in Figure 9-2, for simulating the multiple-channel, multiple-service facility system portrayed in Figure 9-4. Assume that:

a) Arrivals at subsystem 1 are Poisson-distributed with a mean of 1.42 customers per hour;

b) Service time in subsystems 2, 4, 6, and 7 are normally distributed, with means of 1.9, 1.4, 1.6, and 1.8 hours per customer, respectively, each with a standard deviation equal to 1/3 its mean;

c) Service time in subsystems 3, 5, and 8 are uniformly distributed as follows:

Subsystem	Mean	Range
3 .... 1.1 hrs./customer		0.6 through 1.6
5 .... 1.3 " "		0.7 " 1.9
8 .... 0.2 " "		0.1 " 0.3

and simulate operations during the processing of 500 arrivals. Arrange to have printed out:

- *a*)   Percent utilization of the eight service facilities;
- *b*)   Average time in each subsystem, per customer;
- *c*)   The probabilities (based on this sample of 500) of encountering 0 through 18 customers in each of the eight queues.

CHAPTER 10

Management Planning Models

Two MODELS which have particular value for management decision making, and whose development has been greatly stimulated by progress in the computer sciences, have to do with planning. One deals with projects which are, relatively speaking, *one-time* undertakings and which involve a large number of component subprojects which are sequentially interrelated. The other model has to do with short-term forecasting of processes which are relatively *continuous*.

A study of these models will help us develop further skills in computer modeling and will help us equip ourselves for dealing with *total systems* studies.

The first of these models has to do with network analysis, and is most extensively described in current literature as PERT (Program Evaluation and Review Technique) and as CPM (Critical Path Method) analysis.

CPM and PERT evolved independently. CPM was developed by Morgan R. Walker of Du Pont and James E. Kelly of Remington Rand in 1957. PERT was developed in connection with the Polaris weapons system and was first described in an article by Malcolm, Roseboom, Clark, and Fazar in the September 1959 issue of *Operations Research*. Although each of these two techniques has its own modeling language, they differ in only one really fundamental respect: *Whereas CPM endeavors to determine the expected times of completion of the total project and times of completion of the subprojects of which it is composed, PERT goes further and endeavors to estimate variances associated with these expected times of completion.*

Therefore PERT deals more explicitly with the problem of uncertainty, and CPM becomes a kind of subset of PERT in which only expected values are employed in the planning process. We will concern ourselves only with PERT.

PERT NETWORK ANALYSIS

Consider the network of Figure 10-1. In this network a numbered circle corresponds to a significant *completion event,* such as (*a*) an assembly completed, (*b*) a budget prepared, or (*c*) a component tested.

An arrow, on the other hand, corresponds to an *activity,* such as (*a*) manufacture fuselage, (*b*) brief executive committee, or (*c*) prepare plans and specifications.

FIGURE 10-1

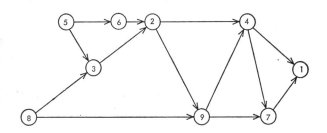

In the pictorial representation of Figure 10-1, the tail of the arrow represents the beginning of the activity and its head represents the ending of the activity. The PERT network is simply the interrelated system of activities and completion events, in which a completion event can be both the terminus of one or more activities and the necessary conditions for the commencement of one or more other activities.[1]

It seems appropriate to speak of events as *completion* events even though some events may not *seem* to represent the terminus of an activity (such as events 5 and 8 in Figure 10-1). However, to the network analyst and the program planner, all events are better thought of as the completion of something, since all events are not "beginning" events (thus event 1 in Figure 10-1).

---

[1] PERT (Program Evaluation and Review Technique) was developed and initially applied by Booz, Allen & Hamilton with Lockheed Aircraft Corporation and the Navy Special Projects Office in 1958. For other references to PERT, see the bibliography at the end of this chapter.

PERT network analysis has as its objective the manipulation of data relative to an interrelated system of activities and completion events so as to yield estimates concerning:

1. The earliest expected time of occurrence of completion events,
2. The latest allowable time of occurrence of completion events,
3. The critical path of the network, and
4. The probabilities of events occurring "on schedule."

For all but elementary networks, analysis "by hand" is too costly to justify. Equipped with a computer model, however, we can analyze and study the behavior of highly complex networks.

Prior to addressing ourselves to the design of a computer model for network analysis we would do well to perform an analysis by hand, both to acquaint ourselves with a number of conventions which we should observe and to acquaint ourselves with what has become rather standard PERT methodology.

First, we need time estimates for activities. In business and industry there is little certainty, so we must deal with probabilities. In network analysis we need two parameters for each time-consuming activity: a mean and a variance. A number of schemes may be employed to arrive at a mean and a variance for the amount of time required for an activity. One that enjoys rather widespread acceptance involves three estimates of the amount of time required for the activity:[2]

1. A most likely amount of time, which we will label m,
2. An optimistic estimate of the amount of time, which we will label a, and
3. A pessimistic estimate of the amount of time, which we will label b.

To arrive, by this scheme, at the mean or expected amount of time required for the activity, which we will label t_e, we give the most likely amount of time a weight of 4 and the optimistic and pessimistic estimates of the amount of time a weight of 1 each. The mean or expected amount of time for the event, t_e, becomes:

$$t_e = \frac{a + 4m + b}{6}.$$

---

[2] The defense for this method of determining the mean and variance of the amount of time required for an activity is dealt with in a number of works on network analysis. See especially Robert W. Miller, *Schedule, Cost and Profit Control with PERT* (New York: McGraw-Hill, 1963), Chapter II.

In this scheme the variance, v, associated with this mean is:

$$v = \left(\frac{b - a}{6}\right)^2 .$$

Let us assume that the expected times (in weeks) for the activities portrayed in the network of Figure 10-1, and their associated variances, have been determined and that they are as shown in Figure 10-2.

FIGURE 10-2

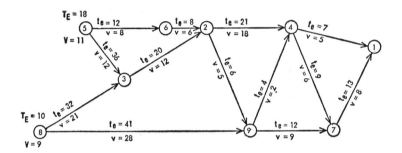

Let us also assume that estimates have been made of the amount of time required for whatever activities precede events 5 and 8, and that estimates have been made of the variances associated therewith. As shown in Figure 10-2, T_E (the earliest expected time of occurrence of completion event 5) is 18 weeks. This may best be thought of as 18 weeks after time zero, the time when the program of activities and events portrayed by our network actually gets underway.

The earliest expected time of occurrence of completion event number 8 is 10 weeks. The variances associated with the earliest expected times of occurrence of completion events 5 and 8 are 11 and 9, respectively.

We would now like to employ these data to determine the earliest expected times of occurrence, T_E, and their associated variances, V, for all the *events* in the network. The calculation of these values involves simply a traverse through the network. We reason thus:

The activity which connects events 5 and 6 cannot *begin* until 18 weeks after time zero (i.e., until after the occurrence of completion event 5, whose earliest expected time of occurrence is 18 weeks after time zero).

Since the activity which connects events 5 and 6 is expected to take 12 weeks, the earliest expected time of occurrence for event 6 is 30 weeks (18 weeks + 12 weeks) after time zero.

We calculate the variance for event 6 by adding the variance associated with its immediate predecessor event (i.e., event 5) and the variance associated with the expected time required for the activity which connects event 6 to its immediate predecessor event. Thus the variance, V, associated with the T_E for event 6 is 19 (11 + 8).

Now that we've determined T_E for event 6, we might move on and determine T_E for event 2—6's immediate successor event. It immediately occurs to us, however, that we cannot determine the earliest expected time of occurrence for event 2 solely on the basis of knowledge about event 6 because event 2 has another immediate predecessor event, namely, event 3. The T_E for event 3 and the t_e for the activity which connects 2 to 3 may pose the constraint which determines the earliest expected time of occurrence of event 2.

Having no knowledge of the T_E for event 3, we are obliged to abandon event 2 for the moment and to determine T_E for event 3. Event 3 has two immediate predecessor events: 5 and 8. To determine T_E for event 3, we simply calculate T_E for event 3 on the basis of its dependence upon event 5, then calculate T_E for event 3 on the basis of its dependence upon event 8, and reason that the earliest expected time of occurrence of event 3 is the *larger* of the two.

T_E for event 3, based on event 5, is 54; and T_E for 3 based on 8 is 42. Therefore, event 5 governs. T_E for event 3 is 54 weeks, and its associated variance is 23.

Equipped now with knowledge about event 3, we can return to event 2. Proceeding as with event 3, we find that event 3 governs for event 2, and that T_E for event 2 is 74 weeks, with an associated variance of 35.

If we continue this process we determine the T_E for each event, as shown in Table 10-1.

Since the T_E for event 1, the final completion event, is 117 weeks, the earliest expected time of completion for the full program of activities represented by the network is 117 weeks after time zero, with a variance of 67.

Table 10-1
Event Numbers

	⑧	⑤	③	⑥	②	⑨	④	⑦	①
T_E:	10	18	54	30	74	80	95	104	117
V:	9	11	23	19	35	40	53	59	67
T_L:	22	18	54	66	74	91	95	104	117
Slack:	12	0	0	36	0	11	0	0	0

We now want to determine T_L for each event. We define T_L to mean the latest expected time which a completion event can be allowed to occur without disturbing the T_E of the final event of the network. Its meaning will become more apparent as we proceed. Let us begin with event 1 and work our way back toward time zero.

If we do not want to disturb the T_E of event 1, clearly, we must cause event 7 to occur not later than 104 weeks after time zero $(117 - 13)$. The latest expected time of occurrence of event 7, i.e., T_L for event 7, is therefore 104 weeks after time zero.

Reasoning in the same fashion, T_L for event 4 is 95 weeks after time zero.

Event 9 has two immediate successor events. T_L for event 9 then would be the *smaller* of the T_L's determined from basing T_L for event 9 first on one and then the other of its two immediate successor events. If event 7 were 9's only immediate successor, T_L for event 9 could be as late as 92 weeks after time zero $(104 - 12)$. But since the latest expected time we can allow event 4 to occur without disturbing T_E for event 7 is 95 weeks after time zero, and since the activity connecting event 4 to event 9 is expected to require 4 weeks, event 9 cannot be allowed to occur later than 91 weeks after time zero $(95 - 4)$. Event 4 therefore governs, and T_L for event 9 is 91.

Continuing in this way, we calculate T_L's for all the events in our network as shown in Table 10-1.

While we spoke, in the preceding development, of T_E and T_L as the earliest and latest times after time zero that an event can occur, it should be recognized that there are variances associated with these values for T_E and T_L, and therefore that T_E and T_L are *expected* values.

Interpretation

If we assume that the distribution for our final event—of which T_E and V are two parameters—approximates a normal distribution, we can calculate the probability of our final completion event's occurring at any time short of or in excess of T_E for event 1 by our knowledge of the normal distribution. For example: approximately 68 percent of the sample of a normal distribution falls within the mean minus 1 standard deviation and the mean plus 1 standard deviation. Therefore approximately 32 percent falls outside this range. Furthermore, approximately 16 percent falls below the mean minus 1 standard deviation. Therefore, the probability that the final event will occur sooner than 108.8 weeks after time zero is 0.16 $(117 - \sqrt{67} = 108.8)$.

A major value in network analysis arises from its usefulness in pointing up improvement opportunities. Suppose, for example, that the program of activities represented by the network in Figure 10-2 is a crucial component of a larger project for which time is of the essence. Suppose it is extremely important that event 1 occur not later than 117 weeks after time zero. At this moment it is apparent that the probability of event 1's occurring by 117 weeks after time zero is only 0.5.

If we were anxious to increase the probability of event 1's occurring by 117 weeks after time zero, how should we go about it? Clearly, we would want to shorten the t_e and perhaps reduce the associated variance of one or more of the network's time-consuming activities. But all the network's activities do not present equally attractive improvement opportunities. Some are critical, and others are not.

It should be apparent that for those events which are critical their T_E's and their T_L's are the same. That is to say, the latest expected time these events can be *allowed* to occur is also the earliest expected time that they *can* occur. For these events we say there is no "slack," or that their slack is zero.

By subtracting each event's T_E from its T_L we obtain the slack, as shown in Table 10-1. Slack is largest for event 6. Under present expectations, event 6 is not expected to occur sooner than 30 weeks after time zero and cannot be allowed to occur later than 66 weeks after time zero—a slack of 36 weeks.

Event 6, therefore, is not critical. The time required for the activity which connects event 6 to event 5 could increase to 48 weeks without disturbing the expected time of occurrence of the final event.

· On the other hand, event 2 *is* critical, and an increase of 1 week in the time required for the activity which connects events 2 and 3 will increase the expected time of occurrence of the final event by 1 week.

The "critical path" through a network is made up of those events which have zero slack and the activities which connect them. In the network of Figure 10-2 the events in the critical path are: 5,3,2, 4,7, and 1.

If we wish to decrease the T_E of our final event we must focus our attention on the events in the critical path and the activities which connect these events.

An optimum "crash program" designed to decrease T_E for the final event would involve a search for the most economical means of reducing the expected times required for the activities in the critical path.

The usefulness of the computer quickly becomes apparent. If we were to obtain cost data on which to base such a search we would almost certainly find that the more we reduce a t_e for any particular activity the more costly it becomes to reduce it further. Thus while the most economical way to reduce T_E for our final event by one week might be to cut a week from the activity which connects critical events 5 and 3, the most economical way to salvage a second week might be to cut from the activity which connects critical events 2 and 4.

The problem is compounded by the fact that as we shorten t_e's we must be alert to what happens to the makeup of the critical path. As we shorten t_e's we may reduce the slack associated with noncritical events and thrust them into the critical path.

Clearly, in a network involving several hundred events, or even several dozen, this repetitive process of searching for improvement opportunities and checking for changes in the makeup of the critical path can become a massive process of data manipulation.

We have by no means touched upon the full scope of uses of network analysis. For further study in this area the reader is referred to the bibliography at the end of this chapter.

Let us develop a general computer model for network analysis. First, however, an additional word about the network in Figure 10-2 is appropriate. Notice that in this network no event has more than two immediate predecessor events and no event has more than two immediate successor events. Clearly, an event in a program of the character which business and industry continually develop can usefully be considered the completion or the beginning of more than two activities.

In the development which follows we will, however, assume that no event will ever have more than two immediate predecessor events and no event will ever have more than two immediate successor events.

By adopting this restriction we make the development of a general computer model easier. Meantime, however, we do not really make our model less general since in fact we could convert a network in which events had more than two successors and more than two predecessors into one in which events had no more than two of each by introducing "dummy" events. The two network segments below, for example, are the same:

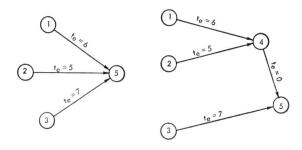

A COMPUTER MODEL FOR NETWORK ANALYSIS

The Determination of T_E

In analyzing a critical path network "by hand," we proceed from one event to another by visual observation of the arrows which connect the events in a pictorial representation of the network. At the outset we identify the final completion event, and then we scan the network backwards, toward time zero, until we finally come upon an event whose T_E is known. Upon encountering an event whose T_E is known, we wend our way forward again, calculating the T_E's of succeeding events until we finally have the T_E's of the immediate predecessors of the final event, whereupon we can determine the T_E of the final event itself. Proceeding in this way we frequently find ourselves at a junction of two activities which culminate in the same completion event. Under these circumstances we are frequently obliged to abandon our forward progress and to retreat in search of an event whose T_E is known; then we can return later to the junction and proceed forward again.

The computer cannot "see" a pictorial representation of a network; but we can, through use of associative memory, tie our events together in computer memory in a fashion precisely analogous to our use of arrows in a pictorial representation.

To see how this might be done, reason that all events, except those earliest events for which a T_E is given at the outset, may have one or two immediate predecessor events. Where an event has two immediate predecessor events, let's arbitrarily designate one of them (either one of them) as that event's first immediate predecessor event and the other as its second immediate predecessor event. When an event has only one immediate predecessor event, we will call it that event's first immediate predecessor.

We would like now to conceive of some scheme for storing all the initial data we have about the network in computer memory in such a way that the following data, applicable to each event, can be retrieved by reference to a common address in core memory:

1.   The number of the event's first immediate predecessor.
2.   The t_e associated with the event's first immediate predecessor.
3.   The v associated with the event's first immediate predecessor.
4.   The number of the event's second immediate predecessor.
5.   The t_e associated with the event's second immediate predecessor.
6.   The v associated with the event's second immediate predecessor.
7.   The T_E of the event, where known.
8.   The V associated with the event's T_E, where known.

With this kind of grouping of data, we can wend our way through the complete network, regardless of which event we start with. That is, the entire network will be "tied together" through associative memory.

Let us use a two-dimension subscripted variable for this memory storage purpose. Let us call this variable EVENT, and let us store:

in EVENT (1,M) all the data relative to event number 1,
in EVENT (2,M) "   "   "   "   "   "   "   2,
in EVENT (3,M) "   "   "   "   "   "   "   3,
etc.

Then for any one event—event N, for example—let,

EVENT(N,1) hold, as a floating-point constant, the number of event N's first immediate predecessor.

EVENT(N,2) hold the t_e associated with N's first immediate predecessor.

EVENT(N,3) hold the v associated with N's first immediate predecessor.

EVENT(N,4) hold the number of event N's second immediate predecessor.

EVENT(N,5) hold the t_e associated with N's second immediate predecessor.

EVENT(N,6) hold the v associated with N's second immediate predecessor.

EVENT(N,7) hold the T_E of event N.

EVENT(N,8) hold the V associated with event N's T_E. (If the T_E and the V of event N are unknown, we will initialize positions 7 and 8 at zero.)

It will be useful if we adopt a practice of giving the final completion event the number "1." All other events can be given any numbers we choose, without regard to the order in which the events might occur. (To conserve memory space, however, we will want to keep these numbers as small as possible; therefore, the number of the event with the largest number should equal the total number of events.)

Now, clearly, we could start with event number 1, our final event, and search backwards—inquiring if an event's T_E is known by examining the contents of the proper position of the variable EVENT (N,M)—until we find an event whose T_E is known (much as we do in the analysis of a network by hand). To avoid duplication of effort, however, it would be wise to keep track of our "path" of travel as we search, so that we can retrace our path as we move forward calculating T_E's. Let us use the one-dimension subscripted variable, PATH, for this purpose. We will let

PATH(1) hold the number of the final event (event number 1).

PATH(2) hold the number of the next event we inquire into, in search of an event whose T_E is known.

PATH(3) hold the number of the next event we inquire into, in search of an event whose T_E is known. Etc.

All positions of PATH(K) might best be initialized at zero. As we work our way backwards, toward time zero, we can replace the zeros with the numbers of the events we have inquired into, and then as we work our way forward, we can return these positions to zero, and thus "empty" them as we retrace our steps.

Let us focus our attention for the moment solely on the construc-

tion of a computer program which will digest the initial data we
have concerning our network and which will calculate and store the
T_E's of all the events in the network. Essentially, we will want to
compose a computer program which will do what is called for
broadly in the flow diagram of Figure 10-3. (In addition to reading
in initial data relative to the events themselves, we should provide
for counting and storing, in the variable NTOTAL, the number of
events read into the network.)

A computer program suitable for calculating and storing the T_E's
of all events appears in Figure 10-4.

The Determination of T_L

In determining the value of T_L for an event, we will want to proceed much as we did in determining the value of T_E. However, to
determine an event's T_L we need to know the identity of its immediate *successor* events and the t_e's associated with these successors. We
did not provide this information as part of the input data applicable
to each event at the beginning of our program. We might do well
to record those data now.

Let us add these data in the array EVENT(N,M). We will let

EVENT(N,9) hold the number of N's first immediate successor.
EVENT(N,10) hold the t_e associated with N's first immediate suc-
        cessor.
EVENT(N,11) hold the number of N's second immediate successor.
EVENT(N,12) hold the t_e associated with N's second immediate
        successor.

These positions had best be initialized, at the beginning of our program, at zero.

Whether we designate an event the first immediate successor or
the second immediate successor is unimportant. Also, it will become
apparent that it is of no consequence if event A is considered event
B's first immediate *predecessor* while B is considered event A's second immediate *successor*.

We might begin with event number 1 (the final event), record its
status as an immediate successor in either position 9 and 10 or 11 and
12 of its first immediate predecessor, and record its status as an
immediate successor in either position 9 and 10 or 11 and 12 of its
second immediate predecessor, then go to event number 2 and repeat

FIGURE 10-3

Flow Diagram for Determining TE's in a Network
(IP = Immediate Predecessor)

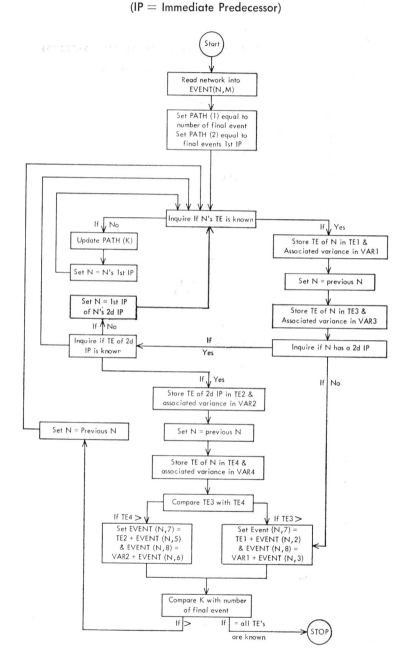

FIGURE 10-4

Program Segment for Calculating and Storing TE's for All Events

```
*
        DIMENSION EVENT (100,20),PATH(100),J(100),E(100)
        NTOTAL = 0.0
  100 READ 1, NUMBER,(EVENT(NUMBER,N),N=1,8)
    1 FORMAT (16,8F6.1)
        NTOTAL = NTOTAL + 1
        IF(NUMBER - 999)100,2,2
    2 NTOTAL = NTOTAL - 1
        K=1
        PATH(K)=1.0
        N=EVENT(1,1)
    3 IF(EVENT(N,7))4,4,5
    4 K=K+1
        PATH(K)=EVENT(N,1)
        N=EVENT(N,1)
        GO TO 3
    5 TE1=EVENT(N,7)
        VAR1=EVENT(N,8)
        K=K-1
        N=PATH(K)
        TE3=TE1+EVENT(N,2)
        VAR3=VAR1+EVENT(N,3)
        IF(EVENT(N,4))6,6,7
    6 EVENT(N,7)=TE1+EVENT(N,2)
        EVENT(N,8)=VAR1+EVENT(N,3)
        GO TO 11
    7 K=K+1
        PATH(K)=EVENT(N,4)
        N=EVENT(N,4)
        IF(EVENT(N,7))4,4,8
    8 TE2=EVENT(N,7)
        VAR2=EVENT(N,8)
        K=K-1
        N=PATH(K)
        TE4=TE2+EVENT(N,5)
        VAR4=VAR2+EVENT(N,6)
        IF(TE3-TE4)9,9,10
    9 EVENT(N,7)=TE2+EVENT(N,5)
        EVENT(N,8)=VAR2+EVENT(N,6)
        GO TO 11
   10 EVENT(N,7)=TE1+EVENT(N,2)
        EVENT(N,8)=VAR1+EVENT(N,3)
   11 IF(K-1)13,13,12
   12 K=K-1
        N=PATH(K)
        GO TO 3
   13 CONTINUE
```

this process, proceeding in this fashion until every event's status as an immediate successor of one or more other events is fully recorded.

We need a computer program which will do what is called for in the flow diagram of Figure 10-5. Figure 10-6 presents such a program.

FIGURE 10-5

Flow Diagram for Recording Identity of Immediate Successor (IS) Events

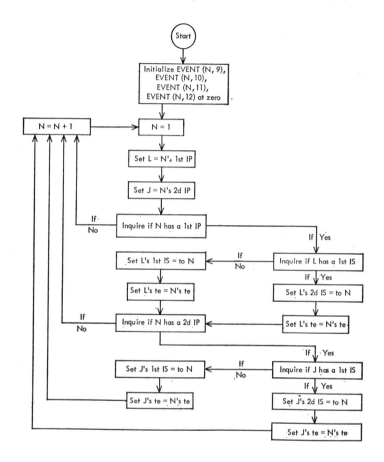

We are now equipped to calculate the T_L's for all the events in the network. The data we will need are stored as follows:

EVENT(N,1) holds the number of N's first immediate predecessor.
EVENT(N,4) holds the number of N's second immediate predecessor.
EVENT(N,9) holds the number of N's first immediate successor.
EVENT(N,10) holds the t_e associated with N's first successor.
EVENT(N,11) holds the number of N's second immediate successor.
EVENT(N,12) holds the t_e associated with N's second successor.

We will want to design a program segment which will calculate for each event its T_L and store it in position: EVENT(N,13).

FIGURE 10-6

Program Segment for Recording the Identity of the Immediate
Successors of Each Event

```
        DO 14  N = 1,NTOTAL
        EVENT(N,  9) = 0.0
        EVENT(N,10) = 0.0
        EVENT(N,11) = 0.0
14      EVENT(N,12) = 0.0
        DO 22  N = 1,NTOTAL
        L = EVENT(N,1)
        J = EVENT(N,4)
        IF(L)22,22,15
15      IF(EVENT(L,9))16,16,17
16      EVENT(L,9) = N
        EVENT(L,10) = EVENT(N,2)
        GO TO 18
17      EVENT(L,11) = N
        EVENT(L,12) = EVENT(N,2)
18      IF(J)22,22,19
19      IF  (EVENT(J,9))20,20,21
20      EVENT(J,9) = N
        EVENT(J,10) = EVENT(N,5)
        GO TO 22
21      EVENT(J,11) = N
        EVENT(J,12) = EVENT(N,5)
22      CONTINUE
```

A procedure such as that employed in the flow diagram of Figure 10-7 should do this for us. Notice that we will keep track of events which we abandon, in pursuit of an event with a known T_L, in the array PATH(K), much as before when we were calculating each event's T_E. However, the record we store in PATH(K) will never be very long. If we employ the procedure suggested in Figure 10-7, and if we begin our inquiry with the final event, then we will find ourselves simply calculating the T_L of each event's immediate predecessors before proceeding toward time zero. Thus the procedure suggested in Figure 10-7 essentially duplicates the procedure we would employ in a "hand" solution.

In Figure 10-8 is a computer program which should do what is required. By the time of completion (computer execution) of this added segment to our total program, the T_E's of all events and the T_L's of all events will have been stored in the appropriate positions of array EVENT(N,M).

FIGURE 10-7

Flow Diagram for Determining T_L's in Network
(IS = Immediate Successor)

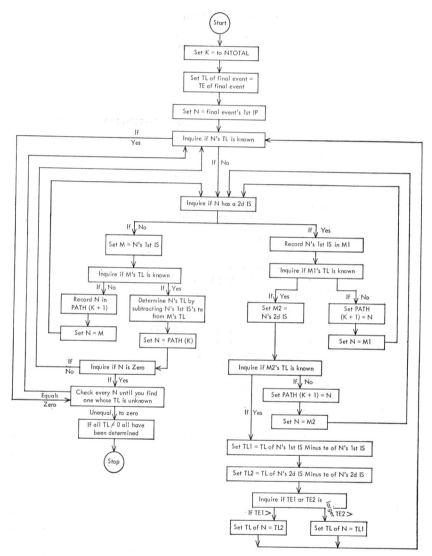

Calculating slack, now that T_E's and T_L's have been determined, is a simple matter:

$$\text{DO } 39 \ N = 1, \text{NTOTAL}$$
$$39 \quad \text{EVENT}(N,14) = \text{EVENT}(N,13) - \text{EVENT}(N,7).$$

FIGURE 10-8

Program Segment for Calculating T_L's of Each Event

```
      K=NTOTAL
      EVENT(1,13)=EVENT(1,7)
      N=EVENT(1,1)
23    IF(EVENT(N,13))24,24,29
24    IF(EVENT(N,11))25,25,31
25    M=EVENT(N,9)
      IF(EVENT(M,13))26,26,27
26    K=K+1
      PATH(K)=N
      N=M
      GO TO 24
27    EVENT(N,13)=EVENT(M,13)-EVENT(N,10)
28    N=PATH(K)
      IF(N)29,29,23
29    DO 30  N9=1,NTOTAL
      N=N9
      IF(EVENT(N,13))24,24,30
30    CONTINUE
      GO TO 38
31    M1=EVENT(N,9)
      IF(EVENT(M1,13))32,32,33
32    K=K+1
      PATH(K)=N
      N=M1
      GO TO 24
33    M2=EVENT(N,11)
      IF  (EVENT(M2,13))34,34,35
34    K=K+1
      PATH(K)=N
      N=M2
      GO TO 24
35    TL1=EVENT(M1,13)-EVENT(N,10)
      TL2=EVENT(M2,13)-EVENT(N,12)
      IF(TL1-TL2)36,36,37
36    EVENT(N,13)=TL1
      GO TO 28
37    EVENT(N,13)=TL2
      GO TO 28
38    CONTINUE
```

It would be useful, for purposes of interpretation, if we provide for having the computer print out values for T_E, slack, and variance in order of earliest T_E's. With a few added statements we can cause to be stored in the various positions of J(L) the numbers of the various events in our network, with the event with the smallest T_E in position 1, the event with the next smallest T_E in position 2, etc.:

```
      DO 40  M = 1,NTOTAL
40    E(M) = EVENT(M,7)
      DO 43  L = 1,NTOTAL
      A = E(1)
      K = 1
      DO 42  M = 2,NTOTAL
      IF(E(M) − A)41,42,42
```

$$41 \quad A = E(M)$$
$$K = M$$
$$42 \quad CONTINUE$$
$$J(L) = K$$
$$43 \quad E(K) = 9999.9$$

With a suitable PRINT and FORMAT statement combination we can cause our print-out to appear as we desire. In Figure 10-9 is a complete program for analyzing a PERT network, composed of

FIGURE 10-9

Program for PERT Network Analysis

```
      DIMENSION EVENT(100,20),PATH(100),J(100),E(100)
      NTOTAL = 0.0
100   READ 1, NUMBER,(EVENT(NUMBER,N),N=1,8)
1     FORMAT (I6,8F6.1)
      NTOTAL = NTOTAL + 1
      IF(NUMBER -999)100,2,2
2     NTOTAL = NTOTAL - 1
      K=1
      PATH(K)=1.0
      K=K+1
      PATH(K)=EVENT(1,1)
      N=EVENT(1,1)
3     IF(EVENT(N,7))4,4,5
4     K=K+1
      PATH(K)=EVENT(N,1)
      N=EVENT(N,1)
      GO TO 3
5     TE1=EVENT(N,7)
      VAR1=EVENT(N,8)
      K=K-1
      N=PATH(K)
      TE3=TE1+EVENT(N,2)
      VAR3=VAR1+EVENT(N,3)
      IF(EVENT(N,4))6,6,7
6     EVENT(N,7)=TE1+EVENT(N,2)
      EVENT(N,8)=VAR1+EVENT(N,3)
      GO TO 11
7     K=K+1
      PATH(K)=EVENT(N,4)
      N=EVENT(N,4)
      IF(EVENT(N,7))4,4,8
8     TE2=EVENT(N,7)
      VAR2=EVENT(N,8)
      K=K-1
      N=PATH(K)
      TE4=TE2+EVENT(N,5)
      VAR4=VAR2+EVENT(N,6)
      IF(TE3-TE4)9,9,10
9     EVENT(N,7)=TE2+EVENT(N,5)
      EVENT(N,8)=VAR2+EVENT(N,6)
      GO TO 11
10    EVENT(N,7)=TE1+EVENT(N,2)
      EVENT(N,8)=VAR1+EVENT(N,3)
11    IF(K-1)13,13,12
12    K=K-1
      N=PATH(K)
      GO TO 3
13    CONTINUE
```

our previously designed program segments, including our "sorter," above, and with our input data added. Notice that it does not matter in what order the input data deck is introduced. We have made provision for a final "dummy" card, referring to fictitious event number 999, to indicate that we have come to the end of the deck and the data relative to all events have been read into the array EVENT(M,N). The dummy card should, of course, be placed at the bottom of the data deck, but the cards presenting data relative to all other events in the network may be shuffled in any fashion.

FIGURE 10-9 (Continued)

```
      DO 14 N=1,NTOTAL
      EVENT(N, 9)=0.0
      EVENT(N,10)=0.0
      EVENT(N,11)=0.0
  14  EVENT(N,12)=0.0
      DO 22 N=1,NTOTAL
      L=EVENT(N,1)
      J=EVENT(N,4)
      IF(L)22,22,15
  15  IF(EVENT(L,9))16,16,17
  16  EVENT(L,9)=N
      EVENT(L,10)=EVENT(N,2)
      GO TO 18
  17  EVENT(L,11)=N
      EVENT(L,12)=EVENT(N,2)
  18  IF(J)22,22,19
  19  IF(EVENT(J,9))20,20,21
  20  EVENT(J,9)=N
      EVENT(J,10)=EVENT(N,5)
      GO TO 22
  21  EVENT(J,11)=N
      EVENT(J,12)=EVENT(N,5)
  22  CONTINUE
      K=NTOTAL
      EVENT(1,13)=EVENT(1,7)
      N=EVENT(1,1)
  23  IF(EVENT(N,13))24,24,29
  24  IF(EVENT(N,11))25,25,31
  25  M=EVENT(N,9)
      IF(EVENT(M,13))26,26,27
  26  K=K+1
      PATH(K)=N
      N=M
      GO TO 24
  27  EVENT(N,13)=EVENT(M,13)-EVENT(N,10)
  28  N=PATH(K)
      IF(N)29,29,23
  29  DO 30 N9=1,NTOTAL
      N=N9
      IF(EVENT(N,13))24,24,30
  30  CONTINUE
      GO TO 38
  31  M1=EVENT(N,9)
      IF(EVENT(M1,13))32,32,33
  32  K=K+1
      PATH(K)=N
      N=M1
      GO TO 24
  33  M2=EVENT(N,11)
```

FIGURE 10-9 (Continued)

```
    IF(EVENT(M2,13))34,34,35
34 K=K+1
   PATH(K)=N
   N=M2
   GO TO 24
35 TL1=EVENT(M1,13)-EVENT(N,10)
   TL2=EVENT(M2,13)-EVENT(N,12)
   IF(TL1-TL2)36,36,37
36 EVENT(N,13)=TL1
   GO TO 28
37 EVENT(N,13)=TL2
   GO TO 28
38 CONTINUE
   DO 39 N=1,NTOTAL
39 EVENT(N,14)=EVENT(N,13)-EVENT(N,7)
   DO 40 M= 1,NTOTAL
40 E(M)=EVENT(M,7)
   DO 43,L=1,NTOTAL
   A=E(1)
   K=1
   DO 42 M=2,NTOTAL
   IF(E(M)-A)41,42,42
41 A=E(M)
   K = M
42 CONTINUE
   J(L) = K
43 E(K)=9999.9
   PRINT 44
44 FORMAT(1H0,9HEVENT NO.,7X,2HTE,7X,5HSLACK,7X,8HVARIANCE)
   DO 45 L=1,NTOTAL
   N=J(L)
45 PRINT 46,N,EVENT(N,7),EVENT(N,14),EVENT(N,8)
46 FORMAT(1H0,2X,I3,8X,F6.1,4X,F6.1,7X,F6.1)
   STOP
   END
   END
```

```
  3   8.0   32.0   21.0    5.0   36.0   12.0   00.0   00.0
  7   4.0   09.0   06.0    9.0   12.0   09.0   00.0   00.0
  4   2.0   21.0   18.0    9.0   04.0   02.0   00.0   00.0
  2   6.0   08.0   06.0    3.0   20.0   12.0   00.0   00.0
  5   0.0   00.0   00.0    0.0   00.0   00.0   18.0   11.0
  8   0.0   00.0   00.0    0.0   00.0   00.0   10.0   09.0
  6   5.0   12.0   08.0    0.0   00.0   00.0   00.0   00.0
  1   4.0   07.0   05.0    7.0   13.0   08.0   00.0   00.0
  9   2.0   06.0   05.0    8.0   41.0   28.0   00.0   00.0
999   0.0   00.0   00.0    0.0   00.0   00.0   00.0   00.0
```

Notice that in the DIMENSION statement we have made provision for only 100 events. To increase the capacity of the program to handle larger networks (limited only by computer memory space available) we would want to increase the space reserved for the various variables mentioned in the DIMENSION statement.

Notice also that in the DIMENSION statement we have made provision for storing for each event not just 14 bits of information but rather 20. Later we might want to read in additional information concerning the cost of shortening the t_e's associated with the immediate predecessors of each event. By doing this we could add a program segment which would cause the computer to determine the most economical means for reducing the time required for completion of the total network of events; that is, for reducing the T_E of the final event.

Data Deck

A further word about the input data, as arranged in the program of Figure 10-9, would be appropriate. As suggested previously, *all* the data required for fully analyzing the network can be read into the computer if the essential data about each event are read into the computer *in association with* that event. In the program of Figure 10-9 we provide for punching all the data pertaining to an event on one card, and thus we will have as many data cards as we have events (plus one for the final "dummy" event). Each of the data fields is 6 columns wide; provision is made for punching the number of the event as an integer constant in the first field, and for punching all other data relative to that event in the remaining columns as floating point constants.

In the second data field is punched the number of the event's first immediate predecessor. In the third data field is punched the t_e associated with the event's first immediate predecessor. In the fourth field is punched the variance associated with this t_e. In the fifth field is punched the number of the event's second immediate predecessor. In the sixth field, the t_e associated with the event's second immediate predecessor is punched, and in the seventh field, the variance associated with this t_e.

Where an event has no second immediate predecessor, a zero is punched in the fifth, sixth, and seventh data fields.

In the eighth field is punched the T_E of the event, when that is known, and in the ninth field is punched the variance associated with that T_E.

Where an event's T_E and variance are unknown, zeros are punched in the eighth and ninth fields.

The solution to the network of Figure 10-2, as analyzed by the program in Figure 10-9, appears in Figure 10-10.

SHORT-TERM FORECASTING

PERT network analysis is a particularly important part of the planning process when the system is characterized by a number of dissimilar, nonrepetitive activities or projects. For short range plan-

FIGURE 10-10

EVENT NO.	TE	SLACK	VARIANCE
8	10.0	12.0	9.0
5	18.0	.0	11.0
6	30.0	36.0	19.0
3	54.0	.0	23.0
2	74.0	.0	35.0
9	80.0	11.0	40.0
4	95.0	.0	53.0
7	104.0	.0	59.0
1	117.0	.0	67.0

ning, when the system is characterized by a more repetitive process, statistical forecasting techniques are particularly useful. Preparatory to building "total system" models we should acquaint ourselves with some of these techniques.

We have already dealt rather fully with processes—phenomena which change in some continuous way through time. The compound interest model, $S = P(1 + R)^N$, describes a discrete, deterministic process in which the amount of growth during a period of time is a function of size: the amount of interest added during a period depends on the size of P at the beginning of that period. When interest is compounded continuously we have a continuous, deterministic process.

The Poisson model,

$$p(r) = \frac{e^{-\lambda}(\lambda)^r}{r!},$$

describes a discrete, stochastic process in which positive integer variables are distributed according to a particular pattern called the Poisson distribution.

The following model—the probability density function of the normal distribution,

$$f(x) = \frac{1}{\sigma\sqrt{2\pi}} e^{-\frac{1}{2}\left[\frac{x-m}{\sigma}\right]^2}$$

—describes a continuous stochastic process in which variables (i.e., x) ranging from minus infinity to plus infinity are distributed "symmetrically" about a mean, m.

Determining the precise output of a deterministic process at some specific future moment in time is simply a matter of computation. Thus, given our initial deposit at time zero, and the interest rate, we can calculate precisely the magnitude of our deposit after some specified period of time has elapsed.

Determining the precise output of a stochastic process at some specific future moment in time is impossible; for example, we cannot determine precisely what the nth variable—which either a Poisson or a normal process is generating—will be. We can, of course, use our knowledge of a specific stochastic process to determine the probabilities associated with a variety of possible outputs and to determine expected values, and hence to improve the quality of our decisions. We did this in our discussion of the inventory problem under uncertainty and in our study of queuing systems.

In our study of the inventory problem under uncertainty (Chapter 6) we were dealing with a stochastic process which was *given*. Thus, it was assumed in the Brown Electronics Company model that daily demand was being generated by a stochastic process with the following probability distribution:

Demand per Day (Units)	Probability
0	.4
1	.3
2	.2
3	.1

Using Monte Carlo simulation, we combined our knowledge of this process with our knowledge of the process which was assumed to generate lead time for Brown Electronics Company to determine the distribution of the process generating demand during lead time.

In a similar way, in our study of queuing systems (Chapters 7 and 9) we used our knowledge of the process which was assumed to generate customer arrivals and our knowledge of the process which was assumed to generate service time in a service facility to determine the distribution of the process generating queues, total time in the system per customer, etc.

In these studies we have always assumed that the parameters of the processes we dealt with were known and that they were constant.[3]

---

[3] Or, if not constant, that their rate of change was known, and hence that their values at any moment in time could be determined.

Our task, given this knowledge, was to determine specific things about the behavior of the systems we were studying so as to provide a basis for sound decision making.

What if we know that the process is constant but we do not know *all* the parameters? Suppose, for example, we are quite confident that the daily demand in a particular market system is being generated by a normal process, and that that process is constant in the sense that the mean and standard deviation do not change through time; but suppose we do not know the values of the mean and the standard deviation. If we wanted to study, through simulation, the behavior of the system of which this daily demand generator is an element, we would want to try to determine the mean and the standard deviation. The mean, by definition, is the simple arithmetic average of the variables generated. We could estimate the mean demand of this process by taking the average of the daily demands after the system has operated for a large number of days. The mean, so determined, might be the true mean of the process generating our daily demands; then again, it might not be. The larger our sample of days of observation, the more closely our sample mean should approximate the true mean.

By analysis of the same sample data we could also estimate the standard deviation of the process, and the larger the sample the more closely our sample standard deviation should approximate the real standard deviation.

If one found himself dealing with a process which was constant in this sense, the logical course would be to employ all past daily demand observations in estimating the unknown parameters. Each day a new estimate could be made on the basis of a new sample, a sample larger than its predecessor by one observation. As time passes, the accuracy of the estimates should improve. However, life is not so simple. Most real systems are characterized by processes whose parameters are unknown and changing. Under these conditions, estimating the parameters of a process on the basis of current and past observations is useful, but, since one or more of the parameters may be changing, observations in the remote past are relatively useless.

We are not prepared to disregard all past observations, of course, because only by averaging can we prevent random fluctuations (noise) from obscuring the parameters of the underlying process entirely. If we assume that change in one or more of the parameters of the process is itself a somewhat orderly process—and we do this when we perceive order rather than complete chaos in our environment—we assert that information from the recent past is quite significant. As a matter of fact, we tend to assume that in the short run the process is a constant process with unchanging parameters.

Forecasting, in this sense, is a matter of estimating what future observations will be (i.e., what the parameters of the process are), assuming the underlying process continues as it has in the recent past.

Essentially, the averaging of past data is a smoothing process which has as its purpose the filtering out of random fluctuations, or noise, in order to reveal the parameters of the underlying process. We get more filtering when we employ more observations. But the larger the sample, the older some of it will be. The more heavily we rely on data from the remote past, the more we discount data in the recent past. This means that changes in the process are detected less quickly.

The basic question in smoothing is: What degree of reliance on past data will maximize the advantages of quick response to process change on the one hand, and the advantages of noise filtration on the other hand?

The Moving Average

One smoothing process, useful for forecasting, involves the moving average. Using the moving average, one simply employs the most recent n observations to calculate an average, which is the forecast for the next period. Suppose, for example, that the following data represented recent daily demand in a given market system:

Date	Actual Demand
Jan. 1	46
" 2	54
" 3	53
" 4	46
" 5	58
" 6	49

We might average these six observations as a means of arriving at a forecast for demand on January 7:

$$\frac{46 + 54 + 53 + 46 + 58 + 49}{6} = 51.$$

On January 7, suppose actual demand proved to be 54, meaning a forecast error on our part of 3. Our new moving average—our forecast for January 8—would now involve the six demand data from January 2 to January 7, inclusive:

$$\frac{54 + 53 + 46 + 58 + 49 + 54}{6} = 52.3.$$

Our thought process in the above can be summed up thus:

On January 6 we forecast that demand on January 7 would be 51. On January 7 demand actually proved to be 54, and we had therefore underestimated the demand by 3. We do not believe that the inaccuracy in our estimate is attributable solely to a change in the process generating our demand; i.e., that the mean of that process rose from 51 to 54 in one day. Nor do we believe that the inaccuracy is attributable solely to random fluctuations; i.e., that the process has not changed. Lacking any thoroughly satisfactory way of sorting out what portion of the inaccuracy can be attributed to each of these elements, we will assume that the excess of the actual demand on January 7 over our estimate of it is partly attributable to:

1. The fact that the mean of the demand-generating process was possibly already higher than our estimate of it on January 6.
2. The fact that the mean of the demand-generating process actually *rose* from January 6 to January 7.
3. Random fluctuations in the demand-generating process which have caused the actual demand on January 7 to be above the true mean.

Under these circumstances, we reason, let us raise our previous estimate of the mean of the process to something less than the actual demand on January 7.

Now let us go back to January 6 and again forecast the demand for January 7, using the moving average again; but this time let us use only the most recent three observations to determine the forecast, those observations pertaining to January 4, 5, and 6. We would have:

$$\frac{46 + 58 + 49}{3} = 51.$$

If we continue to conform to this new sample size, on January 7 we would make a new forecast, thus:

$$\frac{58 + 49 + 54}{3} = 53.6.$$

With this smaller sample, our thought process is much the same as before except that this time we have allowed ourselves to be more heavily influenced by our actual demand experience on January 7. When we employed a 6-day sample, each of the 6 demand observations got equal weight in our moving average. Therefore "old" data received a weight of 5/6 and our current observation (the demand on January 7) got a weight of 1/6.

When we employed a 3-day sample, each of the 3 demand observations got equal weight in our moving average also, but the "old" data received only a weight of 2/3, whereas our current observation received a weight of 1/3.

Our choice of the number of periods to employ in a moving average is a measure of the relative importance we attach to old versus current data. Clearly, if we feel the process is changing slowly, we should adopt a large sample and get greater noise filtering with little sacrifice in change response. On the other hand, if we feel the process is changing rapidly, we should adopt a small sample and get greater change response.

In forecasting with the moving average, the accuracy of the forecast is dependent upon the number of observations, and the optimum number of observations depends upon the rate of change in the process.

Exponential Smoothing

For two reasons the moving average is not as attractive, as a forecasting system, as it might be:

1. With the moving average all data in the sample are weighted equally. If more recent data is more valid than older data, why not give it greater weight?
2. Estimating by the moving average requires that we retain a good deal of data, carrying it along with us from forecast period to forecast period.

In computer work, carrying data along can be inconvenient. Admittedly, in the moving average we could shorten our calculations a bit. Thus in the example above, involving 6 observations, we could arrive at our new forecast by adding to the old forecast 1/6 of the new observation and subtracting 1/6 of the oldest observation. But we still must keep all 6 observations stored and must update the record with each new forecast. If our optimum sample is believed to be several hundred observations, or more (as it sometimes is), this could be a bit inconvenient.

Exponential smoothing gets around these disadvantages. In exponential smoothing we assign weights to observations in indirect proportion to their age, thus being faithful to our conviction that in a changing process recent data is more valid than older data. Furthermore, in exponential smoothing we need only the current forecast, a smoothing constant, and the new observation in order to determine the new forecast, thus eliminating the need for carrying large lists of past data.

In exponential smoothing, the new forecast is the old forecast plus a fraction of the difference between the new observation and the old forecast. The fraction by which the difference between the new observation and the old forecast is discounted is called the smoothing constant, generally designated by the Greek letter *alpha, α*.

We might employ exponential smoothing to get day-to-day demand forecasts from the demand data employed earlier when we discussed the moving average. Let us assume that our smoothing factor is 0.3, and that on December 31 our forecast for demand on January 1 was 51. Our daily demand forecasts for these and succeeding days would be as shown in Table 10-2.

TABLE 10-2

Date	Smoothed Exponential Forecast of Next Day's Demand (i.e., the Forecast of the *Mean* of the Process)	Actual Demand	Forecast Error (i.e., Actual Demand Less Forecast Demand)
Dec. 31	51.0	—	—
Jan. 1	49.5	46	—5.0
" 2	50.9	54	4.5
" 3	51.5	53	2.1
" 4	49.9	46	—5.5
" 5	52.3	58	8.1
" 6	51.3	49	—3.3
" 7	52.1	54	2.7

When we forecast we are really estimating what we believe to be the mean (or, as we shall see shortly, the variance or standard deviation) of the process which we believe is currently generating our demand. Let us refer to that estimate when it is arrived at by exponential smoothing as the "smoothed exponential mean," or SEM.

What we've done in the table above can be expressed by the following general model:

$$SEM_{new} = SEM_{old} + \alpha \text{ (Actual Demand} - SEM_{old}).$$

Our new forecast is the old forecast plus a correction which is proportional to the error in our previous forecast.

It will be more convenient to rearrange some of the terms in this model and to express SEM thus:

$$SEM_{new} = \alpha(\text{Actual Demand}) + (1 - \alpha)SEM_{old}.$$

In using this model SEM_{old} is the immediate predecessor forecast of SEM_{new}. If the new forecast in a sequence of forecasts happened to be the fourth of the sequence, then the old forecast would be the third. Therefore we could write:

$$SEM_4 = \alpha(\text{Actual Demand}_3) + (1 - \alpha)SEM_3;$$

but since:

$$SEM_3 = \alpha(\text{Actual Demand}_2) + (1 - \alpha)SEM_2,$$

then SEM_4 becomes:

$$SEM_4 = \alpha(\text{Actual Demand}_3) + (1 - \alpha) [\alpha(\text{Actual Demand}_2) + (1 - \alpha)SEM_2]$$
$$= \alpha(\text{Actual Demand}_3) + \alpha(\text{Actual Demand}_2) (1 - \alpha) + (1 - \alpha)^2 SEM_2.$$

Continuing, since:

$$SEM_2 = \alpha(\text{Actual Demand}_1) + (1 - \alpha)SEM_1,$$

SEM_4 becomes:

$$SEM_4 = \alpha(\text{Actual Demand}_3) + \alpha(\text{Actual Demand}_2) (1 - \alpha) + \alpha(\text{Actual Demand}_1) (1 - \alpha)^2 + (1 - \alpha)^3 SEM_1.$$

But, finally,

$$SEM_1 = \alpha(\text{Actual Demand}_0) + (1 - \alpha)SEM_0.$$

where SEM_0 is the initial estimate of the mean of the process. From the definition of the exponential smoothed forecast, it is apparent that one must *begin* with a forecast prior to getting the first datum. Actually, the first exponential forecast might be a moving average of past data, or even a subjective judgment.

Now we can finally write:

$$\text{SEM}_4 = \alpha(\text{Actual Demand}_3) + \alpha(\text{Actual Demand}_2)\,(1 - \alpha) +$$
$$\alpha(\text{Actual Demand}_1)\,(1 - \alpha)^2 + \alpha(\text{Actual Demand}_0)$$
$$(1 - \alpha)^3 + (1 - \alpha)^4\text{SEM}_0.$$

By inference, we can write the general model for the nth forecast (factoring out the smoothing constant α):

$$\text{SEM}_n = \alpha[\text{Actual Demand}_{n-1} + \text{Actual Demand}_{n-2}\,(1 - \alpha) +$$
$$\text{Actual Demand}_{n-3}(1 - \alpha)^2 + \ldots \text{Actual Demand}_0$$
$$(1 - \alpha)^{n-1}] + (1 - \alpha)^n\text{SEM}_0.$$

The nature of exponential smoothing is readily apparent from the general model above: the weights given actual observations (values for actual demand in our model) decrease as the observations get older. The most recent observation gets a weight of α. The observation one period old gets a weight of $\alpha(1 - \alpha)$. The observation two-periods-old gets a weight of $\alpha(1 - \alpha)^2$, etc.

If $\alpha = 0.3$, the four most recent observations get weights as shown in Table 10-3:

Table 10-3

	Weight
Current observation	0.3
Observation 1 period old	0.21
" 2 " "	0.147
" 3 " "	0.103
" 4 " "	0.072

A plot of the weights assigned to observations, given that $\alpha = 0.3$, yields an exponential curve; hence the term "exponential smoothing" (see Figure 10-10).

FIGURE 10-10

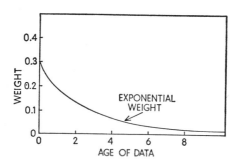

In exponential smoothing, the discounting of past observations is geometrically proportional to their ages, so that *some* weight is given to even the most remote observation. With a moving average involving n past observations, all observations more remote than the nth-most-remote observation get a weight of 0. However, by proper selection of the smoothing constant, α, it is possible to get essentially the same results (i.e., a forecast with the same variance from actual observations) from exponential smoothing that one gets from the moving average.

Let us develop this relationship.

In a moving average the age of the current observation is 0, the age of the one before that is 1, the age of the one before that is 2, etc. In a moving average of n observations, each of the n observations gets the same weight $(1/n)$ regardless of its age. Let us define the average age of the n observations employed in a moving average thus:

$$\text{Average Age} = \frac{0 + 1 + 2 + \ldots n - 1}{n} = \frac{n - 1}{2}.$$

In exponential smoothing, older data gets less weight, but a concept of average age analogous to the definition above for the moving average might be as follows:

$$0 \times \alpha + 1\alpha \times (1 - \alpha) + 2\alpha \times (1 - \alpha)^2 \ldots.$$

The sum of the above terms, as the number of observations approaches infinity, is: $(1 - \alpha)/\alpha$.

We might now define an exponential smoothing system as being equivalent to an n observation moving average if the average ages of their observations are the same, or:

$$\frac{n - 1}{2} = \frac{(1 - \alpha)}{\alpha}.$$

Solving for α we get:

$$\alpha = \frac{2}{n + 1}.$$

We can use the expression above to determine the smoothing constant required if we wish our smoothed exponential forecasts to be equivalent to forecasts obtained by using a moving average involving n observations. Several smoothing constants and the values for n in an equivalent moving average system are shown in Table 10-4.

Table 10-4

Smoothing Constant, α	Corresponding Number of Observations in a Moving Average, n
0.05	39
0.10	19
0.15	12
0.20	9
0.25	7
0.30	5.7
0.35	4.7
0.40	4
0.45	3.4
0.50	3

The variance of the estimates will be approximately the same whether one uses the moving average or exponential smoothing, provided the sample size n and smoothing constant α are related as shown in Table 10-4.[4]

Table 10-3 makes clear the way in which the choice of α influences the weight which older observations get. The smaller the smoothing constant, the more heavily older observations are weighted.

Since we are likely to distrust a sample consisting of only three or four observations in most real processes in business and economics, we will find that our choice for α will generally lie in the range $0.05 \leqq \alpha \leqq 0.30$.

The Impulse Response

We can gain further insight into the nature of exponential smoothing, and particularly the way it contrasts with the moving average, by addressing ourselves at this point to a very important systems concept: the impulse response.

In our discussion of exponential smoothing thus far we've assumed that in the short run the process whose mean we are trying to estimate can be considered constant.

Let us assume that the process generating our demand data has been constant for a long while, and that the mean of that process is

---

[4] This analogy applies only where the process is constant. Thus we could not eliminate seasonal variation from 12 monthly observations by using a smoothing constant of 0.15, whereas we could eliminate seasonal variation from these observations by using a moving average involving $n = 12$ observations.

10. Had we kept track of our forecast errors (see Table 10-2) we could assume that they would add up to 0, since daily demand fluctuations are pure noise in a constant or stable process. Similarly, we might assume that our smoothed exponential mean (the forecast) has been 10 for the past two periods.

Now let us assume that at time zero the mean of the process jumps to 20, but that the next day it returns again to 10, giving us an "impulse" of 10.

Let us assume that we are using, in our forecasting system, a smoothing constant of 0.3. How might the impulse be expected to affect our smoothed forecasts in the immediate future? Now, we know in fact that the demand datum generated when the mean of the process jumped to 20 might be *any* number, since it still generates noise. However, we have posed the question: "How might the impulse *be expected* to affect our smoothed forecasts in the immediate future?" We are, therefore, dealing with *expected values*. Hence, in inquiring about the *impulse response* of our forecasting system, we can concern ourselves only with the mean before, at the time of, and after the impulse.

Employing our exponential smoothing system with $\alpha = 0.3$, we can calculate the value of SEM at the end of the day the impulse occurred:

$$\text{SEM}_{new} = \alpha(\text{Actual Demand}) + (1 - \alpha)\text{SEM}_{old} = 0.3(20) + 0.7(10) = 13.$$

Continuing, our SEM for the next period would be:

$$\text{SEM}_{new} = 0.3(10) + 0.7(13) = 12.1.$$

Table 10-5 shows the forecasts provided by our forecasting system immediately before, during, and after the impulse.

Table 10-5

Time Period	Mean of the Process	Smoothed Exponential Mean (SEM) of the Forecast
−2	10	10
−1	10	10
0	20	13
1	10	12.1
2	10	11.47
3	10	11.03
4	10	10.72
5	10	

By plotting these values for SEM we get an *impulse response curve* for our forecasting system (Figure 10-11):

FIGURE 10-11*

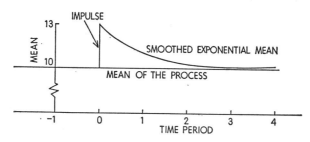

---

* Had our mean before the impulse been zero, and had the impulse been of *unit* magnitude, the immediate response would be a rise in our SEM equal to our smoothing constant, deteriorating exponentially and approaching, but never returning to zero.

The Step Response

Suppose that, instead of an impulse in the mean, our process sustained a sudden rise which lasted indefinitely. We would then have a step rather than an impulse. The response of our system to a step of 10 is shown in Figure 10-12.

FIGURE 10-12

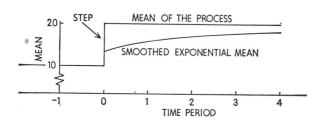

Once again our new SEM approaches but never reaches the new mean. However, it can be made to approach it more quickly. The speed with which the system responds to a step is dependent upon the smoothing constant. The larger the smoothing constant, the fewer the periods required for the value of SEM to rise, say, to 99 percent of the step increase.

When we speak of the weights given past observations in averaging, we are, in effect, describing the impulse response of the averaging system. The impulse response after x observations is the weight given the observation which is x periods old in the smoothing process. In this sense, any discrete, linear, time-invariant system can be completely described by its impulse response.

Some objective judgment is required in real forecasting systems. When a process we are trying to estimate generates an unusually large observation, or perhaps what seems to be an unnaturally long series of larger than forecast observations, when do we deduce that a new mean has developed? In an exponential smoothing system we exercise subjective judgment in selecting the smoothing constant. If we think the process is quite stable, we employ a low smoothing constant and get better noise filtering from our system. On the other hand, if we think we detect a real change in the process, we might switch to a larger smoothing constant to get quicker response.

We identify these process changes by observing the errors in our forecasts. If the process is perfectly stable and our forecast is reasonably close to the true mean, then the sum of our forecast errors should approach zero. That is, overestimates in one period will be cancelled out by underestimates during nearby periods. If, as our forecasting system continues to operate, we keep a running sum of our forecast errors, we can detect process changes.

Observing the forecast errors is useful for another reason. It enables us to forecast another process parameter: the variance or standard deviation from the mean. This parameter is particularly important to us in inventory policy making. We found, in Chapter 6, how a knowledge of the probability of various possible demands during lead time could be used to calculate expected stockouts associated with a variety of order points, and thus we found a way to balance expected stockout costs with expected holding and ordering costs to find the optimum inventory policy.

Many real processes approximate theoretical processes whose properties we understand rather thoroughly: the normal, Poisson, Gamma, etc.

If an analysis of the data generated by a process we are trying to estimate suggests to us that it is a reasonable approximation of the normal process, for example, a forecast of the mean and the standard deviation could be translated into estimates of the cumulative probabilities associated with a variety of reorder points since the normal distribution is completely described by these two parameters.

The variance is defined as the arithmetic average of the squares of the difference between individual observations and the mean of the observations. The standard deviation is the square root of the variance.

If the process we are estimating is stable, the forecast errors are the difference between individual observations and the mean of the individual observations. To estimate the variance of the process, then, we might simply square our forecast errors as they are revealed, keep a running record of the most recent ones, and interpret their arithmetic mean to be the variance of the process.

This would be an estimate of the variance on the basis of a moving average. We've already concluded, however, that the moving average is inferior—in some ways—to exponential smoothing. Why not estimate the variance also by exponential smoothing? Each new period, our estimate of the variance can be the product of our smoothing constant and the old estimate of the variance:[5]

$$\text{VAR}_{\text{new}} = \alpha (\text{Forecast Error})^2 + (1 - \alpha)\text{VAR}_{\text{old}}.$$

The Tracking Signal

We now have an exponential smoothing system for estimating both the mean and the variance of the process, and we are obliged to carry along with us from period to period only the old estimates and the smoothing constant.

We are not prepared to discard all other data, however. As mentioned earlier, we can discern process changes most easily by continuing surveillance over our forecast errors. In a stable process their cumulative sum should be zero.

If we find that our forecast errors do not sum to zero, but rather to some growing positive value, our estimate of the mean is lagging actual observation. If our forecast errors sum to a growing negative value, our estimate of the mean is lagging actual observation in the opposite direction. In the former case, the true mean of the process may have increased. In the latter it may have decreased.

If our only record of past forecast errors is embedded in a smoothed exponential forecast of the variance, then positive or negative "build-up" cannot be discerned.

---

[5] It is necessary, of course, to begin the process of estimating the variance of the process with an initial estimate of the variance—as we are obliged to do with the mean itself.

For "tracking" purposes we would therefore do well to carry with us the sum of the forecast errors. Experience can show us that if the average of our forecast errors exceeds our estimate of the standard deviation (in either direction) by some specified value—which we call a tracking signal—the probability of a change in the process is high enough to warrant increasing our smoothing constant.[6]

Double Smoothing

Thus far we've discussed *single* exponential smoothing. *Double* exponential smoothing merits a comment also.

In single smoothing our new forecast is the old forecast plus a fraction of our forecast error. As suggested before, if there is a trend in the process we are estimating, our forecast errors will tend to be consistently positive. Since we add to our old forecasts only a fraction of these errors, our new forecasts will tend to lag the trend.

We saw how the tracking signal could be used to tip us off that a trend is operative in the process we are estimating, so that we might increase our smoothing constant and thereby reduce the lag. But since we get our new forecast by adding only a fraction of the forecast error to our old forecast, with single smoothing we simply must expect a continuing lag of some size.

When we detect a trend, why not simply add some increment to our forecast and try to eliminate the gap which always trails us? Double smoothing equips us to do this in a fairly satisfactory way. In double smoothing the amount we add can be made proportional to what seems to be the pace of change.

In double smoothing we employ exponential smoothing to smooth our exponentially smoothed forecast:

$$(\text{Double Smoothed Mean}_{new}) = \alpha(\text{SEM}_{new}) + (1 - \alpha)$$
$$(\text{Double Smoothed Mean}_{old}.)$$

Just as the new SEM will lag the true mean in a *trend*, the double smoothed mean will lag SEM. Let us now determine our new forecast as follows:

$$\text{New Forecast} = 2 \times \text{SEM}_{new} - (\text{Double Smoothed Mean}_{new}.)$$

The nature of what we are doing becomes apparent if we present

---

[6] In a normal process, if the sum of the forecast errors exceeds (in either direction) about 4.6 times the standard deviation, one could have a 95 percent confidence that a non-random bias is present in the forecast. Thus a good tracking signal might be in the neighborhood of 4 or 5 times the estimate of the standard deviation.

this graphically. If all noise were eliminated from the system, then our values for the single smoothed mean and the double smoothed mean would give us two points on what we might assume is our trend line. The difference between twice the value of the single smoothed mean and the double smoothed mean is a third point on this trend line, and it constitutes our new forecast for the coming period (see Figure 10-13).

FIGURE 10-13

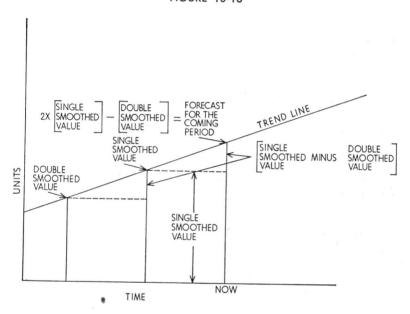

For the case where the new process seems to be increasing at a constant *rate* (i.e., a constant percentage change from period to period), *triple* smoothing may be effective. The triple smoothed mean is a product of the double smoothed mean:

(Triple Smoothed Mean$_{new}$) = α(Double Smoothed Mean$_{new}$) + $(1 - \alpha)$ (Triple Smoothed Mean$_{old}$).

Our new forecast, each period, would be:

New Forecast = 3 (Single Smoothed Mean$_{new}$ − Double Smoothed Mean$_{new}$) + Triple Smoothed Mean$_{new}$.

We will leave the behavior of these systems, their comparative advantages and disadvantages, and particularly their impulse responses, to the exercises.

SUGGESTIONS FOR FURTHER STUDY

BROWN, ROBERT GOODELL. *Smoothing, Forecasting and Prediction of Discrete Time Series.* Englewood Cliffs, N.J.: Prentice-Hall, 1963.

EVARTS, HARRY F. *Introduction to PERT.* Boston: Allyn and Bacon, 1964.

MILLER, ROBERT W. *Schedule, Cost and Profit Control with PERT.* New York: McGraw-Hill, 1963.

EXERCISES

1. Using the normal generator described in Chapter 8, construct a FORTRAN program segment which will generate daily demand, normally distributed, with a mean of 50 and standard deviation of 16.

Forecast demand as the daily demand is generated, and compare the actual standard deviation of forecast errors with the standard deviation of the generating process (i.e., 16) under each of the following conditions:

a) Using a moving average smoothing system
   1) With 3 observations.
   2) With 9 observations.
   3) With 39 observations.

b) Using single exponential smoothing
   1) With a smoothing constant of 0.5.
   2) With a smoothing constant of 0.2.
   3) With a smoothing constant of 0.05.

Repeat part (*b*), using double exponential smoothing, and determine the new forecast each period thus:

New Forecast = 2 × (Single Smoothed Mean$_{new}$) −
Double Smoothed Mean$_{new}$.

Repeat part (*b*), using triple exponential smoothing, and determine the new forecast each period thus:

New Forecast = 3 × (Single Smoothed Mean$_{new}$ − Double
Smoothed Mean$_{new}$) + Triple Smoothed Mean$_{new}$.

Initialize the single, double, and triple smoothed means at 50.

In each of the cases posed above, begin by generating first 20 days' demand of exactly 50 each day. After the 20th day, cause the normally distributed demand-generator to generate random values for demand, as suggested at the outset (i.e., mean of 50, standard deviation of 16).

In each case above, get a cumulative total of the forecast errors over the first 20 days' demand, and a new cumulative total of the forecast errors, beginning with the 21st day and continuing over a total of 1,000 days' simulated demand.

Interpret the results of your experiment.

2. Modify the generator called for in exercise 1 by introducing a *constant trend.* Cause the mean of the daily demand-generator to begin at 50 and to increase by 0.2 units each day after the 20th day. Keep the standard deviation constant at 16.

Repeat what is called for in exercise 1 under this trend condition.

3. Without the computer, determine and plot curves of (1) the impulse response and (2) the step response of the single, double, and triple smoothed forecasting systems called for in exercise 1.

4. Design a self-tracking, single smoothed forecasting system in which the exponential smoothing constant remains at 0.1 *except* when the cumulative sum of the forecast errors rises to four times the standard deviation within 60 observations; at which point: (1) the smoothing constant changes to 0.25 and (2) the cumulative sum of the forecast errors is reinitialized at zero. Provide for returning the smoothing constant to 0.1 when the cumulative sum of the forecast errors fails to increase from 0 to four times the standard deviation within 60 observations.

Test the forecasting system with a normal generator, generating daily demand with a standard deviation of 16 and a mean initialized at 50. Provide for the mean of the generator to remain at 50 for the first 100 days, followed by a period of 100 days in which the mean increases by 2.0 each day, followed by a period of 100 days in which the mean decreases by 2.0 each day.

Arrange for a print-out of the standard deviation of the forecast errors —in addition to other data required—and interpret the results.

5. Compare a double smoothed forecasting system, without tracking signal, to the system you've designed in exercise 4.

6. In estimating a process, if one calculates a single, double, and triple smoothed mean (as called for in exercise 1) from period to period, and if at the end of each period he compares the forecast errors of each of these forecasts, presumably he should base his buying or producing decisions in succeeding periods on that forecast whose forecast error in the current period was least.

Design a forecasting system on this basis and test it in the way called for in exercise 4. Let the smoothing constant equal 0.1.

Repeat the above, this time causing the mean of the demand-generating process to increase by 1.0 percent each period. Thus by a constant *rate* rather than by a constant increment. Interpret the results.

CHAPTER 11

Large-Scale Simulation Models
of the Firm

So FAR we have been concerned with developing computer models
to simulate subsystems of the firm, in which stochastic processes are
inherent. The models and programs of inventory and queuing systems were of this form. We stated in Chapter 1 that when analysis
proceeds from the subsystem to the total system level a significant
step is taken. Restricting analysis to the subsystem results in system
design which is suboptimum. Design of an inventory system cannot be done without considering the relationship of that subsystem
to the other subsystems in the firm. The best possible reorder rule,
for example, cannot be formulated without tracing its effect on such
subsystems as distribution, production, and finance.

To be certain, partial models may be enlarged, as we saw in Chapter 6 where the inventory model was extended to include some
aspects of consumer and supplier behavior. Demand and supplier
delivery time were assumed to be stochastic variables, and the inventory system model accounted for and was responsive to changes
in those variables. However, the model contained no part of the
production system to which it was linked, although admittedly that
production system was organizationally not a part of the Brown
Electronics Company. Profits and losses did not enter the income or
cash flow system of the company. Information flows did not extend
beyond the boundaries of the subsystem model.

In this and in the following chapter we shall examine three large-
scale models, or, more correctly, *types* of models, which have been
developed to simulate total activity in the firm. The Systems Development Corporation model and Professor Bonini's model are the

subject of this chapter. Then, in Chapter 12, we shall also look at Forrester's Industrial Dynamics.

It will become apparent that the three models are similar in the sense that all are computer models designed primarily as research vehicles that enable the investigator to better understand the dynamic and highly complex nature of the behavior of the firm. All make use of the capability of the computer to trace large numbers of simultaneous transactions and to record changes in system states in terms of many hundreds of variables.

The three models focus attention on the information system of the firm, which links activity throughout the firm, and makes available information which is acted upon by the decision-maker.

The models are different in several important ways. The Systems Development model has not become fully operational, and detailed information about it is not readily available. The other two models are operational, and in the case of Industrial Dynamics a special programming language, DYNAMO, is available. The Bonini model is unique because behavioral elements of decision making are simulated.

The purpose in examining these large-scale models is to learn how managerial activity, particularly decision making and control, can be explicitly modeled. A necessary precondition to the writing of a computer program to simulate activity in a firm is a concept of that activity in terms of definitions and relationships which can be translated into the terse language of the computer program. It is exceedingly valuable to observe how these model builders approached and solved this problem. The discipline of reducing organizational concepts to precise formulations and the requirement to specify decision rules and procedures in a straightforward, unambiguous fashion is an education in itself for the business specialist. Most model builders agree that the construction of their models was vastly rewarding even apart from the eventual experimentation with the completed model.

Our comments about model building in Chapter 1 should be recalled. Abstraction and simplification are necessary characteristics of model building. We will not see everything we would wish to include in the models to be examined. We may not agree that certain features of a particular model correspond to what can be observed in the real world.

THE SYSTEMS DEVELOPMENT CORPORATION MODEL

The first model we examine is that of the Management Control Systems group of the Systems Development Corporation, Santa Monica, California. The SDC is a private organization, involved mainly in research for the U.S. government and its military establishment.

Interest in control systems grew from basic work done by the corporation in defense weapons systems, including SAGE. In 1959 the Management Control Systems group began to build a computer model of the firm *to learn how control is effected by using particular decision rules*. The firm modeled was an imaginary but typical manufacturing firm, and the model was dubbed Mark I.

The firm produces a standard product in four models. Specially designed products are available upon customer request. The company has annual sales of $30 million: 90 percent of the total results from sales of four models of a standard product produced to inventory, and 10 percent of the sales are special orders.

Conventionally, the organization of the firm is shown in Figure 11-1. The activities of the president and the controller have been combined. A production controller is responsible for manufacturing, purchasing, warehousing, and maintenance. The accounting department prepares statements and invoices, maintains inventories, and develops prices. The personnel department hires and fires, and maintains records for the 1,600 people employed in the firm.

In less conventional terms, SDC depicts the firm as the complex of systems represented by Figure 11-2.

The Operating System

The first of these systems is the *operating system*. In a manner of speaking, all activity necessary for filling customer orders, producing to stock, developing bids for special orders, etc., comprises the operating system. The major categories of activity in this system do not necessarily correspond to the conventional, functional classification of activity, but rather are the result of the aggregation of "tasks" which are the basic units of activity. A set of transactions ties together the activity network or operating system.

FIGURE 11-1

Organization of the Mark I Firm

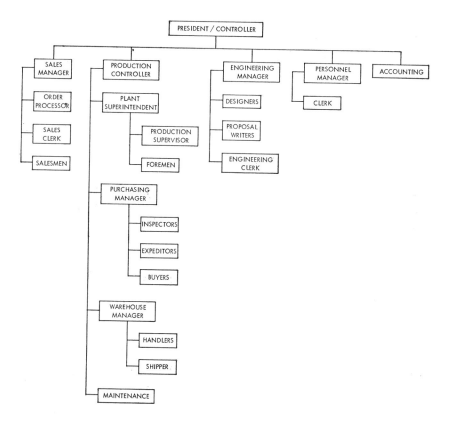

FIGURE 11-2

Major Systems of the Firm

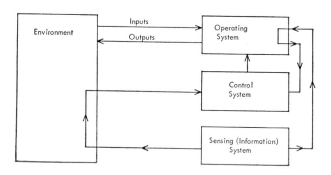

Requests from customers to bid on special products.
Orders for special products.
Orders for standard products.
Production orders.
Move orders.
Purchase orders.

Inputs to the operating system from the environment would include not only resources (labor, capital, etc.) but also information (special and standard orders or requests to bid on special orders). The regular system outputs include special and standard product, bids for special orders, and customer billings for delivered products.

Of special interest is the operational definition of activity and the idea of the task network. The word "task" implies homogeneity. The activity of a sales manager in "signing off" proposals is construed to be one task. This same manager may allocate a sales budget, hire salesmen, and call on customers. Each of the different activities described would require that a separate task be modeled. Queues are associated with tasks. Each task has an input queue, which holds tasks yet to be done, and an output queue which holds completed tasks. When tasks are grouped together and assigned to one individual, that individual is a *task center,* as in the case of our sales manager. Any collection of tasks for purposes of management control would be designated a task center.

Task Design

At each task point resources are consumed and task times are explicitly developed. Task time is made up of waiting, processing, and holding times, which are determined either by the availability of personnel to perform the task or by the exercise of a control decision which determines that waiting or holding times are necessary for any of a variety of reasons. Waiting and holding times result in queues, and, before the next task in a sequence can be done, information about the status of the previous task must be communicated. The manner in which information of this type is routed throughout the activity network will determine its performance.

For each task, six specific decisions must be made.

1. The manner in which resources are allocated to a task.
2. The manner of selecting the next task to be performed; that is, the specification of queue discipline.

3. The manner or method of performing a given task.
4. The manner of picking up or of sensing information necessary for task performance.
5. The decision about what information is to be recorded relative to task performance.
6. The decision about the routing of such information through the organization.

The Control System

Activity in the operating system does not just happen. Tasks are designed, vendors are selected, engineering designs are approved, price is computed, inventory is recorded, a forecast of cash is made, holding times throughout the task network are purposively caused, etc. In fact, there are 66 "control decision areas" and control decision rules in Mark I. Each decision has a required set of information inputs.

We could propose a meaningful view of the firm in terms of these areas which require explicit management decisions. The formulation and application of the control decisions is a major part of what we usually term "managerial activity."

In the SDC scheme, the application of control decisions constitutes the manager's influences over future states of the operating system.

A control decision rule might be defined as a function or rule that transforms a set of information values into a new set of values through the operation of the system. Management's tasks in formulating decision rules are to select the information variables and the nature of the function.

The Sensing System

To repeat, there are necessary information values associated with each control decision. Information can be sensed in the environment about such factors as customers, competitors, unions, and banks. Internally, the records and files maintained will yield information. It is assumed that the very quality of management is a function of the use which is made of information.

If the information is complete, accurate, and recent, intelligent use will be reflected in successful business activity. If information is incomplete, inaccurate or late, intelligent use may not be reflected in business activity. If unintelligent use is made of good information, mediocre performance may result. If unintelligent use is made of poor information, even more degraded performance may result.[1]

Experiments can be designed with the model to evaluate the utility of additional information. This might be done by making modifications of the record or information systems. For example, if previously available information were withheld or delayed additionally, what effect would follow in terms of the decisions made?

Specifically, there are 15 sensing decision rules in the model; and most are designed to treat sales forecasting, costs, and inventory values throughout the operating system. In addition, several decision areas exist in which management decides the routing and transmission of information (procedural decisions), and what information will be kept (recording decisions) about tasks. Procedural decisions are said to "determine organization."

Standard Product Orders

There are two initial transactions that trigger activity in Mark I, and both transactions originate in the environment. One is an order for standard product; the other is a request from a potential customer for a bid or quotation on a special product.

Standard orders are stochastically generated, but demand is determined by relating six factors presumed to influence demand for standard product. Six functions relate price, quality, lateness of delivery, advertising, number of salesmen, and other sales expenditure to demand.

These six "informational variables" take values as the result of management decisions as well as from the occurrence of events (delays, defective product, etc.) not controllable by management. Values of these variables are generated by the model, and the model builders have specified the way in which they combine to determine demand for the firm's standard product. The relationships between several of these variables and demand are worth noting briefly.

Product Quality. In the model, product quality is affected by purchasing, inspection, and workmen. Vendors are modeled to submit stochastically varying percentages of defects. Inspection and

---

[1] J. B. Heyne, *Planning for Research in Management Control Systems* (TM-546), Systems Development Corporation, Santa Monica, Calif., p. 10.

workmanship in the factory account for further quality deterioration in stochastic fashion.

Lateness of Delivery. Delays in order processing contribute to late deliveries of standard product. Information on how delays occur is collected and related to sales. When the transaction flow for the standard order is diagrammed (Figure 11-3), the departments and personnel who contribute to delays can be seen.

It must be pointed out that delays are possible in every task or task center. The particular decision rules employed to govern the way in which the necessary resources are obtained to perform the task affects delay. The decision that governs the release of information needed before a task can be stored affects delay. Time is required to plan and to review plans. Unexpected events occur that result in delays, machine failure, absentee workers, etc. All these factors must be provided for in the model.

Special Product Orders

There is . . . a potential demand for a special product. . . . Functions operating on the potential demand do not result in special product sales; rather they result in a number of requests to submit proposals which may lead to the sale of specially designed products. . . . These . . . functions are relationships between demand and price, quality, lateness of delivery, the advertising budget, the number of special product salesmen, and the cost of special product sales support. Sales support in this case is the same as for standard products.

Another set of . . . functions relates the bids issued in response to requests to a volume of special product orders. These . . . functions are the relationships between proposal acceptance and the size of the order, the delivery date called for on the order, the proposed unit cost and bid due date. The dollar volume of special product orders is added to the dollar volume of standard product orders, forming the preliminary total sales volumes. Orders so included are subject to rejection, cancellation or price variation. Orders, after being filled, are transmitted to the accounting department to be entered as accounts receivable.

Special product orders are treated, beginning with requests for bids, as described before. Such requests are generated as a function of the total market potential. These special product orders, as are standard product orders, are sent through the Sales Department time delay sequence. . . .

Requests for bids are then sent to the Engineering Manager. Holding time in this case might be occasioned by a rule which has the Engineering Manager check his work schedule before undertaking the writing of a proposal. Requests are then sent to the Engineering Clerk, where record of incoming requests is made.

Requests are then transmitted to the Engineering Proposal Writer. At this task center, the request is written during a variable period of time. The proposal may be held for a time if coordination with Production Control is required.

Completed proposals are then sent back through the Engineering Clerk, where record is made, to the Engineering Manager for sign-off.

Completed proposals are directed to the Sales Order Processor, who records on the sales schedule the fact that a proposal has been submitted. The Sales Order Processor then transmits proposals to the Sales Clerk. Proposals are then entered into a file which records an associated dollar value. Proposals are then sent to the Sales Manager for approval. Holding time at this task center may develop if the operative control decision rule requires a credit check of the prospective customer before sign-off. Finally the proposal is sent to the customer.

As in the actual case, the time delay between submission of a bid and receipt of a special order is not governed by the management control system. This delay is stochastically determined by environmental behavior.

On those occasions where proposals are transformed into special orders, they re-enter the company following the time-consuming route to the Sales Department. Special orders are sent to the Engineering Manager and the Engineering Clerks. When special product orders are received, the clerk is instructed to transmit them to Engineering Design. Design then takes place. Holding time between design and blueprinting may be called out by decision rules which govern engineering and administrative procedures. Completed designs are then sent back through Design, the Engineering Clerk, and the Engineering Manager where approval takes place before being sent to Production Control in the form of production orders.[2]

Figures 11-3 and 11-4 help us visualize the activity in the operations system for standard and special orders.

Conclusion

Although it has not been possible to "get inside" the SDC model, a significant effort is represented by this work. The structuring of the operations systems as a task-queue network would seem to have validity. The definition of managerial activity and the modeling of it in terms of information sensing, decision rules, decision areas, and company structure gives explicit form to the more conventional precepts of managerial planning, organization, and control.

---

[2] J. B. Heyne, "On the Empirical Design of Management Control Systems," Systems Development Corporation, Santa Monica, Calif. (1961), pp. 14–19.

The SDC is hopeful that in the not-too-distant future models like Mark I may operate on real data in real time, leaving for management those things which cannot be modeled; namely, sensing the environment and rendering judgment decisions.

FIGURE 11-3

Standard Order Flow

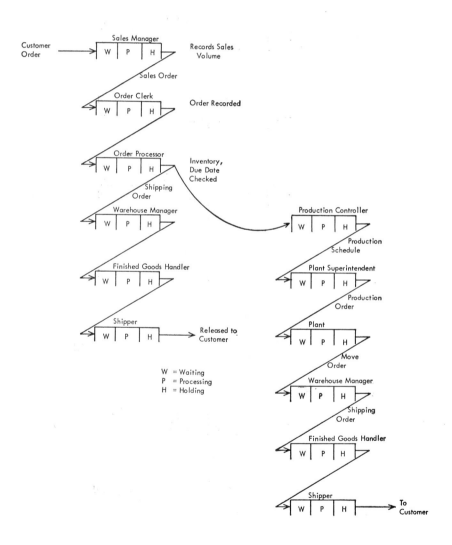

FIGURE 11-4

Special Order Flow

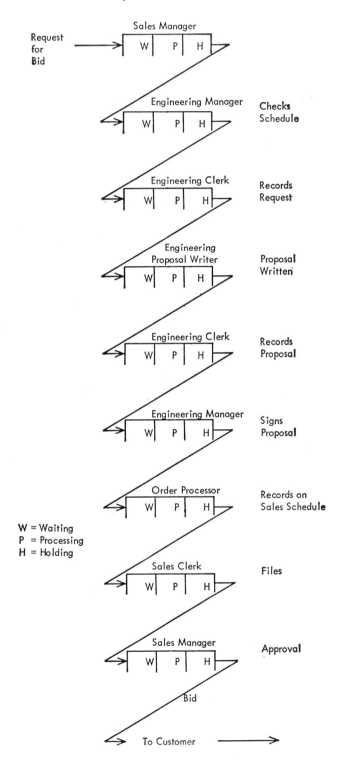

Request for Bid → Sales Manager | W | P | H |

Engineering Manager | W | P | H | — Checks Schedule

Engineering Clerk | W | P | H | — Records Request

Engineering Proposal Writer | W | P | H | — Proposal Written

Engineering Clerk | W | P | H | — Records Proposal

Engineering Manager | W | P | H | — Signs Proposal

Order Processor | W | P | H | — Records on Sales Schedule

W = Waiting
P = Processing
H = Holding

Sales Clerk | W | P | H | — Files

Sales Manager | W | P | H | — Approval

Bid

To Customer →

FIGURE 11-4 (Continued)

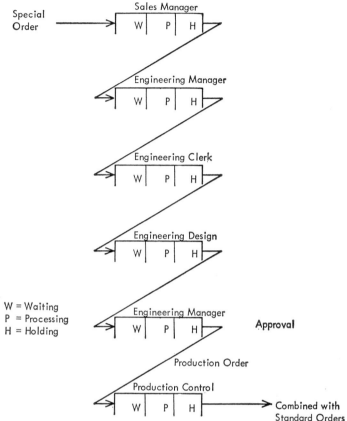

THE BONINI MODEL

The model of Charles P. Bonini differs in several ways from that of the SDC group. In the first place, the Bonini model builds on a theory of the firm postulated by James March and Richard Cyert.[3] The behavioral theory of the firm represents both a departure from and an attempt to draw from the many partial theories of organizational behavior. March and Cyert challenge several basic assumptions which are part of the theory of the firm of classical economics.

They fault the cognitive and motivational assumptions of classical theory. On the one hand, they argue, perfect information is not available to the decision-maker; rather, he must go out and search for it, and even then information is subject to bias. This means that the decision-maker does not know all alternatives; neither does he know with certainty the price tags which go with the set of alternatives. Furthermore, the search for information is both time-consum-

---

[3] See *A Behavioral Theory of the Firm* by Richard M. Cyert and James G. March (Englewood Cliffs, N.J.: Prentice-Hall, 1963).

ing and costly. The second challenge has to do with the motivation of the business decision-maker. There is much evidence that profit is not the only objective, and profit maximization, while described as rational, does not describe what business firms really do about profits. Decision-makers, as individuals and as members of large-scale organizations, have objectives which change through time and which can be ordered in a variety of ways.

There is more dissatisfaction with the economists' classical theory of the firm as an explanation of organizational decision making. Bonini argues that the economist has tended to look at the business firm in terms of its relationships with its environment, and particularly those variables which enter the marketplace, such as output, price, costs, and wages. "From the standpoint of such a market-oriented analysis, the firm is considered as a 'black box' wherein changes in outside variables produced changes in the economic outputs of the box."[4] The economist may be criticized for viewing the firm from a great distance, for failing to differentiate among firms, and for ignoring the contents of the black box.

On the other hand, the social psychologist, the sociologist and the anthropologist, according to Bonini, look at the business firm in terms of its aspects as a social institution. The firm is simply the setting for human interactions. Explanations of organizational behavior take the form of inquiries about how groups are formed, how attitudes develop or change, how aspiration levels are affected, and how social change takes place. No one denies that a better understanding of these processes is desirable, but the fact remains that these aspects of organizational behavior do not constitute its totality.

Prefacing his work, Bonini voices a complaint frequently heard not only in the academic world but also in the business world. The complaint has to do with the very human practice of constructing theory in terms of one's own area of specialization, or of structuring problems in such a way that a particular set of tools can be brought to bear. In each of the disciplines mentioned, as well as in areas of specialization within business administration, the tendency has been to focus on only certain aspects of the total business firm. Those who would regard themselves as generalists have, according to Bonini, foregone analytical characterizations for descriptions that

---

[4] Charles P. Bonini, "Simulation of Information and Decision Systems in the Firm," Stanford University Graduate School of Business, Stanford, Calif., May, 1962.

are not particularly powerful for understanding or controlling complex business systems.

Current theory lacks comprehensiveness and builds on certain assumptions whose reasonableness may be severely questioned. In addition, Bonini points out that many large "pieces of the firm are not replicated in any of the existing models." For example, there is no aspiring middle management group, budget, day-to-day allocation of resources, or explicit modeling of information variables. Analysis in classical economics is static. Equilibrium analysis falls short of explaining the behavior of a management group in the very short run to make the necessary adjustments which are implied by equilibrium.

Given these very summary observations, we come back to the realization that in order to construct models which are more comprehensive, realistic and dynamic, and which replicate the behavioral aspects of goal formation, information processing and decision making, we need modeling techniques which are much more powerful than those used in the past.

Structure of the Firm

In many ways the hypothetical firm which Bonini built is like the one in the SDC model. There are three major areas in the firm for planning and control: manufacturing, sales, and an executive committee. Figure 11-5 represents the formal organization of the model firm. In manufacturing there is a plant supervisor superior to five foremen (one for each of four manufacturing departments and a service department). A staff relationship exists between industrial engineering and production. Industrial engineering reviews and modifies production standards. The general sales manager heads up the sales organization, which includes seven district sales managers. They in turn direct the activities of field salesmen, whose number per district is indicated in the organizational chart.

Figure 11-6 indicates the decisions made at various levels in the firm. Decisions are made at eight points or, as they are defined, *decision centers*. These are the executive committee, manufacturing vice president, general sales manager, plant supervisor, industrial engineering department, district sales managers, foremen, and field salesmen. A decision center is a place in the organization where a decision or part of a decision is made. Such a definition implies that

FIGURE 11-5

Formal Organization of the Simulated Firm*

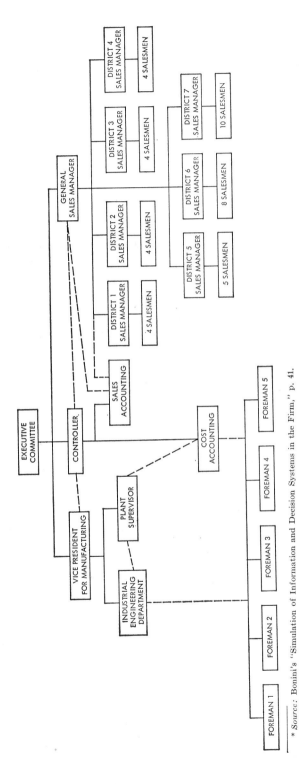

* *Source:* Bonini's "Simulation of Information and Decision Systems in the Firm," p. 41.

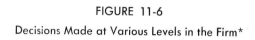

FIGURE 11-6

Decisions Made at Various Levels in the Firm*

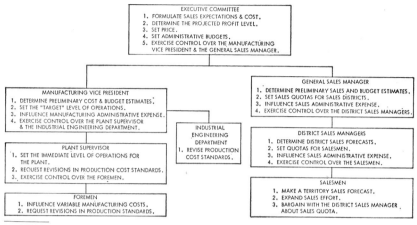

* *Ibid.*, p. 42.

the decision-maker may be an individual, a group, or a nonhuman element.

An *information center* is a place where information is collected, transmitted, stored, analyzed, or compiled. The information relates to the internal operation of the firm as well as the environment. Quite obviously, decision centers and information centers in the firm are inextricably bound together. Decision centers generally transmit decisions to others in the organization, and in a sense act as information centers.

When the decision premises are specified, the decision center acts according to a program which we shall call a *decision rule*. This is a specific procedure. Consider, for example, a decision rule associated with pricing. One such rule would be: Set price to obtain a 10 percent rate of return on investment. Such a rule assumes, as premises, estimates of costs, sales, investment, etc., and there are, of course, many other possible decision rules.

It is also important at this time to distinguish between general decision rules and what we shall term *decision parameters*. A decision parameter is a specific numerical constant associated with a decision rule. In the example above, 10 percent is the decision parameter. This rule could be changed without affecting the essence of the decision.[5]

----

[5] *Ibid.*, p. 21.

Information and decision centers are tied together by information links. Information links determine flows of information among the centers. Such linkage is quite complex in the typical firm and we note that the same decision center may send out different versions of information to different decision centers.

The *information system* of the firm is finally defined as the complete set of linkings of information within the organization. The information system is thus the total information network. "A given information system means complete and explicit specifications so that we will know who receives what information in the firm, where the information is collected, how and when the information is transmitted. . . ." The similarity between the Bonini and the SDC models is apparent concerning information and the decisions about collecting, processing, and transmitting information.

A *decision system,* as defined, totals all the decision rules in the organization. "Thus, a specific decision system means a specific set of decision rules (including specified decision parameters)." Since decision rules are dependent upon information, specification of the information system is implicit.

In order to build his model, Bonini specified the major areas in the firm in which decisions are made. A set of specific decisions to be rendered was identified for each of these areas or decision centers. One of the prior conditions for decision making is the availability of information. Thus there is a flow of information to each decision center in the model about internal as well as external activity or conditions. This information can be accounting data, informational variables which are estimates of the state of the environment, or the reporting of decisions which have been made elsewhere in the organization.

In order to generate activity in the model, decision rules have to be prescribed. For example (as we shall see in the case of sales forecasting), a set of decision rules are specified which, given the information necessary, the decision-maker applies to render a forecast. For the most part, the decision rules to be described are those which have been observed and which pragmatic managers recognize. There is nothing to suggest that any particular rule is the best possible one. Bonini states generally that if we abstract from the practices of managers, the rules included in the model are reasonable.

In other cases, where empirical evidence does not exist or where the decision-making process is so complex as to defy modeling, or where the importance of a decision is relatively minor, Bonini has chosen to produce the results of a decision process rather than to explicitly model the process.

In the case of the industrial engineering department, which re-.views requests for looser production standards, observation of the decision process led to the conclusion that approximately 50 percent of the requests in a given period were approved and 50 percent were disallowed. In this case the decision was judged to be relatively un-important, and the decision process could be modeled as if allowance or disallowance was decided by the flip of a coin. The outcomes of the process were treated as if they were probabilistic and produced by Monte Carlo methods. "In this case, we are not trying to dupli-cate the *procedures* in the real world, but to duplicate the *results* of real world procedures."

Behavioral Concepts

Perhaps the distinguishing element of the model is that decisions are not simply the result of applying a decision rule to a given set of information inputs. If decision making is a behavioral and or-ganizational phenomenon, then the model should reflect those ele-ments of the decision-making process. To achieve this, Bonini makes use of certain behavioral concepts. The first and most important, since it provides the "driving force" in the model, relates to the existence of pressure within the organization and its opposite effect, organizational slack.

When an organization is failing to perform up to expectations, there is a tendency for pressure to build up within an organization, and this pressure generally results in attempts to achieve better performance. On the other hand, when the organization has been successful in achieving its expectations for a period of time, pressure is relaxed and organiza-tional slack in the form of inefficiency creeps in. Consider, as an example, decisions about budgets. If times have been good and the organization has been doing well, then a relaxation of cost conscientiousness may occur and a simultaneous upward trend in departmental budgets may also occur. If the profit picture grows worse, however, pressure may build up in the firm, budgets slashed, and other cost-cutting devices employed. The amount of pressure affects other decisions, of course, besides budget decisions. Control decisions, decision on new plant equipment replace-ment, decisions on maintenance, decisions about dividends are some of the other kinds of decisions that may be affected as pressure builds up and slack is reduced within the firm.[6]

---

[6] *Ibid.*, p. 24.

Identifying things like organizational slack and pressure is one thing, explicit modeling of them is another matter. Each decision-maker in the model is given an "index of felt pressure." The index represents pressure or slack as a function of *performance relative to expectations*. This definition holds whether we are considering the entire organization or one of its decision-makers. The index summarizes and weights those factors, both formal and informal, which are thought to exert pressure on the decision-maker. For example, the factors and corresponding weights which make up the "index of felt pressure" for a salesman are:

Factor	Weight
Index of pressure of his superior	25
His quota as a percentage of his sales the past month	40
Sales of the "average" salesman in his district as a percentage of his sales	10
.75 + (percentage of his products less than 75% of quota)	10
His total quota for the past quarter as a percentage of his total sales for the last quarter	15

Different factors and different weights are used for the other decision-makers in the model. Pressure is partly the result of information which reaches a decision-maker through the accounting information system. Individuals react to information by feeling pressure. Pressure causes them to act—although individuals do not act uniformly given the same information or the same amount of pressure.

The second source of pressure is that which is exerted downward through the organization. Superiors pass on a part of their felt pressure to subordinates. Contagion of pressure is transmitted from one level to the next. The "index of pressure," then, performs a most important function in the model.

In summary, the "index of pressure" is a major mechanism through which the concepts of slack and pressure become operative in the model. The index provides the bridge for tying together information and behavior, and provides for the contagion of pressure within the organization.[7]

Management Planning

Top-level planning is done by the executive committee which renders decisions about budgets and prices. Earlier we noted dis-

---

[7] *Ibid.,* p. 26.

satisfaction with the motivational assumption that managers always make decisions to maximize profits. The *Behavioral Theory of the Firm* substitutes the notion of "satisficing profits": decisions are made in such a way as to achieve *satisfactory* profits. Each period the executive committee follows a procedure which results in the specification of a budget as well as a final price. The procedure, outlined below and diagrammed in Figure 11-7, is iterative.

1. Make preliminary estimates of sales and costs.
2. Use current prices as preliminary prices.
3. Determine profit goal (level of aspiration) as a function of past profits.
4. Estimate expected profit using the preliminary estimates obtained from (1), above.
5. If expected profit is greater than aspired profit, finalize estimated profits.
6. If the expected profit is below aspired profit, revise the estimates of costs, sales, and price in turn and in that order until expected costs reach aspired costs, at which point estimates become finalized.
7. If expected profit, after revisions of costs and sales budgets price, still does not measure up to aspired profits, then the goal or aspiration level is modified downward (aspired profits become a more modest figure).
8. The process is repeated in the above fashion until expected profit measures up to aspired profit, and the last estimate of sales and costs becomes finalized in the budgets; and, correspondingly, the last estimated price is accepted as the final one.[8]

If on the basis of preliminary estimates of costs and price, aspiration levels can be reached, then no problems exist, and the preliminary estimates of price and output become the basis for fixing a budget. If the aspiration level cannot be attained using preliminary estimates of costs and price, then problems exist and a search is begun which is motivated and characterized as "simple minded." This implies that the decision-maker looks first to those factors which are immediate or local, or which he can control and modify in order to attain the desired goals. As alternatives are identified, they are evaluated, and as long as the problem is not resolved, the search expands and the decision-maker negotiates with factors which are outside his control.

We shall see in more detail how these concepts have been

---

[8] *Ibid.*, pp. 27–28.

FIGURE 11-7

Planning Procedure in the Model

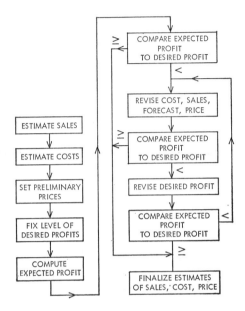

modeled. The planning process is such that if goals are unattainable after modifying or negotiating constraints, then the goals are modified downward. That is, aspiration levels are lowered and the procedure is repeated. If as a result of initial lowering of the profit goal or aspiration level there still exists an inequality between aspiration level and estimated level of profits, the aspiration level is lowered a second time. Eventually, the problem will be resolved and the price and outlook decision will be finalized.

Management is motivated because of the frustration of achieving aspiration levels. The firm is regarded as an adaptive system; organizational learning takes place in the sense that solutions to prior problems can be recalled, and decision rules are modified in the course of resolving conflict situations.

Forecasting

Each quarter the executive committee makes use of preliminary sales estimates and estimated price, as well as preliminary estimates of costs, to develop an estimate of profit for the period. The initial planning begins with the preparation of a sales forecast. The sales estimates are developed through three levels: the field salesmen, district sales managers, and the district sales manager. The flow chart of the sales forecasting process is shown in Figure 11-8. Inputs

FIGURE 11-8

Flow Chart: Sales-Forecasting Procedure*

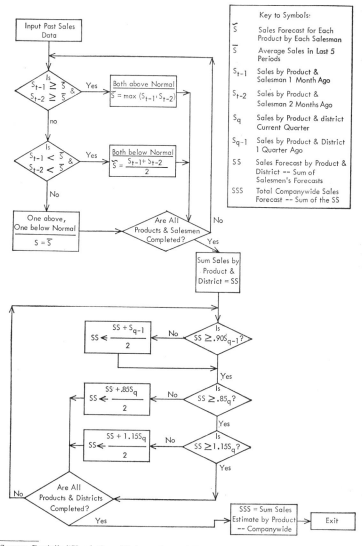

* *Source:* Bonini's "Simulation of Information and Decision Systems in the Firm," p. 48.

of past sales data are first reviewed and field forecasts are developed according to a set of simple rules. Estimates of field salesmen are then aggregated at the level of the district sales manager and reviewed. Aggregation of estimates from the districts is then made, and this figure represents the sales estimate for the company for the coming quarter.

The field salesman begins by comparing his average sales during the past five periods (months) with his sales one month ago and two months ago. If the two most recent monthly sales figures are both above the average, then his sales forecast for the next month is equal to the larger. If, on the other hand, sales for the preceding two months were each below the five-month normal, then the salesman's estimate for next month is the average of the sales for the two preceding months. If, finally, sales in one of the two preceding months was above normal (five-month average) while sales for the other preceding month was below normal, then his estimate for next month is equal to the five-month average.

This procedure is followed until estimates by each salesman have been completed and reported to the district sales level—the estimate of sales in each district is then compared with district sales during the current quarter and one quarter ago. If the estimate for next quarter is equal to or less than 90 percent of the sales for the district one quarter ago, then the estimate for the coming quarter is computed as the average of the estimate for the next quarter and the actual sales one quarter ago. If the sales estimate is equal to or less than 85 percent of sales last quarter in the district, then the estimate is computed as the average of the estimate for next quarter and 85 percent of the sales during last quarter. If the estimate is equal to or less than 115 percent of sales last quarter, then the estimate is computed as the average of the estimate for the next quarter plus 115 percent of sales last quarter. This procedure is followed for the various districts which are included in the sales organization.

Finally, aggregation of the revised estimates for the districts is made. This becomes, as noted above, the preliminary estimate of sales for the coming quarter. One might question the simplicity of the decision rules which are involved in the estimation process; nevertheless, Bonini contends that in actual practice rules similar to these are very much in evidence and, in fact, that the estimating biases that are evident in the procedure do exist. For example, the field salesman reflects optimism if his two most recent months' experience was above the five-month moving average. On the other hand, if both previous months' experience were below the average, he protects himself (in a manner of speaking) by averaging the most recent experience. If the most recent experience is not indicative of a trend, then presumably he does not alter the estimate since he has no hard evidence to serve as a guide. Modifications of a similar nature are made by the district sales manager. We see in this procedure further evidence of the way in which slack has been built into the model.

Budgets

We are still considering the sales organization of the firm; and another kind of planning takes place in the determination of a sales administrative expense budget. The previous budget figure is input and becomes the basis for the sales administrative expense budget for the coming period, given the value of the index of pressure for the general sales manager. If the index for the general sales manager for the most current three periods was greater than 110, then the preceding budget is reduced by multiplying by the factor .98. If, on the other hand, the index value for each of the preceding three periods was less than 95, the expense budget from the preceding period is increased by multiplying by the factor 1.03. If the index values do not fit either of the described conditions, then the expense budget for the coming period is unchanged from the preceding period.

A similar budget is set by the vice president of manufacturing:

Extended low pressure implies a rise in administrative expenses. Extended high pressure implies a cut in administrative expenses. In particular, if the "index of felt pressure" for the vice president of manufacturing is less than 75 for all three periods in the preceding quarter, then the budget is increased by 3 percent. If the index is greater than 110 for all periods in the past quarter, then the budget is decreased by 2 percent. Otherwise, the previous budget remains intact.[9]

The preliminary estimate of unit production cost is made in the manufacturing department. Estimated cost per unit is determined by the following procedure:

Compute the *actual average cost* per unit in the last quarter for each product; determine the *standard cost at "normal" volume* of operations;

---

[9] *Ibid.*, p. 53.

then the expected or estimated cost per unit equals the average of the actual and standard costs computed.

Once again, the procedure involved may be overly simple. Bonini contends that this is a reasonable procedure; and that costs are not expected to be exactly what they were in previous periods, nor is the measure of standard cost taken to be definitive. If costs in the past were high, relative to standard costs, then they should be expected to fall in the future, and vice versa.

The Overall Plan

Returning to the planning procedure for estimating budgets and price, and given the definition of the aspiration level, we may now combine these to trace through the quarterly planning activity of the executive committee. The preliminary estimates of costs per unit, sales by product, and budgeted administrative expenses have been developed by the sales and manufacturing decision-makers. The preliminary estimate of price per product is taken to be the price which existed in the previous period. To operationally define the level of *aspiration,* or *satisfactory profits,* profits for the past ten quarters are averaged.

The expected profit may now be calculated from the standard accounting equation that profits are equal to net sales minus direct costs, minus administrative expenses. If this expected profit is equal to or greater than the profit goal, all of the estimates mentioned up to this point are finalized in the company's quarterly plan. If the expected profit is less than the goal, then some of the estimates must be reexamined.

Costs are the first constraints to which management turns in this model. Standard costs are decreased by 5 percent in the departments which had the best relative performance in the preceding quarter. Given the reduction of these costs, the expected profit is again computed.

If the profit goal is still not met, the sales forecast is modified by increasing by 5 percent the forecast for those products in which sales last quarter were below those of the previous quarter. Once again, expected profit is computed, and if it is equal to or greater than the profit goal, then the revised estimates of price and budgetary items are finalized.

If neither a cut in costs nor an increase in sales forecast results in a projected satisfactory profit, a further price cut is in order. Prices are cut by 5 percent on the two products which have the highest expected percent of gross margin. An assumption about the elasticity of demand is implicit: The sales manager estimates that total revenue will increase 12 percent for each 5 percent decrease in price. Price cuts below a certain point would decrease expected profits, and, if such is the case, the price reduction is not made.

If the combination of modifications discussed so far does not result in a satisfactory level of profits, the profit goal itself is decreased by 5 percent. If expected profits still do not measure up, a second set of modifications is ordered.

A second round of cost reexamination results in reductions of costs on the three departments not previously changed. The reduction is 5 percent. Budgets for administrative expenses for manufacturing and sales are cut 2 percent. With the revised cost estimates, expected profits are recalculated, and, if still unsatisfactory, a second change of the sales forecast is made. The sales estimate is increased by another 5 percent increment. If it is still unsatisfactory, a price cut is made on the two remaining products (those not previously reduced) by 5 percent.

If the profit goal still cannot be achieved, the goal is reduced another 5 percent. The procedure now reverts to the step in which the initial reexamination of costs took place. All subsequent steps may be implemented; the process is iterative, and the gap between estimated and desired profit is finally closed. A flow chart of this process is shown in Figure 11-9.

There is one last planning procedure. A target level of production for each product for the coming quarter is set by the manufacturing vice president who uses sales of the preceding quarter as an estimate of sales by product. The target level of production is fixed in such a way as to meet the expected sales and to maintain an inventory of three months' sales at the end of the quarter.

We are not primarily concerned with the rationale underlying the above. Evidence is persuasive that the procedures and decision rules outlined can be observed in the real world. Our main interest here is to see the way in which a complex planning and decision process has been explicitly modeled.

FIGURE 11-9

Flow Chart: Determination of the Overall Company Plan*

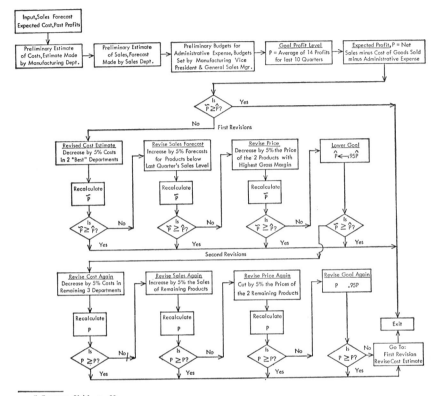

* *Source: Ibid.*, p. 60.

Management Control

Control in the model is accomplished by establishing performance standards which are used to evaluate performance. On the basis of this evaluation, decisions are made which will affect future performance. We may note that the implicit definition of managerial control is orthodox, and that the managerial activities of planning and control are of course linked.

There are two kinds of performance standards which are determined periodically. The first of these is the *sales quota*. Briefly, the overall company sales quota for a product is arbitrarily set at 10 percent above the sales forecast for that product. Quotas are then determined for sales districts, taking into consideration the number of salesmen in the district as well as the comparative past sales performance in that district.

The district managers use a similar procedure to allocate quotas to field salesmen. The district quota is divided among the number of salesmen, with consideration given to the comparative sales performance of the man. Some change of a salesman's quotas is allowed, with upward or downward adjustment based upon a comparison of his quota with his forecast of sales in his territory.

The standard of performance in the manufacturing organization is *standard cost*. Given five manufacturing departments, each with nine accounts, there are 45 standard costs which must be maintained. Standard costs can be increased by 2 percent—or decreased by 2 percent—depending upon a review by the industrial engineering department or upon a request for change initiated by the foreman.

The details of the standard cost adjustment need not concern us, although we should note that in the model actual costs are determined probabilistically, given a distribution and variance for each cost. When actual costs consistently exceed standard costs, requests for loosening the standard may be initiated by the foreman. Standards which are consistently loose (defined as a situation where actual costs are consistently less than the standard), the industrial engineering department seeks to tighten them. "Hence, standard costs are constantly changed over time with the foreman striving to loosen standards, and the industrial engineering department striving to tighten them."[10] We noted earlier that the matter of adjusting standard costs—the allowance or disallowance of a request for change by the foreman—was modeled stochastically. Requests initiated by the foreman are screened by the plant supervisor, who passes along a certain portion to industrial engineering, which grants about 50 percent of them.

We have seen then that the model provides for the generation of standards of performance for each decision-maker or decision-making group in the firm, such as (1) Standard costs for manufacturing, (2) Sales quotas, (3) Sales expense budgets, (4) Manufacturing expense budgets, (5) Target levels of production, (6) Estimated sales, and (7) Estimated profits.

Deviations between standard and actual performance cause an increase in pressure. The mechanism for translating comparative past performance into actions or decisions is the index of felt pres-

---

[10] *Ibid.*, p. 69.

sure, "the major control mechanism in the firm." Pressure from information inputs is built into the index by including those factors which measure actual performance in terms of the standards listed above, quotas, standard costs, etc. Changes in the information system to influence decision making can be made experimentally by changing the weights given the informational factors. To model the effect of an absence of information, the informational factor need only be assigned a zero weight. In this way, changes in the kinds, amounts, and methods of presentation of information can be made to show how the decision system will be modified.

As an example, the effect that inventory level information would have on the general sales manager was studied. If he had information about inventory turnover a weight of 10 or 15 was assigned, depending on the value of turnover. If a change in information transmission were made in which information was *not* available, then the factor would be given a zero weight.

Since these indices are of central importance, we present them below for the General Sales Manager, District Sales Manager, and the Vice President of Manufacturing (the Salesman's index was described earlier).

Index of Pressure for Vice President of Manufacturing

Factor	Weight
Company index of pressure	20
Manufacturing cost relative to standard cost	35
Manufacturing administrative expense relative to budget	10
.75 plus .25 times the number of products in which cost was greater than 10% above standard cost	10
.75 plus the number of departments in which cost was greater than 5% above standard cost	15
The increase of the index of volume of operations	10

The index of pressure for foremen is made up differently from those just listed. The index of pressure of the superior (Vice President of Manufacturing) is weighted 10. The balance, or 90, is the product of the percent of unfavorable cost variances in a department, and the percent of the supervisor's time spent in direct supervision of his department. This time allocation is determined by the number of costs which exceed standards by 10 percent. The net result is to model the concern that a supervisor would feel in the event of poor performance in his department and the need to devote time in the personal supervision of the activity.

The company-wide index represents the pressure felt by the executive committee. This index reflects the difficulty of formulating a satisfactory company plan. Referring to the flow chart of overall company planning (Figure 10-10), if the first preliminary estimate is satisfactory, the index is set at 90. Each revision from the first preliminary plan increases the index by 5.

Index of Pressure for General Sales Managers

Factor	Weight
Company index of pressure	20
Company sales quota relative to actual sales last month	25
Expected company profit relative to actual profit last month	10
Sales administrative expense relative to budgeted expense last month	15
.25 plus .25 times the number of districts and products that achieved less than 85 percent of quota	05
Total company quota relative to company sales last quarter	25

If the company inventory at the end of the month exceeds $3\frac{1}{2}$ months' sales, the index is increased by 10; if inventory exceeds 4 months' sales, the index is increased by 15.

Index of Pressure for the District Sales Manager

Factor	Weight
Index of pressure of General Sales Manager	25
District quota relative to actual sales last month	35
Average sales per salesman in district relative to company-wide average sales-per-salesman	05
District administrative expense relative to budget	10
.75 plus the fraction of the products in his district that were below 80 percent of quota	05
Total district quota relative to total district sales last quarter	20

Activity in the Model

The actual level of production is established by functions which relate target and actual production volume. We noted earlier that target inventory was computed from estimated sales plus an allowance for inventory. Estimates in the case of the manufacturing organization reflect sales a quarter ago. If target volume is within 5 percent of current actual volume, it is determined that the target volume can be produced next month. If target volume is between

5 to 25 percent of current actual volume, production next month is taken to be two-thirds of the way between target and current actual volume. Finally, if target volume is not within 25 percent of current actual volume, production the next month is one-half the way between the target and the current level.

Manufacturing costs vary stochastically to model the unforeseen factors which are not controllable. A distribution is specified for each cost and actual costs are generated. Given the foreman's index of pressure and actual costs incurred, the model provides for a degree of control over costs from period to period. The initial mean and the standard deviation for each cost are specified in the model. The foreman can affect the mean and standard deviation according to the following:

Foreman's Index of Pressure	Change in the Mean of the Cost Distribution	Change in the Standard Deviation of the Cost Distribution
Less than 25	+ 5%	+10%
Between 25 and 75	none	+10%
Between 75 and 125	none	none
Between 125 and 175	none	− 9%
Above 175	−4.5%	− 9%

Thus when pressure is great, the foreman is motivated to reduce costs. When pressure is normal, he does nothing. When pressure is low, organization slack—in the form of increased costs—sets in.

Changes of the standard deviation represent the foreman's efforts to reduce the variability of costs. He tries to reduce the likelihood of extremely high or low costs, since one leads to greater pressure and the other to a tighter standard.

Only when pressure is very high does the foreman resort to a more drastic measure to reduce the mean or average cost: to laying off people, trying new technology, etc. Even so, there are limits to cost reductions which the foreman can effect.

The definition of high, normal, or low pressure was quantified in the above schedule. These values for the index would be different for different foremen. They represent *sensitivity* to pressure. In a sense, they describe action points or limits which trigger activity; in this case, cost-reducing measures. If successful, the index value falls

—and we see how the index provides the motivation for managerial control activity.

In a similar fashion are sales and sales performance modeled. Actual sales are stochastically generated, given a sales probability distribution. Salesmen can modify the mean and standard deviation in response to their pressure index values. Four types of salesmen, who react differently to pressure, "exist" in the model. For example, 20 of the 40 salesmen are constituted to react to pressure by increasing sales effort in all areas, sure customers as well as new prospects. Therefore they realize changes in the mean of the distribution as well as in the standard deviation. A different type of salesman calls only on sure customers, which is translated into a decrease in the standard deviation. Yet other men are presumed to react adversely to pressure by "borrowing" sales from the future; that is, convincing customers to buy for inventory.

Experimentation

The elaborate model we have been discussing was built for the purpose of experimentation. Changes in eight factors were carefully planned to modify the environment, information system, and decision system of the firm. The changes were introduced to test the reasonableness of the model, evaluate critical decision rules or parameters, and generally to test existing hypotheses about behavior of the firm. Each of the eight factors had two values, a normal and an alternative value. These factors were:

Inventory Valuation	Environment Variability
Contagion of Pressure	Market Growth Trend
Sensitivity to Pressure	Industrial Engineering Department
Sales Force Knowledge of Inventory	Past vs. Present Information in Control

There were 2^8 (or 256) possible experiments, but the number was reduced to 64. Each experiment simulated activity in the firm for 108 months.

Observations of the values of a set of system variables were recorded, summarized, and evaluated statistically to measure the effects of the changes. The system variables tracked were price, cost, pressure, inventory, sales, and profit.

The two values for each of the factors were:

Factor	Standard	Alternative
1. Environment	Stable	Variable
2. Market Growth	2% per year with moderate cycle	10% per year (irregular)
3. Industrial engineering	Loose	Tight
4. Contagious pressure	Slight	Much
5. Sensitivity to pressure	High	Low (insensitive)
6. Inventory valuation	LIFO	Average Cost
7. Sales force knowledge of inventory	Knowledge	No Knowledge
8. Past vs. Present Information in Control	Present Information	Past Information

The first two factors change the firm's environment. Modifying the probability distribution for the variable demand is all that is involved when modeling the alternate to relatively stable environment. The next three factors modify decision parameters. Factor 6 changes a decision rule, while the last two factors model different amounts of available information and its content; i.e., whether historical data is reported or merely current data.

Bonini's experimental results will not be discussed here.[11] Most of the experiments were satisfactory and the model was reasonably well-behaved over the range of changes introduced.

BUSINESS GAMES

The subject of this and the following chapter is large-scale simulation of the firm. We cannot pass the opportunity to comment briefly about the most prevalent form of simulation, the business game—or, more generally, *competitive simulation.*

The processing of business games is a principal use of the computer in business and particularly in business education. The computer serves as a central data processor and, given the periodic decisions (price, output, advertising budget expenditure, new plant investment, etc.) of the individuals or teams playing the game, it computes the interaction of these decisions within firms and among firms, and reports the outcome to those playing the game. In this fashion competitive business situations calling for the development of policies and decision making are *simulated.* Business

---

[11] See Chapter 14.

games exist for various levels of complexity and sophistication. Some are designed to simulate an entire industry, others a particular functional area of a single firm. The use of business games (computer and non-computer) has grown steadily during the last ten years.

The American Management Association, International Business Machines, and the management consulting firm, Booz, Allen and Hamilton, were among the first to devise computer models which simulated competitive situations with input-decisions by participants who played the game. Westinghouse, Pillsbury Mills, UCLA, Carnegie Institute of Technology, and the universities of Oklahoma, Washington, Indiana, and Michigan State (among others) also developed games to represent top-management decision making.[12]

Later, functional management—rather than top-management decision making—was the focus of another type of game. The American Management Association created the "Materials Management Simulation." General Electric developed a "Dispatch Game" and "Marketing Strategy Simulation Exercise." The Kroger Company and the Boeing Airplane Company were also in the list of firms constructing and using similar games. Despite differences in complexity or focus, it is possible to generalize about business games.

The simulation of the environment to make possible feedback of the results of their actions to the players is the fundamental "game" idea, and this feature is found in all the games described above. The characteristics of the environment have always been expressed in logical or mathematical relationships. Some of these relations—the rules of the game—are always completely made known to the players, while the remaining relations—which describe the detailed intrinsic characteristics of the environment—are usually made known to the players in only a vague qualitative manner. . . . The interaction of the players and the environment is thus the core of all these games. . . . The interactions between players is another essential idea . . .

A final common characteristic of all these games is their simplicity. Even a very elaborate game . . . is still a radical simplification of the reality it purports to simulate. These simplifications result both from our lack of knowledge of how the real world really is and from our desires to keep the game "playable."[13]

The ultimate use of competitive simulation is to train military

---

[12] Kalman J. Cohen, "Trends in the Educational Uses of Management Games," *Behavioral Theory of the Firm*, Working Paper 37, Carnegie Institute of Technology, Pittsburgh, March, 1962.

[13] *Ibid.*, pp. 4–5.

personnel who are part of a vast man-machine weapons system. For example, simulation is used to present problems to U.S. Air Force air command and warning system personnel. In one such system (SAGE), surveillance, monitoring, identification, and communication about activity in the airspace in which hostile flights may occur are required on a high order of reliability. The system must function effectively the first time, and under various conditions. Simulation of realistic conditions permits the training of personnel and helps maintain a high degree of preparedness.

The advantages claimed for competitive simulation in management education are that it

Permits "cause" and "effect" to be felt.
Aids student in evaluating available information.
Familiarizes the individual with data needed.
Creates high motivation in the student through "involvement."
Provides familiarity with Electronic Data Processing.[14]

To many, the word "simulation" means business gaming. The use of a computer and the construction of a model are common to both forms of simulation, but there are differences of purpose and methodology which should be apparent.[15]

SUGGESTIONS FOR FURTHER STUDY

BONINI, C. P.; JAEDICKE, R. K.; AND WAGNER, H. M. *Management Controls: New Directions in Basic Research.* New York: McGraw-Hill, 1964.

BONINI, C. P. *Simulation of Information and Decision Systems in the Firm.* Englewood Cliffs, N.J.: Prentice-Hall, 1963.

CYERT, RICHARD M., AND MARCH, JAMES G. *A Behavioral Theory of the Firm.* New York: Prentice-Hall, 1963.

ORCUTT, G. H.; GREENBERGER, M.; KORBEL, J.; AND RIVLIN, A. H. *Microanalysis of Socio-Economic Systems.* New York: Harper & Row, 1961.

---

[14] D. G. Malcolm, "The Use of Simulation in Management Analysis: A Survey," *Report of the Second System Simulation Symposium,* American Institute of Industrial Engineers, Evanston, Ill., 1959, p. 18.

[15] See Kalman J. Cohen and Merton H. Miller's "Management Games, Information Processing, and Control," *Management International,* Vol. 3, 1963, pp. 159-77.

CHAPTER 12

Industrial Dynamics

THE THIRD large-scale model, or more accurately, model type, is that of Professor Jay W. Forrester. He has named his form of analysis and simulation "Industrial Dynamics." We begin by turning to some concepts about organization, decision making, and the relationship between information and managing. Management is the process of converting information into action. The conversion process is what we generally recognize and define as decision making. Management success depends on the availability of information and the manner in which conversion takes place. Typically, only a fraction of the available information is used, and then in an incomplete and erratic fashion.

The manager sets the stage for his accomplishments by his choice of which information sources to take seriously and which to ignore. After choice has been made of certain classes of information and certain information sources to carry the highest priority, managerial success depends on what use is made of this information. How quickly or slowly is it converted to action? What is the relative weight given to different information sources in the light of desired objectives? How are these desired objectives created from the information available?[1]

This view corresponds closely with the SDC assumption about the nature of information and its relationship to managerial success. The manager is viewed, almost literally, as an information converter or processor. From the organization and from its environment, information flows to the manager, who in turn outputs a flow of decisions that control activities within the organization. As Forrester notes, the modern manager does not himself convert in-

---

[1] J. W. Forrester, "Managerial Decision Making," *Management and the Computer of the Future*, Martin Greenberger (ed.) (Cambridge, Mass., and New York: The M.I.T. Press and John Wiley & Sons, 1962), p. 38.

formation into physical action, but rather outputs a stream of instructions or decisions which directs the efforts of the human or non-human elements in the organization.

Proceeding from these concepts of decision making and information flows, we can agree that the most critical system of the firm is the information system.

> An industrial organization is a complex, interlocking network of information channels.[2]

At various points throughout this network the information is acted upon by management, in its decision-making role, to control such physical processes as hiring employees, building factories, and producing goods. Those points throughout the network where control is exerted are "action points." Thus we see the important sequence of information, decision making, and control activity (action) illustrated in Figure 12-1.

FIGURE 12-1

Decisions and Information Feedback*

* *Source:* Forrester, "Managerial Decision Making," p. 41.

Figure 12-1 also illustrates an important characteristic of the information network or system in the firm. The decision that leads to control over a physical process is based on information about the prior state of that process. Information about the state of the system is said to be fed back through the information network to the decision point. In actual practice, the decision point relies on information sources which may be located throughout the organization and the system environment itself. We noted the definition of the information feedback system in Chapter 1:

> An information-feedback system exists whenever the environment leads to a decision that results in action which affects the environment.[3]

Managerial decision making is purposive; that is, managers interpret information for the purpose of rendering decisions in such

---

[2] *Ibid.*
[3] *Ibid.,* p. 39.

a way as to influence future system states and in a manner which is satisfactory, given the objectives or the purpose for which the system was designed. However, information feedback systems have properties that result in system behavior which is not always predictable and not always satisfactory. These properties are *structure, delays,* and *amplification.* As we might anticipate, *structure* simply implies the manner in which system parts are interrelated. *Delays* exist because information must be generated and transmitted, and further delays are experienced in the information conversion or decision-making process itself. (Referring again to the SDC model, we may recall the way in which delays in the form of waiting, processing, and holding times were taken into consideration.) *Amplification* is defined in the following way:

> Amplification is manifested by actions being more forceful than might at first seem to be implied by the information inputs to the governing decisions.[4]

Amplification is perhaps best illustrated by specific example. Consumer demand for electrical power is a function of population and of changes in technology. In the United States, at least, demand for electrical energy is increasing, but at a regular and predictable rate. Eventually the demand for electrical energy is translated through information feedback and management decision making at various levels into a demand placed against the manufacturers who produce the electrical generating equipment. This demand for generating equipment has fluctuated as much as ten to one from year to year, with a five- to six-year cycle. The manufacturers, on the other hand, have varied their output as much as four to one from year to year.

Evidence such as this led Forrester to conclude that information-decision making systems are poorly designed in industry; that they react slowly to input variation; that because of the structure through which information is fed back and acted upon, and the delays in the transmission of information, the response or behavior of these systems (measured by such system variables as orders, employment, inventory, cash, investment, etc.) is erratic and inefficient. They can be designed for more effective managerial control.

From the somewhat general nature of the information-decision making process and from the nature of information feedback, we move to the detailed concept of the decision-making process as it is

---

[4] *Ibid.,* p. 40.

modeled in Industrial Dynamics. Decisions based on information reporting the state of the system result in action meant to control physical processes. To explicitly model the system structure within which the decision process exists, Forrester specifies the existence of six interconnected networks which constitute the structure of the basic model. In four of the networks—the *materials, money, personnel,* and *capital equipment* networks—resources flow. The fifth network is labeled the *orders* network. The sixth network is the *information* network, to which we have already referred.

The networks are distinguished one from the other by the kind of material or resource contained. The information network serves to link the other networks and is an integrating network. Briefly, the several networks are described in the following fashion.

The materials network includes flows and stocks of physical goods in all stages of processing.

The orders network includes orders for goods, requisitions for new employees, and contracts for new plant space. "Orders are the result of decisions that have not been executed into flows in one of the other networks."[5]

Money is defined in the cash sense; money flows imply the exchange of payments between points in the network. On the other hand, accounts receivable are not defined as money, and are therefore included in the information network.

"In the personnel network we deal with people as countable individuals. . . . In most situations we shall need to distinguish men in the personnel network from the variables that are in the information network, such as length of work-week and the productivity per man-hour."[6]

"The capital equipment network includes factory space, tools, and equipment necessary to the production of goods. It describes the way that factories and machines come into existence, the stock of existing capital equipment, what part . . . of our capital equipment stock is in use at any instant, and the discard rate of capital equipment."[7]

To better understand the nature of these networks, we can focus momentarily on the material network which is the most conven-

---

[5] J. W. Forrester, *Industrial Dynamics* (Cambridge, Mass., and New York: The M.I.T. Press and John Wiley & Sons, 1961), p. 70.

[6] *Ibid.,* p. 71.

[7] *Ibid.,* p. 71.

tionally defined in the model and the most familiar to us. There are various points throughout the materials network which, at a given instant in time, hold quantities of materials in a variety of forms. Points of interest to us in a materials network might include the raw materials warehouse, various production stages in the plant, the finished goods warehouse in the factory, the shipper's warehouse, the wholesaler's warehouse, and perhaps the retailer's stockroom. Quantities located at such points throughout the network are called "levels." Part of the information which flows through the information network has to do with these levels. In general "A level may be an inventory, the number of employees, the average sales for last month, the accomplishment we believe has been made to date in a research project, the degree of optimism about the economic future, the size of bank balance, etc."[8]

Still considering the material network, we know that changes in the various levels throughout the network take place as the result of the exchange of material from one point in the network to another. Having identified a network of interest to us, and having specified important points along the network, we are thus able to describe the state of the network at a point in time by noting the levels throughout the network. Perhaps more importantly, given information about the *rate* at which material flows between network levels, we are able to anticipate succeeding levels throughout the network. Figure 12-2 illustrates the concepts of levels, flow rates, and decision making. Generalizing, and somewhat simplifying these concepts, the state of the network or subsystem is literally defined by the quantity of resources held at various points throughout the system. Decision making is seen as the managerial activity of deciding future system states by specifying the rates at which resources flow, and hence determining the changes of system levels.

A still closer view of the decision process is represented in Figure 12-3. The figure represents a somewhat conventional view of decision making and its control aspects. Information reporting the apparent state of the system, as well as the desired state of the system, are inputs to the decision point. Depending on the discrepancy between the apparent state of actual conditions and the desired state, action will be prescribed. The greater the discrepancy, presumably the greater the action, and vice versa.

---

[8] Greenberger (ed.), *op. cit.,* p. 43.

FIGURE 12-2

Decision Making in the System Structure*

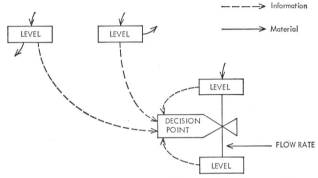

* *Source:* Greenberger (ed.), *Management and the Computer of the Future,* p. 43.

Decision making is being presented here as a continuous process. It is a conversion mechanism for changing continuously varying flows of information into control signals that determine rates of flows in the system. The decision point is continually yielding to the pressures of environment. It is taking advantage of new developments as they occur. It is always adjusting to the state of affairs. It is treading a narrow path between too much action and too little. It is always attempting to adjust toward the desired goals. The amount of action is some function of the discrepancy between goals and observed system states.

We note that we are viewing the decision process from a very particular distance. We are not close enough to be concerned with the mechanisms of human thought. We are not even close enough to see each separate decision as we ordinarily think of decisions. We may not be close enough to care whether one person or a group action creates the

FIGURE 12-3

The Decision Process*

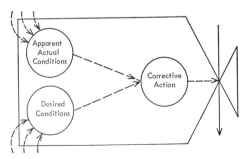

* *Source: Ibid.,* p. 44.

decision. On the other hand, we are not so far away as to be unaware of the decision point and its place in the system. This proper distance and perspective is important to our purposes. We are not the psychologist delving into the nature and sources of personality and motivation, nor are we the bio-physicist interested in the physical and logical structure of the brain. On the other hand we are not the stockholder who is so far from the corporation as to be unaware of the internal structure, social pressures, and decision points.[9]

To preview the nature of an Industrial Dynamics model, its output, and experimental use, we turn to a frequently used illustration. Figure 12-4 represents a simple production-distribution system. Two networks are modeled, the information and the materials networks. A demand function has been specified in order to generate orders from the ultimate customer. At each level (factory, distributor, retailer) an inventory of the stock item is held and periodically replenished. Delays in processing orders are assumed, as

FIGURE 12-4*

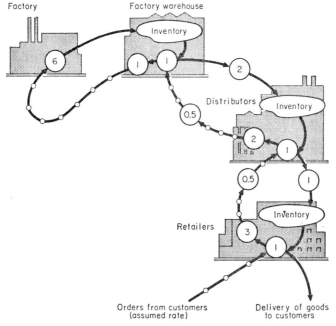

* *Source:* Forrester, *Industrial Dynamics,* p. 22.

[9] J. W. Forrester, *op. cit.,* p. 96.

well as delays in the transmission of orders between levels. Material flows are delayed between levels to represent time required for shipment.

In this system inventories are adjusted to replace goods which are sold, to adjust inventories upward or downward as the level of business activity changes, and to keep the supply pipelines filled with in-process orders as well as shipments.

Thus we have a relatively simple model in which decision rules have been specified to generate actions which lead to the development of orders for product, the processing of orders, and the shipment of the product. Delays in information transmission have been specified. Certain assumptions about the nature of demand have been made. Initially it will be constant through time. The structure of the system has been designed to include the factory, factory warehouse, distributor level, retailer level, and the final customer. Behavior of the system can be noted by changes through time in the levels of the various inventories as well as the levels of orders.

For example, inventory levels for the retailer, distributor, and factory warehouse can be noted. So also can the levels of factory orders from distributors, manufacturing orders to factory, and distributor orders from retailers be noted. In addition, the levels for factory production, factory warehouse unfilled orders, and factory warehouse average order filling delays can be generated.

Using this model, Forrester introduced the following kinds of changes in order to learn the nature of the system response. The first change was a simple step increase of 10 percent in the demand level; i.e., a sudden change from one constant level to another. Amplification took place with respect to the system levels or variables noted earlier. The striking thing, however, is the magnitude of amplification. Changes in distributor orders from retailers lagged changes in demand about a month, and eventually peaked at 18 percent above the pre-change level after 11 weeks. Twenty-seven weeks later the distributor orders from retailers leveled off at 10 percent of the pre-change value. This amplification was explained in terms of the response by retailers to increase inventories as well as to raise the level of orders and goods in transit in the supply pipeline. The inventory and pipeline increments in this case are defined as "transient" or non-repeating additions to the order rate. Once the orders have been placed and the demand satisfied, the retail order level drops back to reflect the increase in customer demand.

FIGURE 12-5*

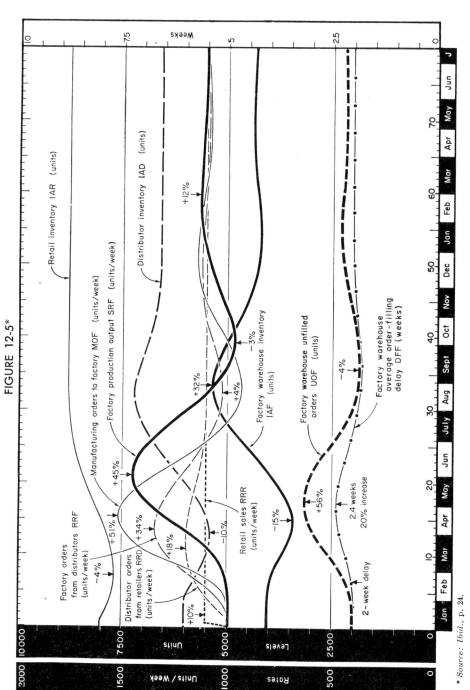

* Source: Ibid., p. 24.

The retail inventory level declined 4 percent seven weeks after the step increase and leveled off about 34 weeks later 20 percent above the pre-change level.

Manufacturing orders to the factory peaked 51 percent above the pre-change level about 15 weeks after the step increase, and even 70 weeks after the change had not stabilized—while factory production rose 45 percent above the pre-change level, peaking about 21 weeks after the introduction of the change.

The response of other system variables is shown in Figure 12-5. One should recall that the pronounced amplification was the result of a modest change in an informational input, a change which was not irregular or complex. While managers may intuitively know that such response frequently occurs, they tend to underestimate the severity of the amplification and heretofore have been at a loss to explain exactly why or when it occurs.

A second change introduced by Forrester involved a 10 percent unexpected rise and fall in retail sales over a one-year period. This was a smoothly fluctuating disturbance, or sinusoid pattern, as opposed to the step increase. As might be expected, amplification was more marked. Without regard to the timing at which maximum and minimum inventory levels occurred, the following was observed: Factory inventories ranged from 62 percent above the pre-change level to −45 percent. Distributor inventories ranged from +32 percent to −33 percent of the pre-change level. Manufacturing orders to the factory peaked at +80 percent about 65 weeks after the change, while factory output fluctuated from a high of +72 percent to a low of −61 percent of the pre-change level. Even after a simulation run of 120 weeks, dampening or mitigation of the amplification had not yet taken place to a significant degree.

More complex input changes were produced by Forrester. In a third experiment an irregular fluctuating retail sales pattern was studied. Additional experiments modeled the effect of reducing certain delays, particularly those involved in the clerical work and data processing of orders.

Constructing an Industrial Dynamics Model

We now turn from the general to the specifics of building a model of a system to gain a working understanding of the concepts discussed above.

The structure of a retailer's distribution system is portrayed by the diagram in Figure 12-6. Requisitions (orders) arrive from customers and go into an unfilled order file. Shipments from the distributor arrive and enter inventory. From this inventory deliveries are made to fill customers' requisitions.

FIGURE 12-6

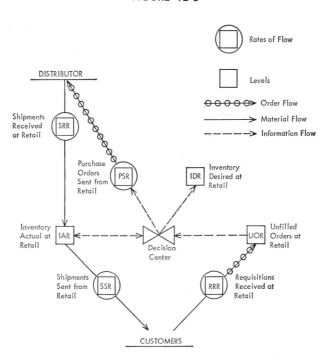

Decisions concerning shipments to customers and quantities to order to replenish the inventory are made at a decision center on the basis of knowledge of (or information from) unfilled orders, actual inventory, and desired inventory.

Three kinds of flow can be traced in the system: material flow, information flow, and order flow.

Let us assume that:

1. The retailer likes to maintain an inventory level equal to 6⅔ of the average requisitions received over each of the past 3 weeks.

2. At the end of each week the retailer orders an amount of new stock equal to: (a) the quantity requisitioned during the week and (b) one-half the difference between his desired inventory and his actual inventory at the end of the week.

3. The retailer's customers experience a 2-week delay in getting their requisitions filled, and the retailer experiences a 3-week delay in getting his purchase orders filled from the distributor.

4. At time zero, actual inventory on hand is 2,000 units; for each of the past 2 weeks, 300 units have been requisitioned by customers; and the retailer has ordered 300 units for each of the past 3 weeks to replenish his inventory.

If we assume that the system is in this "steady state," then at time zero desired inventory would be 2,000 units and the retailer would have 600 units in unfilled backorder.

We might hand-simulate the retailer's system by use of a tabular format (Table 12-1). In our notation system we use the letter R at the end of each three-letter element name to indicate that we refer to the *retail* level. Later we will see how Industrial Dynamics ties the retail level into the distributor and factory levels in order to study "total system" behavior.

Table 12-1

	Week	RRR	SSR	PSR	SRR	UOR	IAR	IDR
	−3			300				
	−2	300		300				
Time	−1	300		300		600	2000	2000
Zero								
	1							
	2							
	3							

We can determine the state of the system at the end of each week after time zero, employing the following relationships, all of which follow from the preceding description of the retailer's system:

1. Requisitions Received at Retail (RRR) = the amount requisitioned in a week (the essential system "input")

2. Shipments Sent from Retail (SSR) = the value of RRR 2 weeks ago

3. Shipments Received at Retail (SRR) = the value of PSR 3 weeks ago

4. Unfilled Orders at Retail (UOR) = $UOR_{old} + RRR - SSR$

5. Inventory Actual at Retail (IAR) = $IAR_{old} + SRR - SSR$

6. Inventory Desired at Retail (IDR) = $6\frac{2}{3}$ (average RRR during *past* 3 weeks)

7. Purchase Orders Sent from Retail (PSR) = $RRR + \frac{1}{2}(IDR - IAR)$

Employing these relationships we find that the system continues in the same state for the first 3 weeks after time zero (see Table 12-2). Now let us assume that in the fourth week customer requisitions jump to 330 per week and continue at that rate; that is, that the system experiences a 10 percent *step* increase. The effect of this change is apparent if we calculate values for the system variables (see Table 12-2) and if we then plot, against time, values for RRR, UOR, and IAR (Figure 12-7).

Table 12-2

	Week	RRR	SSR	PSR	SRR	UOR	IAR	IDR
	−3			300				
	−2	300		300				
Time	−1	300		300				
Zero	1	300	300	300	300	600	2000	2000
	2	300	300	300	300	600	2000	2000
	3	300	300	300	300	600	2000	2000
	4	330	300	364	300	630	2000	2067
	5	330	300	397	300	660	2000	2133
	6	330	330	445	300	660	1970	2200
	7	330	330	428	364	660	2004	2200
	8	330	330	395	398	660	2071	2200
	9	330	330	337	445	660	2186	2200
	10	330	330	288	428	660	2284	2200
	11	330	330	255	395	660	2349	2200
	12	330	330	252	337	660	2356	2200
	13	330	330	273	288	660	2314	2200
	14	330	330	310	255	660	2239	2200
	15	330	330	350	252	660	2161	2200
	16	330	330	378	273	660	2104	2200
	17	330	330	388	310	660	2084	2200
	18	330	330	378	350	660	2104	2200
	19	330	330	354	378	660	2152	2200
	20	330	330	325	388	660	2210	2200
	21	330	330	301	378	660	2258	2200
	22	330	330	289	354	660	2282	2200
	23	330	330	292	325	660	2277	2200
	24	330	330	306	301	660	2248	2200

Preparatory to understanding the nature of DYNAMO, we would do well to observe more closely the character of the elements in our retailer's system. We have two different kinds of elements: levels and rates.

IAR and UOR are *levels,* measured at any moment in time in *number of units.*

RRR, SSR, PSR and SRR are *rates* of flow. RRR and PSR are

FIGURE 12-7

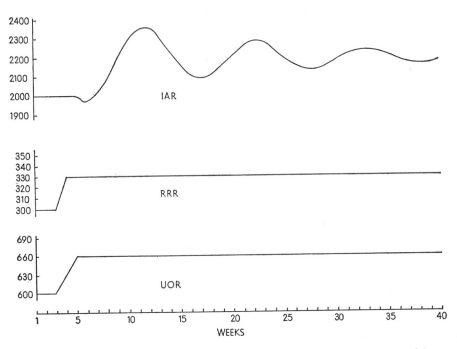

measured in *units ordered per week;* SSR and SRR are measured in *units* of material *sent or received per week.*

If we think of the beginning of a week as moment in time J, the end of the week as moment in time K, and the period of time in between as JK, then the relationship between IAR, SSR, and SRR might be expressed as follows:

$$IAR_K = IAR_J + 1(SRR_{JK} - SSR_{JK}).$$

As the equation above implies, we determine the inventory level at the end of the week by adding to the inventory level at the beginning of the week a quantity equal to the *net rate of inflow* of material during the week, in units per week *times* the amount of time this net rate of inflow has been underway (that is, one week). We see by the following dimensional analysis that our units of measure in the equation are consistent:

$$\text{Units} = \text{Units} + \text{Weeks}(\text{Units/Week}).$$

Now, we could detect changes in our retailer's system more readily if instead of determining the state of the system *once* each week we did so *twice* each week. If we think of J as the beginning of the week, as before, but we now think of K as the *middle* of the week, our equation for IAR as of the middle of the week would be:

$$IAR_K = IAR_J + \tfrac{1}{2}(SRR_{JK} - SSR_{JK}).$$

As before, $SRR_{JK} - SSR_{JK}$ means the *net rate of inflow* of material into inventory, during the period JK, in units per week.

To generalize our model which relates the inventory level to rates of flow in and out of inventory we might write:

$$IAR_K = IAR_J + DT(SRR_{JK} - SSR_{JK}).$$

where DT (Delta T) means: the fraction of a week represented by the interval of time JK.

The usefulness of this more dynamic means of conceptualizing the relationship between the elements of our retailer's system will become apparent if we express the relationship between all the elements of the system in this same fashion.

Our file of unfilled orders would be related to the inflow of new requisitions and delivery on those orders in much the same fashion as the inventory level is related to the inflow and outflow of materials:

$$UOR_K = UOR_J + DT(RRR_{JK} - SSR_{JK}).$$

Preparatory to expressing the relationship between desired inventory and the average weekly requisition rate, let us switch from a simple moving average of the past three weeks to an exponentially smoothed mean of RRR. If we determine our mean by exponential smoothing, we can avoid the necessity of carrying a record of the past three weeks' requisition rates as we move from period to period. In this procedural scheme our new mean requisition rate, each period, is the mean rate used the previous period plus a fraction (the smoothing constant) of the difference between the actual rate of requisitions received in the current period and the previous exponentially smoothed mean. The fraction employed as a smoothing constant can be selected so as to provide the equivalent of 2 weeks, 3 weeks, 4 weeks—or a sequence of any other length—as a basis for our average. A smoothing constant of 0.5, for example, would be the approximate equivalent of a moving average of requisition rates for the past three periods.

If we let RSR represent Requisition rate Smoothed at Retail, and let DRR represent the *reciprocal* of our smoothing constant, the current week's RSR would be related to the current requisition rate and last week's RSR in the following way:[10]

$$RSR = RSR_{old} + \frac{1}{DRR} (RRR - RSR_{old})$$

Now if we return to our use of J and K to represent the beginning and end of the week, respectively, we would have:

$$RSR_K = RSR_J + \frac{1}{DRR} (RRR_{JK} - RSR_J)$$

and the general model for a fractional part of one week, DT, would be:

$$RSR_K = RSR_J + \frac{DT}{DRR} (RRR_{JK} - RSR_J)$$

Now we can determine the desired inventory level at moment in time K. For the general relationship, we will let AIR (constant for Inventory at Retail [in weeks]) represent the constant which relates our desired inventory to the smoothed mean of recent requisition rates (this was $6\frac{2}{3}$ in our earlier hand-simulation). Then we would have:

$$IDR_K = AIR(RSR_K)$$

To express the relationship between purchase orders sent from retail, the current rate of requisitions received from retail, and the desired and actual inventory levels, let us let DIR represent the *reciprocal* of the fraction of the difference between our desired and the actual inventory, which we will add to the current requisition rate. (As in the case of DRR, DIR can be thought of as a delay in adjusting Inventory at Retail [in weeks].)

We need also to think of rate-of-purchase-orders-sent as applying to a *succeeding* period. That is, if RRR_{JK} represents the rate of requisitions received in the current period, the value for PSR calculated from RRR_{JK} would be the rate at which purchase orders will be sent in the immediately *succeeding* period. For the general model, then, let us let KL represent the interval of time, DT in duration, which begins at moment in time K. Our model for PSR_{KL} then would be:

---

[10] The reciprocal of DRR can be thought of as a delay, measured in number of weeks. Thus DRR means Delay in smoothing Requisitions at Retail, in weeks.

$$PSR_{KL} = RRR_{JK} + (1/DIR)(IDR_K - IAR_K).$$

It should be apparent that if DT is one week, our equations for IAR, UOR, and PSR represent precisely the relationship we employed in conducting our hand-simulation of the retailer's system.

Before expressing shipments sent from retail, we want to enrich our model a bit and make it more realistic.

In real systems of the type we are modeling, we know that the rate of shipment to customers tends to be proportional to the magnitude of backorders. If we let DFR (Delay in Filling Orders Retail [in weeks]) represent the reciprocal of the constant which relates shipments sent from retail to our unfilled order file, we would have:

$$SSR_{KL} = UOR_K/DFR.$$

We need to make another provision in determining the rate of shipments sent from retail. If our actual inventory at moment in time K is less than $(UOR/DFR)DT$, then the rate of shipments sent from retail in interval of time KL will not be UOR_K/DFR, but rather IAR_K/DT.

Our rate equation for SSR, during interval of time KL, would then be the minimum of these two quantities and, as a general model, we might express it thus:

$$SSR_{KL} = MIN(UOR_K/DFR, IAR_K/DT).$$

It will be recalled that (in our hand-simulation) shipments received at retail in a given week were equal to purchase orders sent from retail three weeks previously. If we let DTR (Delay in Transit at Retail [in weeks]) represent the number of weeks of delay between the sending of a purchase order and the receipt of materials, and if we think of PSR_{JK} as representing the rate of submission of purchase orders DTR weeks ago, then we might use the following notation to represent the rate of receipt of shipments at retail in interval of time KL:

$$SRR_{KL} = DELAY(PSR_{JK}, DTR).$$

Let us hand-simulate the retailer's system again, this time using the equations we have just developed which portray the relationships between the elements of the system as the system moves from state to state in intervals of time (DT). We will begin with the following initial conditions (with J representing the beginning of the *last* period, DT, before time zero, and K representing time zero):

$$IAR_J = 2{,}000 \text{ units} \qquad RSR_J = 300 \text{ units}$$
$$IDR_J = 2{,}000 \text{ units} \qquad RRR_{JK} = 300 \text{ units per week}$$
$$UOR_J = 600 \text{ units} \qquad SSR_{JK} = 300 \text{ units per week}$$

And let us give our constants the following values:

$$DRR = 0.67 \text{ weeks} \qquad DFR = 2 \text{ weeks}$$
$$AIR = 6\tfrac{2}{3} \text{ weeks} \qquad DTR = 3 \text{ weeks}$$
$$DIR = 2 \text{ weeks}$$

Given these initial values, we can calculate values for RRR_K, then IAR_K, and then UOR_K and IDR_K. Then, having these values, we can proceed to determine: SSR_{KL}, PSR_{KL}, RSR_{KL}, and SRR_{KL} for the coming period.

It is evident that there is a required order in calculating the values of the elements from moment in time to succeeding moment in time, just as in our previous hand-simulation of the retailer's model. But this time it is different: Given, as initial values, *levels* at the *beginning* of a period, DT, and *rates* of flow *during* the period, we calculate *levels* at the *beginning* of the next period, then *rates during* the period.

A hand-simulation of the retailer's system, beginning with the initial conditions set forth above, would yield the sequence of "states" shown in Table 12-3, assuming that $DT = 0.2$ weeks and assuming that the rate of requisitions received at retail increases by 10 percent at the beginning of the second week after time zero—that is, after the lapse of 5 intervals of time.

Were we to continue these calculations over 300 time periods (60 weeks of simulation) and plot curves for our variables, we would get step response curves similar to those of Figure 12-7. Curves for IAR, PSR, and SSR are shown in Figure 12-8.

The Impulse Response

It should be apparent that the fashion in which our retailer's system *responds* to an input *stimulus* (such as the 10 percent increase in rate of requisitions received) is determined by the structure of the system; that is, the way in which its various elements are interrelated. The fashion in which the elements are interrelated determines the way in which an input stimulus will influence the state of the system in the next period.

Table 12-3

Elements (in Order of Determination) for Each Period

		RRR	RSR	IDR	IAR	UOR	PSR	SSR	SRR
	−15*						300		
	−14						300		
	−13						300		
Time	−1	300	300	2000	2000	600	300	300	300
Zero									
	1	300	300	2000	2000	600	300	300	300
	2	300	300	2000	2000	600	300	300	300
	3	300	300	2000	2000	600	300	300	300
	4	300	300	2000	2000	600	300	300	300
	5	300	300	2000	2000	600	300	300	300
	6	330	309	2000	2000	606	330	303	300
	7	330	315	2060	1999	611	330	306	300
	8	330	320	2102	1998	616	361	308	300
	9	330	323	2131	1997	621	383	310	300
	10	330	325	2152	1995	625	398	312	300
	11	330	326	2166	1992	628	410	314	300
	12	330	328	2176	1989	631	419	316	300
	13	330	328	2184	1986	634	425	317	300
	14	330	329	2188	1983	637	430	318	300
	15	330	329	2192	1979	639	435	320	300

* The system has been in a steady state for the past 3 weeks (15 DT's). We need to retain data relating to purchase orders sent 3 weeks ago to determine SRR in the current period.

The impulse response of the file of unfilled orders to a unit increase in the rate of receipt of requisitions could be developed from the following two relationships:

$$UOR_K = UOR_J + DT(RRR_{JK} − SSR_{JK})$$
$$SSR_{JK} = UOR_J/DFR.$$

Substituting the second in the first, we get:

$$UOR_K = UOR_J + DT(RRR_{JK} − UOR_J/DFR)$$
$$= UOR_J(1 − DT/DFR) + DT(RRR_{JK}).$$

Now, if we begin (at time zero) with:

$$UOR_J = 2.0$$
$$RRR_{JK} = 1.0,$$

and if we assume that:

$$DT = 0.2$$
$$DFR = 2.0,$$

then:

$$UOR_K = 1.0.$$

FIGURE 12-8

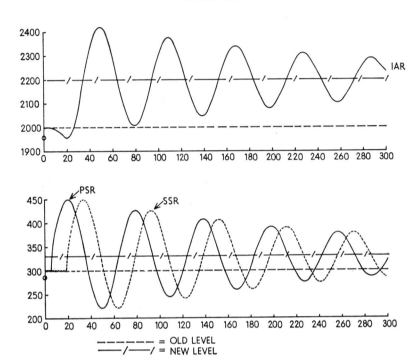

——————— = OLD LEVEL
———/———/ = NEW LEVEL

If we hand-simulate the "unfilled order file-requisitions received" subsystem, and if we input an increase of unity in the rate of receipt of requisitions at the beginning of the third time interval, we get an impulse response for this subsystem (Table 12-4 and Figure 12-9).

Table 12-4

PERIOD	RRR	UOR	PERIOD	RRR	UOR
1	1.00000	2.00000	13	1.00000	2.06974
2	1.00000	2.00000	14	1.00000	2.06276
3	2.00000	2.20000	15	1.00000	2.05649
4	1.00000	2.18000	16	1.00000	2.05084
5	1.00000	2.16200	17	1.00000	2.04575
6	1.00000	2.14580	18	1.00000	2.04118
7	1.00000	2.13122	19	1.00000	2.03706
8	1.00000	2.11810	20	1.00000	2.03335
9	1.00000	2.10629	21	1.00000	2.03002
10	1.00000	2.09566	22	1.00000	2.02702
11	1.00000	2.08609	23	1.00000	2.02432
12	1.00000	2.07748	24	1.00000	2.02188

FIGURE 12-9

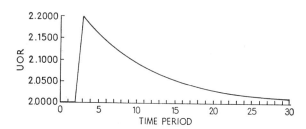

The expression $UOR_J(1 - DT/DFR) + DT(RRR_{JK})$ is analogous to the "transfer function" in engineering and biological systems. It specifies how conditions at the input will be transferred to the output.

We could develop a similar expression to specify how any other subsystem of our retailer's system responds to an impulse.

The concept of an impulse response is very important in systems analysis. It develops that any discrete, linear, time-invariant system can be completely described by its impulse response.

In complex systems it becomes difficult to develop an analytical expression for the impulse response of the total system. We can, however, examine the impulse response by simply subjecting the system to a unit impulse and observing the response of any of the elements of the system to the impulse.

DYNAMO

To facilitate simulation of systems of the character we have dealt with in this chapter, DYNAMO was developed. DYNAMO is a computer language in the same sense that FORTRAN is a computer language. As with FORTRAN, programs written in DYNAMO language must conform to the peculiar conventions of the language. A few of the DYNAMO conventions will be described.

In DYNAMO, subscripts are expressed by use of a decimal point. Thus IAR_K can be written in DYNAMO as IAR.K, and SSR_{KL} can be written SSR.KL.

In DYNAMO the relationship between our retailer's actual inventory at one moment in time and (1) the actual inventory at a previous moment in time and (2) the net rate of inflow can be expressed:

$$IAR.K = IAR.J + (DT)(SRR.JK - SSR.JK).$$

The equation above is one of a *class* of DYNAMO equations, which has the form:

$$V.K. = V.J + (DT)(\pm P, \pm Q).$$

There are approximately 60 admissible DYNAMO equation forms. To translate an ordinary algebraic statement into DYNAMO, one sometimes has to do a bit of maneuvering. For example, there is no DYNAMO form into which the following expression can be translated directly:

$$SSR.KL = MIN(UOR.K/DFR,IAR.K/DT).$$

But there *is* one which reads:

$$V = MIN(\pm P, \pm Q).$$

in which P and Q are two *variables*, but not *ratios*.

Furthermore, we have another DYNAMO equation of the form $V = P/Q$. Therefore, if we let NIR (Negative Inventory at Retail) correspond to P, we can write:

$$NIR.K = IAR.K/DT.$$

And if we let STR (Shipments "Tried" at Retail) correspond to Q, we can write:

$$STR.K = UOR.K/DFR.$$

Then finally we can express the relationship between SSR, UOR, and IAR by the three following legitimate DYNAMO equations:

$$NIR.K = IAR.K/DT$$
$$STR.K = UOR.K/DFR$$
$$SSR.KL = MIN(STR.K,NIR.K).$$

Another legitimate DYNAMO equation is:

$$V.KL = DELAY\ 3(\pm P,C),$$

which can be employed to express the relationship between SRR and PSR:[11]

$$SRR.KL = DELAY3(PSR.JK,DTR).$$

---

[11] For a full discussion of DYNAMO and how the DYNAMO compiler works, see *DYNAMO User's Manual*, Alexander L. Pugh, III (2d ed.; Cambridge, Mass.: The M.I.T. Press, 1963).

The DYNAMO compiler is so constructed that some functions which one would have to structure—were he to do this kind of systems simulation in FORTRAN—are accommodated automatically, or in a short-cut fashion, by systems functions in the compiler.

Another virtue of DYNAMO for this kind of simulation is the use it makes of the printer as a plotter. By use of what amounts to a variable FORMAT specification, DYNAMO can cause to be printed out, as a system moves from state to state, a number of curves, each corresponding to a system element. In this arrangement, letters, rather than short lines, form the curve, as shown in Figure 12-10.

Distributor and Factory Levels

In our retailer's system we concerned ourselves only with the retail level. We know, of course, that just as elements at the retail level are interrelated, and just as these elements are related to customer requisitions as an input, so also are elements within the distributor level interrelated, and related to the retail level as an input. Similarly, the factory level is made up of interrelated elements, and is related to the distributor level and to its own sources of supply.

Forrester's system of notation:

RRR for Requisitions Received at Retail
DPC for Delay in Purchasing at Consumer sector
MAF for Manufacturing Average rate at Factory

quickly becomes intelligible, so that the structure of a "total" system can be translated into DYNAMO equations, and thus into a DYNAMO program, rather readily.

SUGGESTIONS FOR FURTHER STUDY

Forrester, Jay W. *Industrial Dynamics.* New York: John Wiley & Sons, 1961.

Greenberger, Martin. *Management and the Computer of the Future.* Cambridge, Mass., and New York: The M.I.T. Press and John Wiley & Sons, 1962.

FIGURE 12-10*

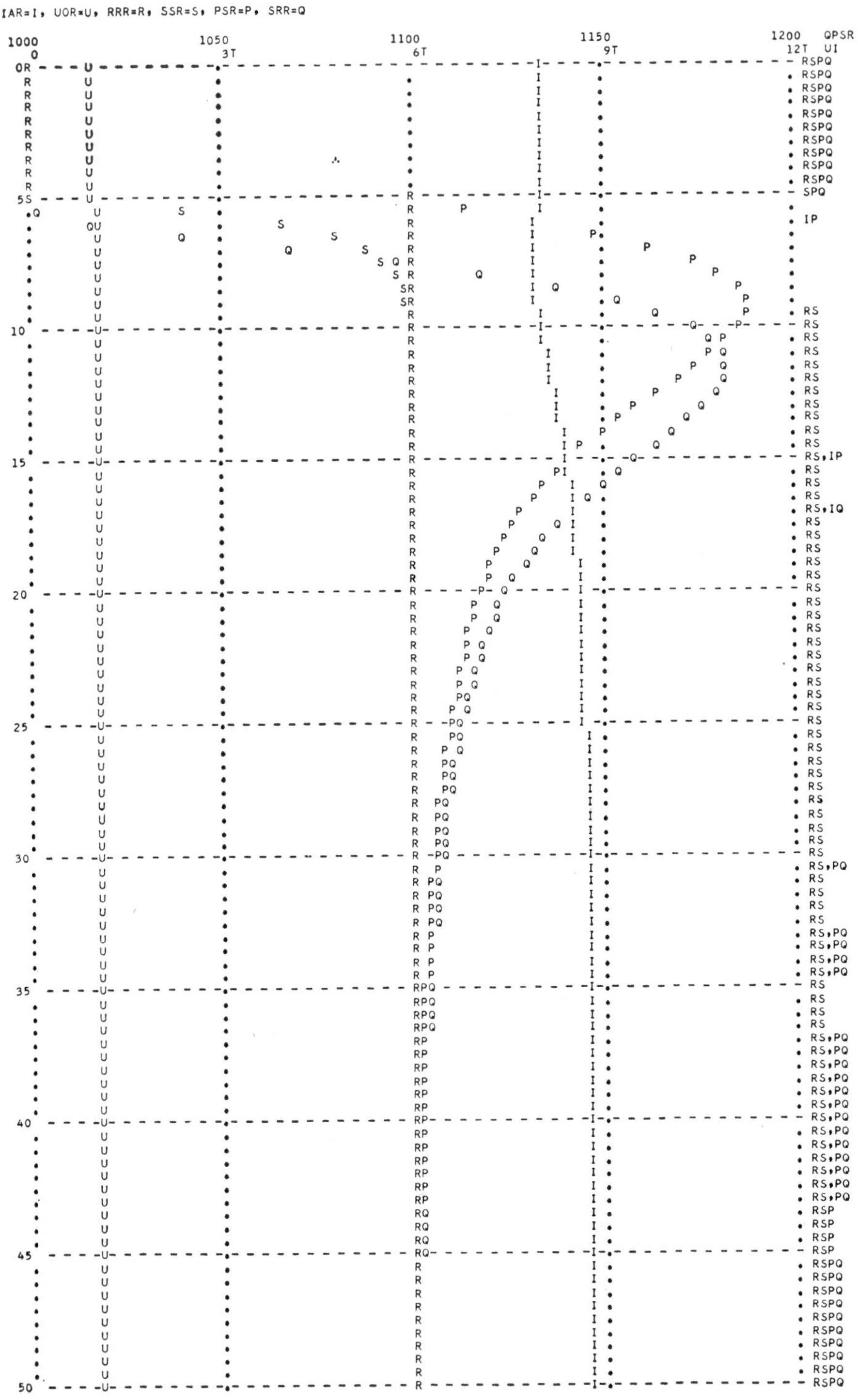

* *Source:* Pugh, DYNAMO *User's Manual,* p. 13.

EXERCISES

1. Write a FORTRAN program which will simulate the retailer's system, as portrayed by the equations on page 276 of this chapter.

2. Write a FORTRAN program which will simulate the retailer's system, as portrayed by the equations beginning on page 278, in which the state of the system is determined at succeeding moments in time, DT, where DT is 0.2 weeks.

CHAPTER 13

A Study in Total Systems Simulation

IN DEVELOPING simulation models, one is continually tempted to abandon specific cases and to pursue the elusive but intriguing *universal* model, the general systems simulator—or, as an ultimate, the "general problem solver."

From a theoretical point of view, the universal model is potentially a powerful analytical construct by means of which we can immensely improve our understanding of the decision-making process. But in dealing with applied problems in business and industry we must concern ourselves with the specific. Thus we find ourselves building models which portray specific systems with specified parameters.

To improve our feel for total systems simulation, we will build a model for a specific system with specified parameters. We will then employ that model, in the exercises at the end of this chapter, to study the behavior of the total system which it represents.

The total system with which we will deal is a business firm which we will call the "Simco Sales Company."

SIMCO SALES COMPANY

Simco Sales Company sells one product, an electronic air purifier, for domestic use. Simco has these units custom made by a variety of suppliers and it resells them under the brand name "Filtron."

Lead time for delivery of new stock from their suppliers, Simco has found, varies in a random fashion, with the following distribution:

Lead Time (Weeks)	Probability
4	.10
5	.15
6	.50
7	.15
8	.10

While Simco management is uncertain about demand from week to week (and employs a sales forecasting strategy which will be described shortly), demand is in fact normally distributed about a mean of 50 Filtrons per week, with a standard deviation of 15.

When customers request Filtrons, and Simco is unable to deliver immediately due to stockouts, customer orders are backordered; and customer backorders are first satisfied out of new stock received. New stock is received over the weekend.

At the end of each week, Simco management appraises its operating experience during the week, updates records, and makes two decisions (1) whether to declare a price markdown, if demand has been less than that deemed satisfactory, and (2) how much new stock to order, if any. The order itself, however, is not placed until early Monday morning.

If demand during the week was less than 70 percent of the forecasted demand that week, the sales price for the coming week is marked down from the normal retail price of $100 per Filtron to $85. The price markdown, however, is made only if the inventory of Filtrons on hand at the end of the week, plus new stock scheduled to arrive over the weekend, is more than 150 percent of forecast demand for the coming week. At the end of each week Simco management currently forecasts demand for the coming week simply by averaging the demand during the past 3 weeks.

Experience has shown that during a week in which the special reduced price of $85 per Filtron prevails, demand is stimulated to a 5 percent increase.

Simco currently determines at the end of the week how much to order. The amount to order is determined by adding the quantity of Filtrons sold during the week to one-half the sum of:

a)   The difference between the desired and actual inventory,
b)   The difference between the desired and actual supply backorder
     (pipeline).

The desired inventory is three times the demand forecast for the coming week. The desired pipeline is the expected demand during lead time, based on the demand forecast for the coming week.

Simco has observed that about 20 percent of the backordered demand which is not filled the following week is lost.

Simco pays $50 per Filtron received from its suppliers, and payment is due during the week following receipt of a new shipment of stock.

Fixed costs amount to $2,000 per week, and variable costs are as follows:

1.   20 percent of the investment in inventory at the beginning of the
     week, at a yearly rate, and
2.   8 percent of the investment in accounts receivable at the beginning of the week, at a yearly rate.

The above costs are all cash costs, and constitute a cash drain at the end of the week.

At the beginning of the period of operations with which we are concerned, the state of the Simco system is as follows:

Demand during the past 10 weeks has been 50 units each week;
Simco is destined to receive, on each of the coming 6 weekends, 50
   units of new stock;
The actual inventory on hand is 150 units;
There are no customer backorders outstanding;
Demand forecast for the current week is 50 units;
There is no price markdown planned for the current week;
$2,500 is scheduled to be received from accounts receivable collections
   over each of the coming 4 weeks (thus total accounts receivable are
   $10,000);
Cash on hand stands at $4,000.

Half of Simco's weekly sales are cash sales. Charge sales do not bear interest and are payable four weeks later.

It is desired to construct a program by which Simco's operating experience can be simulated so that certain policy decisions (notably the demand and forecasting strategy and the inventory management policy) can be tested to determine their influence on profits, etc.

It would be preferable to design subroutines for (1) Generating demand and determining lead times; (2) Making policy decisions.

A TOTAL SYSTEM MODEL FOR SIMULATING THE OPERATIONS OF SIMCO SALES COMPANY

Let us construct a FORTRAN program by means of which we can cause the computer to simulate the operating experience of Simco Sales Company, and let it determine and print out summary data which will enable us to test various demand forecasting strategies and various inventory management policies.

We will begin by constructing a supply subroutine whose purpose will be to determine how much new stock was received over the weekend and to update our backorder pipeline. We will assume that it is early Monday morning, prior to the hour Simco opens for business.

The Supply Subroutine

Since we review weekly our inventory on hand and our stock on order, and since we may place an order at the beginning of each week, we may have outstanding at any one time orders "destined to be delivered" in 1, 2, 3, 4, 5, 6, 7 or 8 weeks. (A reexamination of Simco's expected lead time distribution will make it apparent that we will never have outstanding an order which will take longer than 8 weeks to arrive.)

In order to simulate weekly receipts of new shipments from our suppliers we will have to keep a record of when our various past orders (our pipeline) is "destined to be delivered." It will be convenient for us to use a one-dimension subscripted variable here. Let us designate the variable, $PIPLIN(K)$, for this purpose. We will let:

PIPLIN(1)   hold the amount of previously backordered stock which is destined to be delivered to Simco in 1 week;

PIPLIN(2)   hold the amount of the previously backordered stock which is destined to be delivered to Simco in 2 weeks; etc.

Since that stock which we were destined to receive last week in 2 weeks is now destined to be received in 1 week, and that which we were destined to receive last week in 3 weeks is now destined to be received in 2 weeks, etc., it is necessary to update, each Monday, Simco's supply pipeline.

```
          DO 2 K = 1,7
      2   PIPLIN(K) = PIPLIN(K + 1)
          PIPLIN(8) = 0.0
```

In composing the supply subroutine, let us assume that the initial state of Simco's backorder pipeline will be loaded into the program at the beginning of our *main* program. Under this circumstance it will be necessary to make provision for the variable, PIPLIN(K), in our CALL and SUBROUTINE statements.

Let us also assume that the decision as to how much to order, always made at the end of the week, has been made; and that by the time we are ready in the main program to call our Supply Subroutine, the variable UO (units ordered) will have been given the value of the order quantity decided upon.

Basically, then, the function of our supply subroutine, which we will "call" the first thing Monday morning, will be:

a) To inquire how much stock was delivered over the weekend;

b) To determine when the order quantity UO—decided upon at the end of last week—will be delivered (thus we "negotiate" delivery terms with our suppliers and place an order for UO Filtrons Monday morning), and with this information we update our supply pipeline. (This means that while the lead time Simco can expect is random, when Simco places a Monday morning order Simco gets a delivery date commitment from its suppliers. We assume that the commitment date is always honored, so that Simco *knows* the delivery dates of all stock in its backorder pipeline at all times.)

The following program segment, constructed so as to simulate the lead time distribution Simco expects to experience, should do this:

```
        M = RANDOM(X)*100.0
        IF (M − 9)3,3,4
    3   LT = 4
        GO TO 11
    4   IF (M − 24)5,5,6
    5   LT = 5
        GO TO 11
    6   IF (M − 74)7,7,8
    7   LT = 6
        GO TO 11
    8   IF (M − 89)9,9,10
    9   LT = 7
        GO TO 11
   10   LT = 8
   11   CONTINUE
```

Now, if a currently simulated lead time should tell us that our ordered quantity of Filtrons is destined to be delivered, for example, in 5 weeks, we would want to add this quantity to our updated pipeline, increasing any outstanding backorder which was already destined to be delivered in 5 weeks by an amount equal to the current value of UO.

Letting SR hold the stock just received, over the weekend, our supply subroutine might appear as follows:

```
         SUBROUTINE SUPPLY (PIPLIN,SR,UO)
         DIMENSION PIPLIN(9)
         SR = PIPLIN(1)
         DO 2 K = 1,7
    2    PIPLIN(K) = PIPLIN(K + 1)
         PIPLIN(8) = 0.0
         M = RANDOM(X)*100.0
         IF (M − 9)3,3,4
    3    LT = 4
         GO TO 11
    4    IF (M − 24)5,5,6
    5    LT = 5
         GO TO 11
    6    IF (M − 74)7,7,8
    7    LT = 6
         GO TO 11
    8    IF (M − 89)9,9,10
    9    LT = 7
         GO TO 11
   10    LT = 8
   11    CONTINUE
         PIPLIN(LT) = PIPLIN(LT) + UO
         RETURN
         END
```

The Main Program

We will want to provide in our main program for initializing the state of Simco at the beginning of our simulation of Simco's operating experience. We might do this with the following statements:

```
      DO 5 M = 1,6
   5  PIPLIN(M) = 50.0
      PIPLIN(7) = 0.0
      PIPLIN(8) = 0.0
      TMU = 50.0
      SD = 15.0
      UO = 50.0
      ULS = 0.0
      AIEW = 150.0
      CBQ = 0.0
```

(Variables which have not already been identified are:

ULS—Units of Lost Sales

AIEW—Actual Inventory at End of Week

CBQ—Customer Backorder Queue [more will be said about this shortly]

```
      DO  6  J = 1,10
  6   DDP(J) = 50.0              DDP(J)—Past Demand, by weeks, for 10
                                   weeks
      FD = 50.0                  FD—Demand Forecast for current week
      PMD = 0.0                  PMD—Price Markdown
      SSF = 0.0                  SSF—Sales Stimulation Factor
      DO  7  K = 1,4
  7   AR(K) = 2500.0             AR(K)—Accounts Receivable, by weeks
      TAR = 10000.0              TAR—Total Accounts Receivable
      COH = 4000.0               COH—Cash on Hand)
```

Let us assume that it is Monday morning of our first week of simulated operations. By calling SUBROUTINE SUPPLY we can:

1. Determine stock received over the weekend (the current value of SR), and
2. Update our backorder pipeline.

This requires the statement: CALL SUPPLY (PIPLIN,SR,UO).

Now, in our main program we would do well to record the arrival of new stock over the weekend and to apply any new stock received over the weekend to customer backorders, if any. In a program segment designed to deal with this, we will let the variable BS represent Backordered Sales—those sales resulting from reducing the customer backorder queue by delivery of Filtrons at the beginning of the week (from stock which we received over the weekend) to customers whose orders we were unable to fill during the previous week.

The variable CBQ, Customer Backorder Queue, holds the quantity of backordered Filtrons; the variable AIEW will hold the Actual Inventory at the End of the Previous Week (and prior to the receipt of any new stock over the weekend); and AIBW will hold the Actual Inventory at the Beginning of the Week (i.e., AIEW plus SR.)

The following program segment should do these things for us:

```
                AIBW = AIEW + SR
                IF  (CBQ − AIBW)8,8,9
          8     BS = CBQ
                AAIBW = AIBW − CBQ
                CBQ = 0.0
                ULS = 0.0
                GO  TO  10
          9     BS = AIBW
                AAIBW = 0.0
                ULS = (CBQ − AIBW)*0.20
                CBQ = (CBQ − AIBW)*0.80
```

```
10   N = CBQ
     CBQ = N
     N = ULS
     ULS = N
```

In the above program segment we employ AAIBW, Adjusted Actual Inventory at the Beginning of the Week, to hold the value of inventory *after* customer backorders at the beginning of the week, if any, have been dealt with, but before the current week's demand has been considered.

We provide for reducing the customer backorder queue and units of lost sales to zero if the Actual Inventory at the Beginning of the Week (AIBW) is greater than CBQ, and we provide for reducing AAIBW to zero if CBQ is greater than AIBW.

Recalling that 20 percent of customer backorders which are *not* satisfied at the beginning of the week are lost, we also provide for reducing unsatisfied CBQ by 20 percent, then we record in the variable ULS (Units of Lost Sales) the number of Filtrons we failed to sell due to stockout.

Finally, in the last four statements we truncate any fractional part of the customer backorder queue and units of lost sales.

We are now ready to accommodate the current week's customers. We need a demand subroutine to determine what demand we are "destined to experience" this week.

The Demand Generator Subroutine

We would like to construct a demand subroutine in such a way that, each time we call the subroutine, the demand which Simco is "destined to experience" during the coming week will be determined for us. Since Simco's demand pattern will be normally distributed, we can employ the normal generator described in Chapter 8 to simulate weekly demand.

However, we must make special provision for modifying the demand thus generated under two conditions:

1.   When a negative demand is generated. With a mean demand of 50 units and a standard deviation of 15, it is extremely unlikely that a negative demand will be generated, but it is a distinct possibility; and under this condition we should simply give demand a value of zero.

2.   When, because of the past week's unsatisfactory demand, Simco's markdown policy calls for reducing the sale price by 15 percent, yielding an expected 5 percent stimulus in the succeeding week's demand.

In composing our demand subroutine we will assume that by the time this subroutine is called (from the main program), demand the *previous* week has been compared to demand *forecast* for the previous week, and that the variable PMD (Price Markdown) has been given a value of 0.0 or 0.15—as the past week's demand has been judged satisfactory or unsatisfactory.

We employ the variable SSF as a Sales Stimulation Factor. If last week's demand was judged unsatisfactory, and it was decided to reduce the price of Filtrons by 15 percent, SSF will be given a value of 0.05 and employed to increase this week's demand, just generated, by 5 percent. Otherwise, SSF will be given a value of 0.0.

In the CALL and SUBROUTINE statements we will want to make provision for transferring values for PMD and also ADDW (Actual Demand During the current Week) in and out of the subroutine.

To permit us to test a variety of policies under a variety of conditions, let us treat the mean and the standard deviations of the demand pattern as variables. We can read in values for these variables at the beginning of our main program. These variables—TMU for the mean and SD for the standard deviation—must also be provided for in our CALL and SUBROUTINE statements.

A subroutine suitable for generating weekly demand might appear as follows:

```
      SUBROUTINE DEMAND (ADDW,PMD,TMU,SD,SSF)
      V = (−2.0*LOGF(RANDOM(X)))**0.5*COSF(6.283*
         RANDOM(X))
      D = TMU + SD*V
      IF (D)1,2,2
   1  D = 0.0
   2  IF (PMD − 0.15)3,4,4
   3  SSF = 0.0
      GO TO 5
   4  SSF = 0.05
   5  ADDW = D*(1.0 + SSF)
      N = ADDW
      ADDW = N
      RETURN
      END
```

In the first IF statement, in SUBROUTINE DEMAND, we provide for making demand zero if our generator has generated a negative demand.

In the second IF statement (statement 2) we determine whether a decision was made in the main program to reduce the price—in which event PMD will have been given a value of 0.15—and therefore whether we should stimulate demand by 5 percent.

In the two statements just preceding the RETURN statement we truncate the decimal part of the demand just generated to avoid sales with a fractional part of a unit.

Now we are ready to conduct normal sales operations during the current week, and we call our demand subroutine to determine the demand which we are "destined to experience" during the week. We simply: CALL DEMAND (ADDW,PMD,TMU,SD,SSF), and the variable ADDW gets a new value corresponding to the quantity of Filtrons customers will demand during the current week.

Let us now assume that the week's operations have been conducted, the end of the week has arrived, and we are ready to record and interpret the week's experience, to update our accounts, to forecast next week's demand, and to make a reorder decision.

First we should provide for dealing with the current week's demand. Let us add a program segment which will translate our knowledge of the current week's demand (ADDW), inventory on hand after customer backorders were dealt with (AAIBW), and backorder sales at the beginning of the week (BS) into:

1. Total sales during the week,
2. Actual inventory at the end of the week, and
3. Gross profit and gross income from the week's sales.

We will let the variable TUS (Total Units Sold) hold the value of the week's total sales in number of Filtrons; the variable WGP hold the Week's Gross Profit; and the variable GIS hold Gross Income from Sales during the week. The following statements should determine what is required:

```
      IF (ADDW − AAIBW)11,11,12
   11 TUS = BS + ADDW
      GO TO 13
   12 TUS = BS + AAIBW
      CBQ = CBQ + (ADDW − AAIBW)
   13 GIS = 100.0*(1.0 − PMD)*TUS
      WGP = GIS − 50.0*TUS
      AIEW = AAIBW − ADDW
      IF (AIEW)14,15,15
   14 AIEW = 0.0
   15 CONTINUE
```

In the program segment above, when Actual Demand During the Week (ADDW) exceeded our Adjusted Actual Inventory at the Beginning of the Week (AAIBW),

1. We calculated Total Units Sold (TUS) on the basis of units available (AAIBW) rather than units demanded (ADDW).
2. We "lengthened" our Customer Backorder Queue (CBQ) by an amount equal to the unsatisfied demand.
3. We reduced Actual Inventory at the End of the Week (AIEW) to zero (see the statement preceding statement 14).

When actual demand was equal to or less than adjusted inventory at the beginning of the week, total units sold was based on actual demand, and therefore the customer backorder queue, already zero, was not altered.

In the statement after statement 13 in the above program segment, the week's gross profit is determined. The sale price, it will be recalled, is $100 per Filtron except when a price markdown has been declared. And the cost per Filtron to Simco is $50.

Let us now update our Cash on Hand (COH). Cash on hand will be increased by:

1. Accounts receivable collected during the week, and
2. Income from cash sales during the week.

And cash on hand will be decreased by:

1. Payment for new stock received over the past weekend (recall that payment to our suppliers must be made during the week following delivery of new stock);
2. Fixed charges (FC) of $2,000 per week; and
3. Variable charges, including:[1]
a) Inventory holding charges, at a rate of 20 percent per year, calculated on the basis of the dollar cost of the Actual Inventory at the Beginning of the Week (AIBW), and
b) Accounts receivable investment charge, calculated at a rate of 8 percent per year on the Total Accounts Receivable at the beginning of the week (TAR)

With the following statements we can update our cash on hand account:

$$FC = 2000.0$$
$$COH = COH + AR(1) + 0.5*GIS - SR*50.0 - FC$$
$$- (0.20/52.)*50.0*AIBW - (0.08/52.0)*TAR$$

---

[1] Some of these would not normally be considered cash costs, but rather would be deferred charges. To simplify our model, let us assume that these are all costs which constitute an immediate cash drain.

We might now update our accounts receivable. Recall that half the week's sales are cash sales, and that charge sales are collected four weeks later. We have designated AR(J) as a one-dimension subscripted variable for keeping track of our accounts receivable (see the initializing statements at the beginning of our main program).

As with our supply pipeline, we will want to update our accounts receivable record. This might be done thus:

```
       DO 18 J = 1,3
   18  AR (J) = AR (J + 1)
       AR (4) = 0.5* GIS
       TAR = AR (1) + AR (2) + AR (3) + AR (4)
```

One-half the current week's gross income from sales will be an addition to accounts receivable, and will be collected four weeks from now. In the next to last statement in the program segment above we make provision for this as part of the process of updating the accounts receivable record.

In the final statement above we sum our Total Accounts Receivable (TAR) to prepare for printing out our statement of accounts later.

We can determine the Week's Net Profit (WNP) using our knowledge of the Week's Gross Profit (WGP), already calculated, and the operating costs employed above to update our cash on hand account:

$$WNP = WGP - (0.20/52.0)*50.0*AIBW - (0.08/52.0)*TAR - FC$$

We are now ready to make decisions concerning:

1. Whether to declare a price markdown next week;
2. How much new stock to order.

Recall that Simco declares a price markdown if these two conditions prevail:

a) The current week's demand was less than 70 percent of forecast demand;
b) The Actual Inventory on hand at the End of the Week (AIEW), plus the stock destined to be received over the coming weekend (PIPLIN(1)), is more than 150 percent of the demand forecast for the coming week.

The variable FD holds our last weekend's forecast of the current week's demand (see the initializing program at the beginning of the main program).

With the following statement we can determine whether condition (*a*), above, warrants a price markdown:

IF $(ADDW - 0.7*FD)19,21,21$.

But now, to determine whether condition (*b*) warrants a price markdown, we must forecast sales for the coming week.

As suggested earlier, it will be convenient to design subroutines for demand forecasting and for reorder decisions. These are the two management practices we are interested in testing, and it will be convenient if we can manipulate the program segments having to do with these practices without disturbing the remainder of the program. Subroutines serve this purpose nicely.

The Demand Forecasting Subroutine

We have designed DDP(L) as the one-dimension subscripted variable in which we want to store demand during the past, and with:

DDP(1)   holding the demand 1 week past
DDP(2)   holding the demand 2 weeks past, etc.

As before, we will want to update this record each week. This might be done as follows:

$$DO\ 1\ IB = 1,9$$
$$L = 11 - IB$$
$$1\quad DDP(L) = DDP(L - 1)$$
$$DDP(1) = ADDW$$

Let us design this subroutine initially to test Simco's *current* demand forecasting strategy. Later we will alter it to test alternative strategies.

At present, Simco forecasts demand during the coming week simply by averaging the demand during the past three weeks. We will let the variable FD hold the current value of forecast demand, determined thus: $FD = (DDP(1) + DDP(2) + DDP(3))/3.0$.

Our demand forecasting subroutine, then, is simply:

```
SUBROUTINE FORECAS (DDP,FD,ADDW)
DIMENSION DDP(11)
DO 1 IB = 1,9
L = 11 - IB
```

```
1   DDP(L) = DDP(L − 1)
    DDP(1) = ADDW
    FD = (DDP(1) + DDP(2) + DDP(3))/3.0
    RETURN
    END
```

Now, with the statement, CALL FORECAS (DDP,FD, ADDW), we can cause FD to be given the value of our demand forecast for the coming week, and we are equipped to decide whether actual inventory on hand (AIEW), plus new stock to be received over the weekend (PIPLIN(1)), is sufficient, compared with the demand forecast for the coming week, to warrant a price markdown. This requires only an IF statement: IF (AIEW + PIPLIN(1) − 1.5*FD)22,22,20.

From the above it should be apparent that our pricing decision can be made by the following program segment:

```
        IF (ADDW − 0.7*FD)19,21,21
    19  CALL FORECAS (DDP,FD,ADDW)
        IF (AIEW + PIPLIN(1) − 1.5*FD)22,22,20
    20  PMD = 0.15
        SSF = 0.05
        GO TO 23
    21  CALL FORECAS (DDP,FD,ADDW)
    22  PMD = 0.0
        SSF = 0.0
    23  CONTINUE
```

In the above program segment, when the conditions dictating a price markdown prevail, we set PMD, the variable holding the value of the price markdown, equal to 0.15; and we provide a sales stimulation factor of 5 percent by setting SSF = 0.05; otherwise we set PMD = 0.0 and SSF = 0.0.

By the addition of statement 21 in the program segment above, we make certain that SUBROUTINE FORECAS has been called— regardless of whether a price markdown was declared—and thereby prepare for determining how much stock should be ordered.

The Reorder Subroutine

Recall that under Simco's *present* policy, an order is placed at the end of the week for a quantity of Filtrons equal to total units sold during the week plus half the sum of (*a*) the difference between the desired and the actual inventory and (*b*) the difference between the desired and the actual supply backorder pipeline—where Desired Inventory = 3 times the demand forecast for the coming week and Desired Supply Backorder = expected demand during lead time, based on the demand forecast for the coming week.

Actual inventory on hand is AIEW. With the following statements we can determine Desired Inventory (DI), Actual Supply Backorder (ASB), and Desired Supply Backorder (DSB):

```
      DI = 3.0*FD
      ASB = 0.0
      DO 1 N = 1,8
   1  ASB = ASB + PIPLIN(N)
      DSB = 6.0*FD
```

If our ordering policy should yield a decision to order a negative quantity of Filtrons, we will, of course, want to order zero. An order subroutine suitable for Simco's *present* ordering policy might therefore be:

```
      SUBROUTINE ORDER (PIPLIN,UO,TUS,AIEW,FD,
        ASB,DI,DSB)
      DIMENSION PIPLIN(9)
      DI = 3.0*FD
      ASB = 0.0
      DO 1 N = 1,8
   1  ASB = ASB + PIPLIN(N)
      DSB = 6.0*FD
      UO = TUS + 0.5*(DI − AIEW + DSB − ASB)
      N = UO
      UO = N
      IF (UO)2,3,3
   2  UO = 0.0
   3  CONTINUE
      RETURN
      END
```

To determine the number of Filtrons to be ordered at the end of the week we simply: CALL ORDER (PIPLIN,UO,TUS,AIEW, FD,ASB,DI,DSB).

Report Generating

We would like to study the behavior of Simco. Let us simulate Simco's operating experience over a sample of 100 weeks and store, after each week's simulation, data required for determining the mean and the variance associated with each account we are interested in. To do this, we might store in the one-dimension subscripted variable $R(K)$ the cumulative sums of the accounts we are interested in and the cumulative sums of their squares, as these are generated weekly. Thus:

$R(1)$	holds the cumulative sum of the values generated weekly for	ADDW
$R(3)$	" " " " " " " " " "	CBQ
$R(5)$	" " " " " " " " " "	AIEW
$R(7)$	" " " " " " " " " "	ASB
$R(9)$	" " " " " " " " " "	AR
$R(11)$	" " " " " " " " " "	COH
$R(13)$	" " " " " " " " " "	TUS
$R(15)$	" " " " " " " " " "	GIS
$R(17)$	" " " " " " " " " "	WGP
$R(19)$	" " " " " " " " " "	WNP
$R(21)$	" " " " " " " " " "	ULS

and:

$R(2)$	holds the cumulative sum of the squares of values generated for	ADDW
$R(4)$	" " " " " " " " " " "	CBQ
$R(6)$	" " " " " " " " " " "	AIEW
$R(8)$	" " " " " " " " " " "	ASB
$R(10)$	" " " " " " " " " " "	AR
$R(12)$	" " " " " " " " " " "	COH
$R(14)$	" " " " " " " " " " "	TUS
$R(16)$	" " " " " " " " " " "	GIS
$R(18)$	" " " " " " " " " " "	WGP
$R(20)$	" " " " " " " " " " "	WNP
$R(22)$	" " " " " " " " " " "	ULS

We would want to initialize these variables at zero, at the beginning of our main program:

$$\text{DO } 4 \text{ K} = 1,22$$
$$4 \quad R(K) = 0.0.$$

Toward the end of our main program we might employ the following set of statements to store the required data, as it is generated:

$$R(1) = R(1) + \text{ADDW}$$
$$R(2) = R(2) + \text{ADDW**2}$$
$$R(3) = R(3) + \text{CBQ}$$
$$R(4) = R(4) + \text{CBQ**2}$$
$$R(5) = R(5) + \text{AIEW}$$
$$R(6) = R(6) + \text{AIEW**2}$$
$$R(7) = R(7) + \text{ASB}$$

$$R(8) = R(8) + ASB**2$$
$$R(9) = R(9) + AR$$
$$R(10) = R(10) + AR**2$$
$$R(11) = R(11) + COH$$
$$R(12) = R(12) + COH**2$$
$$R(13) = R(13) + TUS$$
$$R(14) = R(14) + TUS**2$$
$$R(15) = R(15) + GIS$$
$$R(16) = R(16) + GIS**2$$
$$R(17) = R(17) + WGP$$
$$R(18) = R(18) + WGP**2$$
$$R(19) = R(19) + WNP$$
$$R(20) = R(20) + WNP**2$$
$$R(21) = R(21) + ULS$$
$$R(22) = R(22) + ULS**2.$$

After simulation of 100 weeks of operating experience we can summarize and translate these data into means and standard deviations—(A(I) for the means, and STDEV(I) for the standard deviations)—by the following statements:

```
    DO 26 I = 1,21,2
    A(I) = R(I)/100.0
26  STDEV(I) = SQRTF((R(I + 1) − R(I)**2/100.0)/99.0)
```

Now, by the addition of the required DIMENSION statement at the beginning of the main program, we are ready to simulate one week's experience:

```
    DIMENSION(AR(5),PIPLIN(9),DDP(11),R(22),
    A(22),STDEV(22)
```

By adding a suitably placed DO statement, we can oblige the computer to conduct the simulation over the desired 100 weeks of operations. Finally, we would want to add suitably composed PRINT and FORMAT statements to print out for us the desired data.

Our complete program for simulating the experience of Simco Sales Company over 100 weeks operations is portrayed in the Flow Diagram of Figure 13-1. And in Figure 13-2 we have a complete computer program, with comment statements liberally interspersed to facilitate interpretation.

The print-out of the program in Figure 13-2 is shown in Figure 13-3.[1] During this sample of 100 weeks of simulated experience,

---

[1] This output is the result of a particular random number generator. Since the sample is small other generators can be expected to yield somewhat different results.

FIGURE 13-1

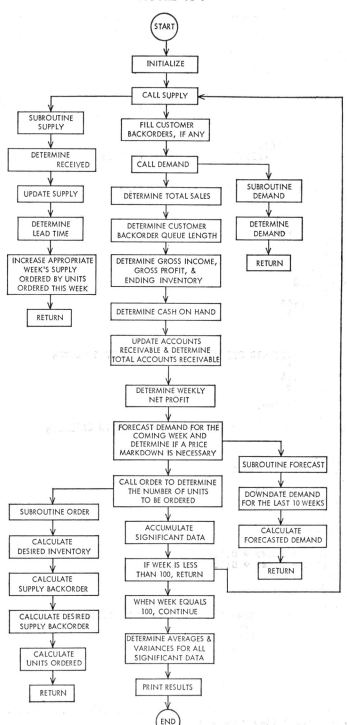

FIGURE 13-2

```
      PROGRAM SIMCO
      DIMENSION AR(5), PIPLIN(9), DDP(11),R(22), A(22),STDEV(22)
    1 FORMAT(14H WEEKLY DEMAND,F27.4,F25.4/23H BACKORDER QUEUE LENGTH,F1
     18.4,F25.4/25H INVENTORY AT END OF WEEK,F16.4,F25.4/17H SUPPLY BACK
     2ORDER,F24.4,F25.4/20H ACCOUNTS RECEIVABLE,F21.4,F25.4/13H CASH ON
     3HAND,F28.4,F25.4/6H SALES,F35.4,F25.4/24H GROSS INCOME FROM SALES,
     4F17.4,F25.4/20H WEEKLY GROSS PROFIT,F21.4,F25.4/18H WEEKLY NET PRO
     5FIT,F23.4,F25.4/20H UNITS OF LOST SALES,F21.4,F25.4)
    2 FORMAT(//33X,8H AVERAGE,10X,19H STANDARD DEVIATION)
    3 FORMAT(///3X,4HWEEK,5H ADDW,5X,3HCBQ,5X,4HAIEW,5X,3HABS,7X,3HTAR,
     19X,3HCOH,5X,3HTUS,6X,3HGIS,7X,3HWGP,7X,3HWNP,4X,3HULS,5X,2HFD,3X,3
     2HPMD/)
      PRINT 3
C     INITIALIZE VALUES.
C     INITIALIZE DATA ACCUMULATION VALUES AT ZERO.
      DO 4 K = 1,22
    4 R(K) = 0.0
C     INITIALIZE PIPELINE FOR THE NEXT 8 WEEKS.
      DO 5 M = 1,6
    5 PIPLIN(M) = 50.0
      PIPLIN(7) = 0.0
      PIPLIN(8) = 0.0
      TMU=50.0
      SD=15.0
      UO=50.
      ULS = 0.0
      AIEW = 150.0
      CRQ = 0.0
      DO 6  J = 1,10
    6 DDP(J) = 50.0
      FD = 50.0
      PMD = 0.0
      SSF = 0.0
C     INITIALIZE ACCOUNTS RECEIVABLE FOR THE NEXT 4 WEEKS.
      DO 7 K = 1,4
    7 AR(K) = 2500.0
      TAR = 10000.0
      COH = 4000.0
C     RUN FOR 100 WEEKS.
      DO 25 JWKS = 1,100
C     CALL SUPPLY TO DETERMINE LEAD TIME FOR UNITS ORDERED.
      CALL SUPPLY (PIPLIN,SR,UO)
C     FILL CUSTOMER BACKORDERS, IF ANY.
      AIBW = AIEW + SR
      IF  (CBQ - AIBW) 8,8,9
    8 BS = CBQ
      AAIBW = AIBW - CBQ
      CRQ = 0.0
      ULS=0.0
      GO TO 10
    9 BS = AIBW
      AAIBW = 0.0
      ULS = (CBQ - AIBW) * 0.20
      CRQ = (CBQ - AIBW) * 0.80
   10 N = CRQ
      CRQ = N
      N = ULS
      ULS = N
C     CALL DEMAND TO DETERMINE DEMAND FOR THIS WEEK.
      CALL DEMAND (ADDW, PMD, TMU, SD, SSF)
C     DETERMINE TOTAL SALES DURING THE WEEK.
      IF (ADDW - AAIBW) 11,11,12
   11 TUS = BS + ADDW
      GO TO 13
   12 TUS = BS + AAIBW
C     DETERMINE CUSTOMER BACKORDER QUEUE LENGTH.
      CRQ = CBQ + (ADDW - AAIBW)
C     DETERMINE GROSS INCOME, GROSS PROFIT, AND ENDING INVENTORY.
   13 GIS = 100.0 * (1.0 - PMD) * TUS
```

FIGURE 13-2 (Continued)

```
      WGP = GIS - 50.0 * TUS
      AIEW = AAIBW - ADDW
      IF (AIEW) 14,15,15
   14 AIEW = 0.0
   15 CONTINUE
   16 FC = 2000.0
C     DETERMINE CASH ON HAND.
   17 COH=COH+AR(1)+.5*GIS-SR*50.-FC-(.2/52.)*50.*AIBW-(.08/52.)*TAR
C     UPDATE ACCOUNTS RECEIVABLE AND DETERMINE TOTAL A.R.
      DO 18  J = 1,3
   18 AR(J) = AR(J + 1)
      AR(4) = 0.5 * GIS
      TAR = AR(1) +AR(2) + AR(3) + AR(4)
C     DETERMINE WEEKLY NET PROFIT.
      WNP = WGP -(0.2 / 52.) *50. * AIBW - (0.08 / 52.)*TAR- FC
      IF (ADDW - 0.70 *FD) 19,21,21
C     FORECAST DEMAND FOR THE COMING WEEK AND DETERMINE IF A PRICE MARKDOWN
C     IS NECESSARY.
   19 CALL FORECAS (DDP,FD,ADDW)
      IF(AIEW + PIPLIN(1) - 1.5 * FD) 22,22,20
   20 PMD = 0.15
      SSF = 0.05
      GO TO 23
   21 CALL FORECAS (DDP,FD,ADDW)
   22 PMD = 0.0
      SSF = 0.0
   23 CONTINUE
C     CALL ORDER TO DETERMINE THE NUMBER OF UNITS TO BE ORDERED.
      CALL ORDER (PIPLIN,UO,TUS,AIEW,FD,ASB,DI,DSB)
      PRINT 24, JWKS,ADDW,CBQ,AIEW,ASB,TAR,COH,TUS,GIS,WGP,WNP,ULS,FD,PM
     1D
   24 FORMAT(I7,F6.0,F8.2,2F9.2,F11.2,F12.2,F6.0,3F10.2,F6.1,F6.0,F5.2)
C     ACCUMULATE SIGNIFICANT DATA.
      R(1) = R(1) + ADDW
      R(2) = R(2) + ADDW**2
      R(3) = R(3) + CBQ
      R(4) = R(4) + CBQ**2
      R(5) = R(5) + AIEW
      R(6) = R(6) + AIEW**2
      R(7) = R(7) + ASB
      R(8) = R(8) + ASB**2
      R(9) = R(9) +TAR
      R(10) = R(10) +TAR**2
      R(11) = R(11) + COH
      R(12) = R(12) + COH**2
      R(13) = R(13) + TUS
      R(14) = R(14) + TUS**2
      R(15) = R(15) + GIS
      R(16) = R(16) + GIS**2
      R(17) = R(17) + WGP
      R(18) = R(18) + WGP**2
      R(19) = R(19) + WNP
      R(20) = R(20) + WNP**2
      R(21) = R(21) + ULS
   25 R(22) = R(22) + ULS**2
C     IF WEEK IS LESS THAN 100, RETURN TO THE TOP OF THE DO LOOP.
C     WHEN WEEK EQUALS 100, CONTINUE.
C     DETERMINE AVERAGES AND VARIANCES FOR ALL SIGNIFICANT DATA.
      DO 26 I = 1,21,2
      A(I) =R(I) / 100.
   26 STDEV(I)=SQRTF((R(I+1)-R(I)**2/100.0)/99.0)
C     PRINT COLUMN HEADINGS.
      PRINT 2
C     PRINT RESULTS.
      PRINT 1, (A(I),STDEV(I),I=1,21,2)
      STOP
      END
C     DETERMINE DEMAND.
      SUBROUTINE DEMAND (ADDW, PMD, TMU, SD, SSF)
```

FIGURE 13-2 (Continued)

```
      V = (-2.0 *LOGF(RANDOM(X)))**0.5 * COSF(6.283 * RANDOM(X))
      D = TMU + SD *V
      IF (D) 1,2,2
    1 D = 0.0
    2 IF (PMD - 0.15) 3,4,4
    3 SSF = 0.0
      GO TO 5
    4 SSF = 0.05
    5 ADDW = D * (1.0 + SSF)
      N = ADDW
      ADDW = N
      RETURN
      END
      SUBROUTINE SUPPLY (PIPLIN,SR,UO)
      DIMENSION PIPLIN(9)
C     DETERMINE SHIPMENTS RECEIVED.
      SR = PIPLIN(1)
C     UPDATE SUPPLY.
      DO 2 K=1,7
    2 PIPLIN(K) = PIPLIN(K + 1)
      PIPLIN(8) = 0.0
C     DETERMINE LEAD TIME.
      M = RANDOM(X) * 100.
      IF (M - 9) 3,3,4
    3 LT = 4
      GO TO 11
    4 IF (M - 24) 5,5,6
    5 LT = 5
      GO TO 11
    6 IF (M - 74) 7,7,8
    7 LT = 6
      GO TO 11
    8 IF (M - 89) 9,9,10
    9 LT = 7
      GO TO 11
   10 LT = 8
C     INCREASE APPROPRIATE WEEKS SUPPLY ORDERED BY UNITS ORDERED THIS WEEK.
   11 PIPLIN(LT) = PIPLIN(LT) + UO
      RETURN
      END
      SUBROUTINE FORECAS (DDP,FD,ADDW)
      DIMENSION DDP(11)
C     DOWNDATE DEMAND FOR THE LAST TEN WEEKS.
      DO 1 IB = 1,9
      L = 11 - IB
    1 DDP(L) = DDP(L-1)
      DDP (1) = ADDW
C     CALCULATE FORECASTED DEMAND.
      FD = (DDP(1) + DDP(2) + DDP(3)) / 3.0
      RETURN
      END
      SUBROUTINE ORDER (PIPLIN,UO,TUS,AIEW,FD,ASB,DI,DSB)
      DIMENSION PIPLIN(9)
C     CALCULATE DESIRED INVENTORY.
      DI = 3.0 * FD
C     CALCULATE SUPPLY BACKORDER.
      ASB = 0.0
      DO 1 N=1,8
    1 ASB = ASB + PIPLIN(N)
C     CALCULATE DESIRED SUPPLY BACKORDER.
      DSB = 6.0 * FD
C     CALCULATE UNITS ORDERED.
      UO = TUS + 0.5 * (DI - AIEW + DSB - ASB)
      IF(UO) 2,3,3
    2 UO = 0.0
    3 CONTINUE
      RETURN
      END
      END
```

Actual Inventory at the End of the Week (AIEW) dropped to zero twice and customer backorder queues formed both times. The price of Filtrons was marked down during 17 of the 100 weeks. Simco lost money during 40 of the 100 weeks but experienced an average weekly net profit of \$368.51, with a standard deviation of \$802.01. Cash on Hand (COH) built up rather steadily during the 100 weeks. Simco is a profitable company and no dividends are currently being paid out.

Whether alternative policies relative to forecasting, price markdown, and inventory management would be superior remains to be seen. By adjusting the model of Figure 13-2 we could test a variety of policies under a variety of market conditions and thus improve our understanding of the system and equip ourselves to make better management decisions (see Figure 13-3, pp. 312–14).

EXERCISES

1. Write a complete FORTRAN program that will print out the mean weekly demand for a given product for one year. The mean is 35 units the first 5 weeks, then it increases at a rate of 11 percent per week until the 25th week, is constant for 5 more weeks, then decreases at a rate of 5.5 percent for the rest of the year. Below is a graphical representation of mean demand as a function of time.

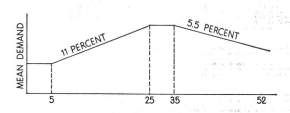

2. Rerun the program of Figure 13-2, and with the following variables initialized at zero: COH,AR,TAR,AIEW, and with CBQ = 500.0. Comment on the results.

3. Eliminate the print and format statements in the program of Figure 13-2 which cause *weekly statements* to be printed out, and arrange to have Simco's operations simulated for 500 weeks rather than 100 weeks.

a) Run a 500-week operations simulation.

b) Arrange to have the mean of weekly demand begin at 50.0, as in the model of Figure 13-2, but cause the mean to increase by one-half unit each week. Let the standard deviation be one-third of the weekly demand and run the simulation called for in *a)* under these conditions.

FIGURE 13-3

WEEK	ADDW	CBQ	AIEW	ABS	TAR	COH	TUS	GIS	WGP	WNP	ULS	FD	PMD
1	37.	.00	163.00	300.00	9350.00	3796.15	37.	3700.00	1850.00	-202.85	.00	46.	.00
2	40.	.00	173.00	264.00	8850.00	3740.81	40.	4000.00	2000.00	-54.58	.00	42.	.00
3	56.	.00	167.00	224.50	9150.00	4484.31	54.	5600.00	2800.00	743.04	.00	44.	.00
4	54.	.00	163.00	23.25	9350.00	5128.50	55.	5400.00	2700.00	643.88	.00	50.	.00
5	55.	.00	158.00	264.63	10250.00	5173.15	55.	5500.00	2750.00	693.27	.00	55.	.00
6	45.	.00	153.00	305.81	11000.00	5367.38	45.	5500.00	2750.00	694.88	.00	52.	.00
7	54.	.00	158.00	327.41	10450.00	5861.42	54.	4500.00	2250.00	651.42	.00	51.	.00
8	36.	.00	115.00	351.20	10450.00	8662.65	36.	4500.00	2250.00	194.88	.00	45.	.00
9	54.	.00	92.50	388.60	9500.00	10497.06	36.	3600.00	1800.00	-233.33	.00	48.	.00
10	54.	.00	38.50	389.60	9450.00	13914.65	54.	5400.00	2700.00	667.67	.00	54.	.00
11	55.	.00	44.25	388.80	9900.00	13843.72	54.	5400.00	2700.00	665.88	.00	51.	.00
12	46.	.00	60.84	369.18	9950.00	13676.53	55.	5500.00	2750.00	712.41	.00	52.	.00
13	53.	.00	186.41	282.11	10450.00	7138.40	46.	4600.00	2300.00	239.23	.00	51.	.00
14	54.	.00	133.41	326.35	10400.00	10436.47	53.	5300.00	2650.00	598.15	.00	51.	.00
15	45.	.00	166.10	293.78	10400.00	9443.38	54.	5400.00	2700.00	641.67	.00	51.	.00
16	55.	.00	121.10	347.34	9900.00	12395.44	45.	4500.00	2250.00	202.83	.00	48.	.00
17	45.	.00	132.05	330.17	10350.00	12599.70	45.	4500.00	2250.00	700.03	.00	52.	.00
18	54.	.00	132.03	335.08	9950.00	12700.00	55.	4500.00	2250.00	200.65	.00	51.	.00
19	52.	.00	161.51	279.54	10050.00	11868.69	54.	5400.00	2700.00	692.98	.00	54.	.00
20	52.	.00	151.76	302.21	10450.00	12551.56	54.	5400.00	2700.00	444.35	.00	53.	.00
21	54.	.00	192.66	267.36	10300.00	11193.32	52.	5200.00	2600.00	537.10	.00	54.	.00
22	55.	.00	140.22	277.29	10650.00	11302.07	52.	5400.00	2700.00	536.27	.00	57.	.00
23	61.	.00	85.22	330.53	10600.00	14698.34	54.	5400.00	2700.00	646.34	.00	54.	.00
24	37.	.00	113.05	358.13	11100.00	18105.07	55.	5500.00	2750.00	706.65	.00	51.	.00
25	47.	.00	143.03	371.57	10350.00	14313.12	61.	6100.00	3050.00	999.65	.00	48.	.00
26	33.	.00	154.01	322.78	9647.50	16056.72	37.	3700.00	1450.00	-200.54	.00	39.	.15
27	57.	.00	121.01	348.88	7920.00	18412.26	47.	3995.00	1650.00	-408.50	.00	46.	.00
28	95.	.00	148.94	288.07	10820.00	18796.07	33.	3300.00	1650.00	-392.77	.00	62.	.15
29	44.	.00	158.19	225.01	11177.50	17781.15	57.	9500.00	4750.00	52.15	.00	65.	.15
30	79.	.00	121.59	357.29	11322.50	18860.79	95.	4400.00	1995.00	2686.44	.00	73.	.00
31	73.	.00	106.95	357.17	14450.00	16577.66	44.	4750.00	3950.00	144.16	.00	65.	.15
32	71.	.00	113.95	469.47	13350.00	18626.96	79.	3950.00	3650.00	1883.60	.00	74.	.15
33	93.	.00	99.04	594.39	15800.00	26676.72	73.	7900.00	3550.00	1590.13	.00	79.	.00
34	50.	36.05	231.37	738.72	14339.62	26497.19	71.	7100.00	4650.00	1495.24	.00	71.	.15
35	92.	.00	135.37	594.95	12547.46	25131.51	14.	9300.00	497.46	2605.13	.00	78.	.15
36	54.	.00	171.68	510.80	13489.62	20028.31	128.	1394.93	4481.78	-1324.42	.00	65.	.00
37	96.	.00	299.67	500.52	13972.46	26693.06	96.	10884.31	2700.00	2415.89	.00	81.	.15
38	35.	.00	233.67	570.26	12227.50	23515.12	87.	5400.00	3750.00	624.37	.00	62.	.15
39	87.	.00	177.89	462.60	11477.50	25096.28	39.	8160.00	3045.00	1295.63	.00	73.	.00
40	39.	.00	320.89	402.80	10202.50	26445.89	66.	7395.00	1950.00	-311.60	.00	54.	.00
41	66.	.00	421.94	402.80	11252.50	25255.61	56.	3045.00	2310.00	972.08	.00	64.	.00
42	56.	.00	382.94	438.56	12096.54	27744.97	32.	5410.00	2400.00	-132.79	.00	54.	.15
43	32.	.00	436.47	263.35	8905.00	22196.54	40.	5600.00	1400.00	-236.67	.00	51.	.15
44	40.	.00	320.89	122.29	8050.00	26690.78	39.	3900.00	1950.00	737.75	.00	43.	.00
45	40.	.00	421.94	35.76	6900.00	19350.93	33.	3300.00	1650.00	-481.95	.00	37.	.15
46	39.	.00	382.94			17371.85				-702.54	.00		.00
47	33.	.00	436.47							-143.53	.00		.00
48		.00								-450.90	.0		.00

0.00	53.	0.00	2400.99	4500.00	9000.00	90.	21037.51	9950.00	.00	345.24	.00	90.	50
0.15	51.	0.00	-531.08	1555.00	3100.00	31.	22455.81	9550.00	157.38	314.24	.00	31.	51
0.05	61.	0.00	128.30	2205.00	5355.00	63.	24708.18	10577.50	189.57	251.24	.00	63.	52
0.15	42.	0.00	-514.13	1550.00	3100.00	31.	26043.60	10277.50	308.17	220.24	.00	31.	53
0.00	52.	0.00	114.70	2170.00	5270.00	62.	31120.43	8412.50	308.01	158.24	.00	62.	54
0.15	49.	0.00	704.78	2750.00	5500.00	55.	33377.06	9412.50	370.87	103.24	.00	55.	55
0.00	50.	0.00	-432.82	1600.00	3200.00	32.	35618.92	8535.00	410.87	-71.24	.00	32.	56
0.00	41.	0.00	-727.20	1330.00	3230.00	38.	28858.72	8600.00	267.93	190.62	.00	38.	57
0.00	49.	0.00	643.48	2700.00	5400.00	54.	30528.09	8665.00	235.74	166.81	.00	54.	58
0.00	48.	0.00	631.45	2700.00	5400.00	54.	29729.71	8615.00	154.87	233.40	.00	54.	59
0.00	42.	0.00	-258.45	1800.00	3600.00	36.	29321.57	8815.00	233.73	197.40	.00	36.	60
0.00	34.	0.00	-251.80	1800.00	3600.00	36.	30687.04	9000.00	270.16	161.30	.00	36.	61
0.00	41.	0.00	-500.79	1550.00	3100.00	31.	30887.54	7850.00	239.48	170.30	.00	31.	62
0.00	48.	0.00	892.71	2950.00	5900.00	59.	31340.75	8100.00	176.68	219.96	.00	59.	63
0.00	46.	0.00	-410.88	1650.00	3300.00	33.	36356.74	7950.00	176.43	183.40	.00	33.	64
0.15	46.	0.00	491.54	2750.00	5100.00	51.	28728.52	8700.00	178.28	174.10	.00	51.	65
0.00	40.	0.00	692.24	2550.00	5500.00	55.	30356.46	8600.00	225.21	219.96	.00	55.	66
0.00	33.	0.00	692.19	1650.00	3300.00	33.	30714.59	8500.00	256.61	134.09	.00	33.	67
0.00	33.	0.00	-497.46	1550.00	3100.00	31.	31143.85	6330.00	275.80	102.09	.00	31.	68
0.15	41.	0.00	-402.19	1600.00	3200.00	36.	32130.46	7380.00	253.50	188.52	.00	36.	69
0.00	40.	0.00	642.01	2700.00	5400.00	54.	33044.48	7480.00	253.50	240.17	.00	54.	70
0.00	40.	0.00	-435.52	1650.00	3300.00	33.	30634.12	7500.00	115.77	209.17	.00	33.	71
0.00	54.	0.00	-507.73	1550.00	3100.00	55.	30634.63	8650.00	115.97	154.17	.00	55.	72
0.15	55.	0.00	-414.07	2750.00	5500.00	75.	28559.94	9700.00	149.44	107.59	.00	75.	73
0.00	57.	0.00	696.96	3750.00	7500.00	36.	30858.17	9850.00	178.11	71.59	.00	36.	74
0.15	43.	0.00	1699.80	1800.00	3600.00	61.	33839.10	11350.00	217.23	10.80	.00	61.	75
0.00	48.	0.00	-235.84	3050.00	6100.00	33.	35253.49	8667.50	371.23	86.23	.00	33.	76
0.15	56.	0.00	-390.55	1650.00	3300.00	51.	34268.57	9246.17	434.82	183.41	.00	51.	77
0.00	59.	0.00	101.77	1785.00	3300.00	85.	34268.33	10250.00	412.84	145.41	.00	85.	78
0.00	44.	0.00	-247.29	2378.67	4335.04	36.	38015.78	9867.50	449.78	56.41	.00	36.	79
0.15	61.	0.00	355.30	3471.33	4757.34	57.	40171.97	10372.66	366.30	86.23	.00	57.	80
0.00	65.	0.00	1625.45	1995.00	7342.66	38.	36865.41	11776.33	317.28	183.41	.00	38.	81
0.15	47.	0.00	-67.60	3115.00	4845.00	89.	31167.58	10644.00	390.94	145.41	.00	89.	82
0.00	41.	0.00	-151.23	2700.00	7565.00	52.	33183.44	10372.50	390.40	56.41	.00	52.	83
0.00	53.	0.00	1068.92	2700.00	5200.00	36.	37300.69	11070.00	532.26	86.23	.00	36.	84
0.00	63.	0.00	656.11	1800.00	5400.00	34.	41543.06	10982.50	448.48	126.54	.00	34.	85
0.15	54.	0.00	-248.00	2400.00	2890.00	48.	37825.41	10882.50	454.38	197.69	.00	48.	86
0.00	49.	0.00	-867.70	3800.00	4800.00	76.	35667.66	8545.00	346.22	149.69	.00	76.	87
0.00	43.	0.00	-349.14	2450.00	7400.00	49.	33567.94	9445.00	272.57	147.35	.00	49.	88
0.15	47.	0.00	1742.52	2450.00	6400.00	48.	37286.36	10845.00	375.61	83.35	.00	48.	89
0.00	49.	0.00	415.74	1650.00	4800.00	48.	36524.78	11850.00	492.13	258.92	.00	48.	90
0.15	53.	0.00	322.75	2030.00	4900.00	33.	42105.78	10500.00	288.82	209.92	.00	33.	91
0.00	63.	0.00	100.00	2750.00	4900.00	58.	31199.08	8950.00	304.45	176.92	.00	58.	92
0.00	54.	0.00	384.05	2750.00	3300.00	87.	35381.95	9315.00	315.27	338.48	.00	87.	93
0.15	49.	0.00	-404.14	1650.00	4930.00	52.	30022.36	11215.00	95.71	283.48	.00	52.	94
0.00	43.	0.00	-60.04	3350.00	5500.00	36.	33093.47	8965.00	146.61	209.92	.00	36.	95
0.00	47.	0.00	670.58	4350.00	8700.00	55.	37824.63	11265.00	205.57	176.92	.00	55.	96
0.15	49.	0.00	2278.23	3400.00	3400.00	87.	34858.75	11137.50	306.57	246.37	.00	87.	97
0.00	67.	0.00	-371.44	4700.00	4700.00	34.	37596.35	11137.50	327.64	247.37	.00	34.	98
0.00	59.	0.00	-139.71	1925.00	4675.00	55.				192.37	.00	55.	99
0.15													100

FIGURE 13-3 (Continued)

	AVERAGE	STANDARD DEVIATION
WEEKLY DEMAND	51.7000	16.7468
BACKORDER QUEUE LENGTH	.7348	5.1703
INVENTORY AT END OF WEEK	163.9244	88.1368
SUPPLY BACKORDER	313.2099	125.4132
ACCOUNTS RECEIVABLE	10023.1598	1712.9372
CASH ON HAND	24437.6888	10533.0383
SALES	51.7000	18.1259
GROSS INCOME FROM SALES	5010.3924	1668.3601
WEEKLY GROSS PROFIT	2425.3924	802.7297
WEEKLY NET PROFIT	368.5059	802.0908
UNITS OF LOST SALES	.0000	.0000

SIMCO SATISFACTORILY COMPLETED.

c) Arrange to have the mean of weekly demand begin at 50.0, but cause the mean to increase by 0.5 percent each week. Let the standard deviation continue to be 1/3 of the mean weekly demand. Run the simulation under these conditions. Interpret the results of these experiments.

4–1. Alter Simco's program in Exercise 3 to cause the demand forecast (FD) to be determined by single exponential smoothing with a smoothing constant of 0.3. Rerun parts (*a*), (*b*), and (*c*) of Exercise 3 under these conditions.

4–2. Repeat what is called for in 4–1, but employ double exponential smoothing with a smoothing constant of 0.3. Interpret the results of these experiments.

5–1. Employ the model called for in Exercise 3 with mean weekly demand constant at 50.0. Alter this program to cause weekly demand to be gamma-distributed, with a mean of 50.0 and a standard deviation equal to 1/3 of the mean. Run the simulation under this condition.

5–2. Repeat what is called for in 5–1, but with a standard deviation of twice the mean. Run the program under this condition and interpret the results of these experiments.

ADDITIONAL SYSTEMS EXERCISES

6. A local retailer of combination heating-air conditioning units is concerned with maximizing his profits over the coming year. He has discovered over the past few years that his demand takes on the following characteristics:

a) During the first 10 weeks of the year demand is normally distributed, with a mean of 65 and a standard deviation of 10.

b) During the next 15 weeks the mean demand increases at a rate of 5 percent per week.

c) During the next 20 weeks the mean demand is constant.

d) During the last 7 weeks the mean decreases at a rate of 7 percent per week.

When a purchase order is placed with the manufacturer of these units, the lead time distribution is as follows:

Lead Time (Weeks)	Probability
2	.29
3	.38
4	.10
5	.03
6	.07
7	.13

Our retailer buys his units at a cost of $150 per unit and sells them at $250 per unit, a profit per unit of $100.

His inventory holding costs are $20 per unit per week.

Each time he places an order with the manufacturer of the units he experiences a $600 ordering and shipping cost, regardless of the number of units ordered.

His beginning inventory is 400 units.

This retailer finds it extremely necessary to maintain a good public image. Thus when demand exceeds inventory he has the required number of units flown in from the manufacturer at an additional cost of $250 per unit.

Our retailer's inventory ordering policy is as follows: When inventory drops below 210 units, he orders an amount equal to 3 times that week's demand.

His weekly profit, then, equals: Demand × (selling price—purchase price)—cost per order (if an order has been placed that week)—inventory holding cost × inventory at the end of the week—stockout cost × (demand—inventory) (if a stockout occurs).

A necessary order of calculations is as follows: each week

1. Determine if a shipment from the manufacturer is due this week. If so, add it to inventory.
2. Determine demand for this week, and satisfy it.
3. Recalculate inventory. If demand exceeded inventory, calculate stockout cost.
4. If it is necessary to place an order, do so; determine lead time and thus the week in which the order is due.
5. Determine inventory costs on the remaining inventory.
6. Calculate profit for the week.

In order to determine an average profit under these conditions, we find it necessary to simulate this retailer's experience for 100 *noncumulative* years. In effect, we are simulating the same year 100 times; that is, we are beginning each year with an inventory of 400 units, a mean demand of 65, etc. Thus we want to simulate this retailer's experience in the marketplace 100 times. At the end of each year of calculation we want to print out:

TOTAL STOCKOUT COST
TOTAL ORDERING COST
TOTAL HOLDING COST
TOTAL PROFIT.

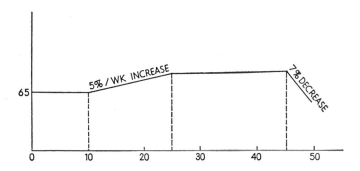

At the end of the 100 years these figures should then be averaged and the average stockout cost, average ordering cost, etc., printed out.

7. The Z Company operates a power plant to provide electricity and steam for heating the company's various buildings. The electrical power is provided by means of three turbogenerators. Steam is fed into the turbines, producing electricity. Also, steam is extracted from two of the turbines for heating the buildings. Each turbine's efficiency varies according to the electrical load and the (extracted) heating steam load placed on the turbine.

The steam is produced by a system of boilers. A relationship of linearity exists among the amount of steam produced, the amount of coal required, and the cost of the coal. Thus a minimization of the steam required to produce a specific electrical load and heating load will also represent a minimization of total cost of satisfying these requirements. The problem then is, given certain electrical and heating loads, to determine the minimum amount of steam required and the allocation of the steam to each of the three turbines.

For each combination of requirements there are several thousand combinations of possible allocations of steam to each of the turbines; the problem is to find the minimum combination in each case. From information furnished from the turbine manufacturers, it is seen that although turbine 2 is the most efficient in generating electricity, it is not capable of furnishing heating steam. Turbine 3 is more efficient than turbine 1 in generating electricity, but turbine 1 is the more efficient heating steam producer. Obviously, then, only turbines 1 and 3 are capable of furnishing heating steam; if the heating requirements exceed the amount of steam extracted from these two turbines, the remaining required steam must be taken directly from the boilers.

Rules and Assumptions

a)   All three turbines must be kept operating under normal conditions. Starting and stopping of the turbines is unduly hard on them; thus they must be kept running at points equal to, or above, their minimum operating points at all times.

b)   The turbines are naturally most efficient at maximum heating steam extraction.

c)   From the graphs supplied by the manufacturers, equations have been developed which describe the limits of the operating range for each turbine. Since each line appearing on the performance curves is a straight line, an equation of the form $Y = a + bX$ can be developed to describe these lines. For example, in turbine 1:

$$Y = \text{Throttle Flow (steam required)}$$
$$X = \text{KW (kilowatt load)}$$
$$a = 0.65 \text{ (heating extract)} + 10,000$$
$$b = 15.4 \, .$$

The following parameters exist for the three turbines:

Turbine 1

Throttle Flow $= 15.4 \times (\text{KW}) + 0.55 \times \text{Heat} + 10,000$
Maximum Extraction $= 12,310 + 9.23 \times \text{KW}$
Minimum KW $= 2500$ Maximum KW $= 6500$

Turbine 2

Throttle Flow $= 5000 + 6.3 \times \text{KW}$
Maximum Throttle Flow $= 8000 + 21.5 \times \text{KW}$
Minimum KW $= 800$ Maximum KW $= 3200$

Turbine 3

Throttle Flow $= 8000 + 8.25 \times \text{KW} + 0.9 \times \text{Heat}$
Maximum Throttle Flow $= 8500 + 20.5 \times \text{KW} + 0.8 \times \text{Heat}$
Maximum Extraction $= 25,000$
Minimum KW $= 800$ Maximum KW $= 3200$

We want the work of determining the most efficient combination to be done by the computer. The method is to specify a load on the system and then to calculate the most efficient method of providing the load.

The print-out should include the system load in terms of electricity and heat, the amount of steam required, the amount of steam directed into each turbine, the amount of heating steam extracted from each turbine, and the amount of heating steam drawn directly from the boilers (if necessary). This should be done for electrical loads of 4500

KW up to 12,500 KW, increasing by increments of 500 KW; and heating loads of 40,000 pounds to 140,000 pounds, increasing by increments of 20,000 pounds.

Method of Calculation

The steps of the calculation might be as follows:

1. Specify an electrical load.
2. Specify a heating load.
3. Set load on turbine 1 = 2000 KW.
4. Increase the load on turbine 1 by 500 KW.
5. Set load on turbine 2 at 600 KW.
6. Increase load on turbine 2 by 200 KW.
7. Set the load on turbine 3 to meet the demand.
8. If turbine 3 is overloaded, go to step 7.
9. Set heat extraction on turbine 1 at its maximum.
10. Increase heat extraction on turbine 1 by 10,000.
11. Set heat extraction on turbine 3 to meet the demand.
12. If turbine 3 is overloaded, determine the amount of direct steam required.
13. Determine the steam required to provide this loading.
14. If this is cheaper than the previous method, save and return to step 12. If not cheaper, do not save, but return to step 12.
15. Return to step 2 until all heating loads have been satisfied.
16. Return to step 1 until all electrical loads have been satisfied.

For a clearer picture of the system see the figure below.

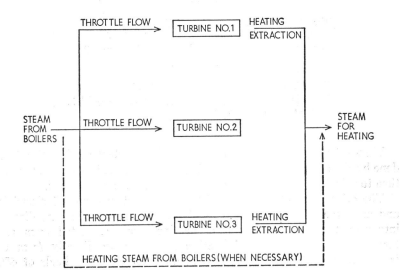

8. Esto Oil Company is considering bidding on a contract to supply fuel oil to a port in the United Kingdom. Esto's plan is to tap its production facilities in Africa and transport the oil in its own tankers.

The fuel is to be delivered to the customer's tank facilities in port in the U.K. The capacity of these facilities is 1,250 units of oil and the customer's invitation to bid specifies that the supplier must not permit the supply to drop below 250 units more than 5 percent of the time.

Demand on the tank facilities in the U.K. is found to be normally distributed with a mean of 100 units per day and a standard deviation of 25 units.

Esto management wants to know if it can maintain this service level by employing on a full-time basis 3 of its standard 625 unit tankers. Other constraints are:

1. The limited storage capacity in the U.K. (i.e., 1,250 units maximum capacity);
2. Berth facilities both in the U.K. (one berth) and Africa (2 berths). One day is required to load a ship berthed in Africa, and one day is required to unload a ship berthed in the U.K.;
3. Travel time. Eight days are required for a ship to make the trip from Africa to Britain and eight days are required for the return trip;
4. Weather. While weather does not influence the speed of travel at sea, a ship cannot enter or leave a berth during a storm. Storms are seasonal with the following pattern:

		Probability of a Storm Each Day	
		April 1 to Sept. 30	Rest of Year
In Africa harbor		0.2	0.1
In U.K. harbor		0.1	0.2

Esto's production facilities in Africa do not pose a constraint.

Esto's plan is that ships which cannot unload in the U.K. because the customer's tank facilities are loaded will anchor in the harbor and wait, constituting a floating inventory.

Construct a computer model for simulating Esto's proposed transportation system and determine if the required service level can be met with 3 of its ships.

Suggestions

It is useful to think of the 8 days travel time as involving intervals between 7 successive positions in the ocean, plus the harbor (see diagram below). Each day after a ship leaves harbor it advances one interval. Positions 1 through 7 represent the trip from the U.K. to Africa and positions 10 through 16 represent the return trip. Each day of simulated operations the location of each of the 3 ships should be updated.

A subscripted variable, SHIP(M), might be employed to keep track of the position of each ship:

SHIP(1) = 12.0   means ship 1 is in position 12, etc.

The system might be initialized with all 3 ships at sea, perhaps as follows: SHIP(1) = 1.0, SHIP(2) = 5.0, and   SHIP(3) = 12.0.

BERTH(1) = 0.0 might mean that berth 1 is empty.
BERTH(2) = 1.0 might mean that berth 2 is occupied.

Assume the simulation begins on January 1, with 750 units of oil in storage in the U.K., and run the simulation for 6 years.

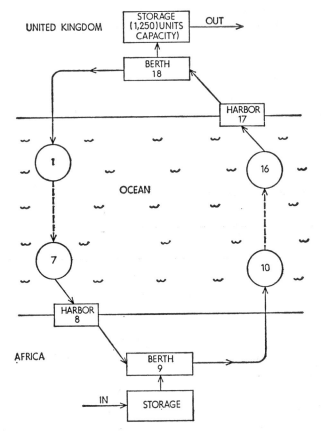

9.   (*A General Inventory Model with Quantity Discounts*) Semiannually, Townsend Products Company reviews its recent sales experience and produces a new monthly demand forecast consisting of a mean, TMU, and its associated standard deviation, SD, for each of the 1,000 products Townsend supplies to its industrial customers.

Townsend figures that the optimum order quantity can be determined independently of the optimum reorder point by virtue of the price break structure (quantity discounts) quoted by Townsend's suppliers. The optimum order quantity at Townsend, therefore, is determined by balancing annual materials cost, holding cost, and ordering cost (i.e., finding the minimum of the total of these three). Given a new monthly demand forecast, a quantity discount schedule consisting of a minimum order quantity, and five order quantity ranges and their associated per unit delivered costs (specified by the supplier), Townsend determines its optimum order quantity, $\hat{Q}$, as follows:

Step 1. Total annual materials cost, holding cost, and ordering cost are calculated, using the minimum allowable order quantity specified by the supplier.

Step 2. The "advantage" associated with moving into the next order quantity bracket (price break) is calculated.

Step 3. If this advantage is positive, then Step 2 is repeated. If not, or if the final order quantity bracket (price break) has been reached, the order quantity currently being considered is adopted as optimum.

It can be shown that the optimum probability of a stockout during lead time* is:

$$\text{Optimum probability of a stockout} = \frac{\text{(Unit Holding Cost, UHC)} \times \text{(Cost per Unit, CPU)} \times \text{Optimum Order Quantity, } \hat{Q}}{\text{(per unit Stockout Cost, STKCOS)} \times \text{(Demand per Year, DPY)}}.$$

The optimum probability of a stockout means the optimum probability that demand during lead time exceeds the reorder point, and therefore it is the cumulative probability associated with R, the reorder point.

Given a table of cumulative probabilities associated with the mean plus various multiples of the standard deviation above the mean, we could calculate the optimum reorder point from the relationship above.

Assume that Townsend Products Company's demand pattern is gamma distributed. Employ the probability density function of the gamma distribution (Chapter 8) and Simpson's rule for approximating an integral (Exercise 8–2), Chapter 8) to develop tables for the cumulative probabilities associated with X as X varies from the mean, plus three multiples of the standard deviation, by 100 equal increments, for *each* of the following ratios of the standard deviation to the mean:

$$3/6, 4/6, 5/6, 6/6, 7/6, \text{ and } 8/6.$$

Provide for storing the values of these tables in the matrix PROB(N, M) such that:

---

* See Fetter and Dalleck, *Decision Models for Inventory Management* (Homewood, Ill.: Richard D. Irwin, Inc., 1961), p. 18.

a)   For the gamma distribution with ratio of standard deviation to mean = 3/6:

   PROB (3,1)   holds the probability of generating a value greater than the mean plus 1/100 multiples of 3 standard deviations;

   PROB (3,2)   holds the probability of generating a value greater than the mean plus 2/100 multiples of 3 standard deviations; etc.

b)   For the gamma distribution with ratio of standard deviation to mean = 4/6:

   PROB (4,1)   holds the probability of generating a value greater than the mean plus 1/100 multiples of 3 standard deviations;

   PROB (4,2)   holds the probability of generating a value greater than the mean plus 2/100 multiples of 3 standard deviations; etc., through . . .

f)   For the gamma distribution with ratio of standard deviation to mean = 8/6:

   PROB (8,1)   holds the probability of generating a value greater than the mean plus 1/100 multiples of 3 standard deviations;

   PROB (8,2)   holds the probability of generating a value greater than the mean plus 2/100 multiples of 3 standard deviations; etc.

Using the concepts advanced above, design a FORTRAN algorithm which will conduct Townsend's semi-annual inventory management review and will determine and print out, along with the product number (ranging from 0001 through 1000), the optimum order quantity, reorder point, expected annual stockout in units short,[†] and expected service level given for each product:

1   Monthly demand forecast: TMU and associated standard deviation, SD;

2   Supplier's delivered price schedule;

3   Estimates of:

   a)   Annual Holding Cost, AHC, as a percent of the investment in inventory,

   b)   Ordering cost, CPO, the cost of processing one order,

   c)   Stockout Cost, STKCOS, the cost of being short one unit.

---

† For a short-cut method of determining expected units short during lead time, see Fetter and Dalleck, *op cit.,* Appendix F.

CHAPTER 14

Experimentation

IN ALL the preceding we have directed attention to constructing specific models and implementing them; i.e., translating them into computer programs. Purposely, nothing has been said about (*a*) proposing experiments which employ the models and (*b*) carrying out or executing the experiments. These topics have not been treated heretofore, even though it would seem reasonable to bring them up preliminary to the first experimental use of a systems model. That this was not done reflects our primary objective, which was to acquaint the student with particular model forms and to demonstrate how the computer program may be written and used as a simulator.

As we considered models of increasing complexity, we chose to omit general discussion of experiment planning and execution. Some intuitive (and we hope reasonable) experiments were proposed and carried out for each of the models discussed. The various experiments could have been replicated (copied, rerun under various conditions, or run longer) in order to generate systems behavior in addition to that which was produced or traced. Where a model was used to evaluate several forms of a decision rule, we could have replicated the experiment on many sets of data, or for other forms of the decision rule. But given the introductory level of the material presented, focus until now has been the conceptualization of the system, construction of the model, and the use of the model in limited experiments which were arbitrarily selected because they yielded information that could not be easily obtained—if at all—using other methods, and which would be generally valuable or interesting to the decision-maker.

The second and more compelling reason for deferring discussion of the design and execution of experiments is that simulation, as we have described it, is a very new analytical procedure. There are many unanswered methodological questions which simply have not been tackled. The major effort so far has been devoted to formulating and implementing models; i.e., overcoming the problems of constructing models which not only parallel real systems, but doing so within the limits imposed by the computer.

Without question, impressive strides have been made in this phase of simulation. Practitioners of the art have been quick to make use of increasing computer size and sophistication. Special simulation languages (procedure-oriented) have been devised which facilitate the tasks of modeling systems, stepping the models through time, and generating reports of system behavior. If we define simulation to include not only model construction, but design, execution, and evaluation of the results of experiments, then we conclude that there remain few obstacles to building sizable and complex models of particular or theoretical systems. This comment is not meant to deprecate the difficulties that have been surmounted, but it does imply that initial simulation efforts have concentrated on obtaining operational models whose reasonableness was judged in terms of how well they reproduced data which had been obtained by observing the real system.

A Critical Comment.   The foregoing helps us understand current criticisms of simulation methods. It is contended that while all sorts of data can be generated from the models, procedures have not been developed for:

1. Determining the implications that changes of inputs (parameters, exogenous variables) will have generally.
2. Planning and executing experiments efficiently.

The purpose of this chapter is to offer some suggestions to guide the student so as to preclude grossly inefficient experimental work. However, before proceeding—especially considering the newness of the technique—we should like to comment on the more serious criticisms.

Those with extensive experience with simulation point out that they are able to produce results which have reasonable posterior explanations. Yet they admit that they have no way of deriving general implications of changes in their models. When one speaks of "solving" a simulation model, he means that from a set of starting conditions the model will track a set of system variables. One then seeks to explain "the way in which forces in the systems interact," or the output is displayed in a form that has been labeled "pictorial graphics."

Reviewing several large simulations recently, Sprowls[1] concluded that these shortcomings in methodology were persistent, fundamental, and disturbing. He noted that two analysts (C. P. Bonini and E. B. Roberts) conducted experiments with decision-information models of the firm in which both specified similar starting conditions but obtained contradictory results. Bonini defined a highly variable environment in terms of customer orders and market growth trend, and his model produced lower costs and higher sales and profits. Roberts, using Forrester's techniques, observed that a similar environment led to great fluctuations of inventory, backorders, employment, and, we presume, profits.

In each case a reasonable sounding explanation of the results was offered. We would agree that repeated instances such as this would cast doubts about the methodology, but we cannot agree fully with Sprowls who contends that, given such evidence:

> I can only conclude at this time that there is no question but that a computer simulation model can generate time paths of many variables from many kinds of initial conditions. There is still a very large question whether anyone understands the model, although reasonable sounding explanations can be given for almost any input-output phenomenon observed. . . . I am prepared only to look at each of them as an interesting isolated case which can be described to me but from which I shall draw no conclusions.[2]

For the models compared above, the inputs were not identical, and there were important differences in assumptions as well as in the procedures for simulating decision making. Obviously, if a model, operating on identical inputs, produced different results, the model would be suspect. But it would seem that some of the current criticism is a bit premature. The method, as we pointed out, is new, and our knowledge of the nature of decision making is highly incomplete.

It is more difficult to evaluate or generalize the output of a model

---

[1] Clay Sprowls, "Simulation and Management Control," *Management Controls: New Directions in Basic Research* C. P. Bonini, R. K. Jaedicke, and H. M. Wagner (eds.) (New York: McGraw-Hill, 1964), pp. 146–48.

[2] *Ibid.*, p. 147.

being used to explore a behavioral theory of decision making, as contrasted to evaluating a model which simulates a physical system in which it is only desired to compare *relative* behavior of the system under variations of a particular decision rule. In the second case, the output can be used to indicate which rule to select without raising serious doubts about the generality of the model or its output under greatly modified assumptions.

The important thing is that simulation can be helpful to the on-line decision maker. R. W. Conway notes that,

> Fortunately, a large number of investigations appropriate for simulation compare a sequence of alternatives. With proper operating procedures a simulation model can produce *relative results* much more efficiently than *absolute results*.[3]

Such comparative information provides an adequate basis for making a choice among the alternatives.

Ideally, the contrast of alternatives should be performed by using the same "experimental media" (as Conway calls it) or, as we commonly say, the experiments should be performed under identical conditions. In simulation, identical conditions are maintained by specifying initial values for each variable, system parameters, and the data representing sequences of exogenous events: customer orders, shipments received, machine failures, etc.[4] The unique advantage of simulation is that not just closely identical but *absolutely identical* conditions can be maintained through repeated experiments or runs. For example, to evaluate alternative inventory reorder rules, the same sequence of orders and material receipt delays can be reused. Perfect homogeneity of the experimental media is thus possible.

From this aside, we turn now to some specific suggestions about designing and executing experiments.

Planning Experiments

Given an operational model of a system, there is almost no end to the variety of changes that might be introduced, and hence some limitations must be imposed. On the one hand we wish to ignore trivial changes, and on the other hand combinations of changes

---

[3] R. W. Conway, "Some Tactical Problems in Simulation Method," Memorandum RM-3244-PR, The Rand Corporation, Santa Monica, Calif., October, 1962, p. 13.

[4] Alternately, as we have seen, a procedure for generating values of the exogenous random variables may be used in place of a list of events.

whose effects cannot be readily measured by statistical methods. At the same time we need to remember that the execution of experiments is not without cost.[5] It is simply not feasible to perform a complete replicate of even modest designs involving small sets of changes. Recall Bonini's design in which 8 changes were introduced, each having 2 values or "cases." This means that 2^8, or 256, experimental runs would have been necessary to obtain a complete replicate of the experiment; i.e., one run for each of the possible combinations of changes. Depending on the length of the runs (number of simulated time periods), we are now talking of requirements of time of large-scale computers on the order of hours—not to mention computation time for obtaining estimates of parameters for numerous distributions, as well as to evaluate the significance of observed differences.

Therefore fractional factorial design is used in which high-order interaction effects are not computed.[6] The use of conventional analysis of variance techniques is subject to question as regards evaluation of the so-called observed differences. Some experimenters hypothesize that changes or combinations of changes will not modify system behavior (the *null hypothesis*). Others insist that such a hypothesis is not appropriate for the rather typical experiment in which changes really represent such alternatives as a set of alternative decision rules. These rules, it is contended, are different, and differences, however slight, of system behavior will follow. Failure to reject the null hypothesis indicates only that the test is not sensitive to the differences for the given sample size or length of run. In addition, the analyst wants to identify the best alternative, or he would like to rank the alternatives; he does not wish to conclude that they are merely different.[7]

The question remains, "What experiments should we undertake?" Generally, two kinds of experiments should be considered:

1. Those that serve to test the reasonableness of the model, and
2. Those that evaluate or obtain estimates of important properties of the model.

---

[5] See Daniel Teichroew and John F. Lubin, "Computer Simulation: Discussion of the Technique and Comparison of Languages," Working Paper No. 20, Graduate School of Business, Stanford University, Stanford, Calif., 1964.

[6] See C. P. Bonini, *Simulation of Information and Decision Systems in the Firm* (New York: Prentice-Hall, 1963), pp. 85–96.

[7] R. W. Conway, *op. cit.*, p. 16.

Reasonableness of the Model. Such criteria (above) are more easily spelled out than applied, and it goes without saying that from this point on judgment and *a priori* feelings about the nature of the system modeled play an important part. With respect to experiments of the first kind:

> Some tests should be made upon the reasonableness and stability of the model. This can be done by studying the effects upon the firms of different external factors. In other words, we should test to see whether under different conditions in the external environment the firm of our model behaves reasonably (in line with the way we would expect a real world firm to behave). For example, we should not expect the model to "blow up" and go off to infinity as a result of only relatively minor changes in its external environment.[8]

To achieve such a test we might simply redefine the probability distribution (for an exogenous variable) as having a greater variance than in the initial or standard version of the environment. If it is desired to introduce a fast and irregular growth rate for a variable, random fluctuations can be superimposed on the trend of the variable. Precisely what constitutes fast or slow rates and irregular or smooth cyclical patterns is left to the discretion of the analyst.

Evaluating Properties of the Model

Parametric Changes. Parameters (particularly of decision rules) may be modified to obtain a parametric value that optimizes a measure of effectiveness of system behavior. The very first models taken up in this text involved simulation of inventory systems, the search for parameter values for the reorder point, and the reorder quantity so that total inventory cost could be minimized. Recall in these examples that not all parameter values were considered, and that we compared sequential costs and stopped searching when total cost began to increase.

Evaluation of parameters (sensitivity analysis) has been demonstrated in numerous examples throughout the text, so that further discussion is not necessary. This is an obvious but highly useful form of change and experimentation. The values proposed are usually indicated by *a priori* knowledge of what values are reasonable or possible in the real world. Evaluation of parameter values that are not available to the decision-maker results in data which

---

[8] C. P. Bonini, *op. cit.*, p. 75.

cannot be acted upon. Finally, even within a specified interval it is not necessary to consider very small incremental changes of a parameter. Many functions of measures of effectiveness are insensitive to slight absolute differences—as we can recall, for example, from the shape of the inventory total cost curve.

Decision Rule Changes. A second type of change is the modification, or rather substitution, of decision rules. Virtually each example in the text demonstrated or proposed such substitutions. Inventory reorder rules, queue discipline rules, forecasting rules, and pricing rules (among others) have been altered or substituted in our examples. In addition, the information flows, delays, and links, which we regard as decisions about organizational structure, can be modified to test the effects on decision making.

Simulation is usually undertaken because we have raised questions or posed hypotheses about the system behavior under various decision rules. We thus begin with the purpose of sampling behavior or response subject to alterations that are feasible but about which we have only vague notions of the consequences of repeatedly applying the rules. The output of the model furnishes comparative system performances which are then used to select a particular rule. The model can be made to operate successively on a real or synthetically produced sequence of exogenous events, and here we may note that the use of the same sequence for all runs of an experiment minimizes residual variation and obtains comparable data with smaller sample size than is possible if different sequences are used for each run.

The use of a common sequence of events to test alternatives (decision rules in this case) is the most important procedural question in simulation.[9] The procedure is preferred because it permits smaller sample sizes and sharpens differences among alternatives. If the analyst has a sequence obtained by observation of the real system, he would be led to use this procedure simply because of the cost of obtaining the data.

Starting Conditions

We have continually assumed that (given a model) not only is a sequence of exogenous variables generated or "read in," but that the initial state of the system is specified; that is, that values are pro-

---

[9] R. W. Conway, *op. cit.*, p. 14.

vided for system variables at simulated time zero. Here the problem is that the output of the model will be biased by the set of initial values until the model has "warmed up," or, more precisely, has obtained the steady state where that term is taken to mean an arbitrarily close approximation to the system's equilibrium state.

Several suggestions are usually proposed, but they are difficult to apply and require considerable exercise of judgment:

1. Discard data generated during an initial interval of the simulation run.
2. Select starting conditions that reduce the duration of the warmup or transient period.
3. Select starting conditions such that bias is not introduced.

As for the third suggestion, if the analyst had such knowledge that he could start the model in its steady state, he would not have to resort to simulation.

Assume for the moment that the state of a system is defined on a single variable. The steady state is assumed to exist and is described by the probability distribution of the variable. The distribution is said to be a property of the system and is constant. Thus it is incorrect to suggest that the variance of the steady-state distribution decreases through time. The variance which decreases (as the simulation is extended) is that obtained by simulation, which we treat as an estimate of the system parameter. These estimates or approximations approach the inherent or limiting distribution at a rate which is influenced by the starting conditions.

Differences between the system parameter and the obtained estimate decrease with time, but Conway cautions that for complex systems the rate of approach is slow and the error (difference) remains large (even after long runs)! This can be verified from our own experience with the Simco model. Although we would not call 100 periods (two years) a long time, nevertheless the variances obtained were disappointingly large.

The suggestion to eliminate the bias that is induced by a particular set of starting conditions by the discarding of some portion of the output really poses the problem of when to begin measurement. The following guides are proposed.[10]

1. Delete an early portion of the output of a run. A rule of thumb is to truncate a series of measurements when the first of the series is neither the maximum nor the minimum of the remaining set.

---

[10] *Ibid.,* p. 5.

2. Deletion should be done with due consideration, given the complexity of the system; i.e., the number of elements in the system as well as the number of events that take place. The more complex the system, the longer the bias persists.

3. All runs of a given experiment should be treated similarly when deletion is done.

The suggestion to select starting conditions to minimize or rather shorten the warmup period is really an alternative to starting the system in the empty or idle condition. Such a choice (empty or idle) has the disadvantage of being artificial (except for simple queuing systems), and the consequent time to achieve the steady state is long. The selection of non-empty conditions requires *a priori* knowledge of the system but, as Conway notes, it is rare that the analyst has no such information.

Length of the Run. Determination of the length of the simulation run is implied in the preceding discussion. It is tempting to exploit the computer to generate extremely long runs but economy usually rules against such a practice. When our purpose is to trace systems response, the simulation is continued until the variables have "settled down." Recall the demonstrations of impulse response for the Simco model. For many purposes, however, we are interested in short-run effects and settle on simulation periods of relatively short duration. Bonini decided on an interval of 9 years in his experiments, with the model moved through 108 monthly periods. In much of Forrester's work intervals of 2–3 years are common, although activity was generated in fractional parts of a day.

There seem to be no objective rules for fixing the proper length of the run. Variances are reduced through time, but at a cost which should be appraised in terms of the precision gained. We are also warned that such gains in complex systems require extremely lengthy runs. In many cases the proper length cannot be decided beforehand simply because we desire to process the model until specific conditions result. Thus we are in fact interpreting time as one of the information outputs rather than as the mere magnitude of sample size.

On this point it seems evident that the analyst should use all the data generated and that he need not resort to sampling from the output. If additional data is required, the simulation should be *continued*—rather than started again from a second set of initial conditions. The expanded output is then treated as a single sample.

Characterizing the Output. It is not our purpose to discuss statistical methods used to summarize the output of the simulation. In addition to depicting output graphically, descriptive statistical measures, such as the mean, the standard deviation, the variance, and the trend, are used to characterize system variables.[11] The use of classical analysis of variance seems widespread in simulation despite the awareness that the null hypothesis may be improper and that independence of samples is often assumed—when in fact, as we noted, because of common starting conditions or because of the use of a common sequence of exogenous events, dependence is the case.

In summary, Conway concludes:

. . . a single experimental run should be made for each alternative tested. Variability should be reduced and replication provided by extending the length of the run rather than executing completely separate and independent runs. Performance measures will be based on the entire run (except for the "warmup" and possibly a "cooling-off" period at the end of the run) but the run must be subdivided and a sequence of interval measures obtained in order to estimate the precision of the results. The positive correlation that almost surely exists between neighboring measurements guarantees that the estimate of variance computed under the usual assumption of independence will understate the true variance. . . . It clearly requires some investigations of the degree of autocorrelation.[12]

The manner of treating these tactical problems should be described when reporting simulations, along with the description of the model and its output. Criticism of methodology will continue, and for the present each simulation will be judged in terms of its credibility and utility. However, we trust that the exposition contained in this text has been persuasive in pointing out the present usefulness of simulation as well as the areas in which refinement is needed.

SUGGESTIONS FOR FURTHER STUDY

BONINI, C. P.; JAEDICKE, R. K.; AND WAGNER, H. M. *Management Controls: New Directions in Basic Research.* New York: McGraw-Hill, 1964.

CONWAY, R. W. "Some Tactical Problems in Simulation Method" (RM-3244-PR), The Rand Corporation, Santa Monica, Calif., 1962.

---

[11] For example, SIMSCRIPT provides a COMPUTE statement which can be used to obtain any one of seven statistics, including the mean, standard deviation, and variance.

[12] *Ibid.*, p. 34.

TEICHROEW, DANIEL, AND LUBIN, JOHN F. "Computer Simulation: Discussion of the Technique and Comparison of Languages," Working Paper No. 20, Graduate School of Business, Stanford University, Stanford, Calif., 1964.

TOCHER, K. D. *The Art of Simulation.* Princeton, N.J.: Van Nostrand, 1963.

Index

*This book has been set on the Linotype in
11 point Modern #21, leaded 2 points, and
10 Modern #21, leaded 1 point. Chapter
numbers and titles are in Bulmer italic. The
size of the type page is 27 by 45½ picas.*